DUTCH WEIGHT.

THE WORKS OF
WASHINGTON IRVING

KNICKERBOCKER'S HISTORY OF NEW YORK

KNICKERBOCKER MISCELLANIES

WITH FRONTISPIECE

NEW YORK AND LONDON
THE CO-OPERATIVE PUBLICATION SOCIETY, Inc.

4

CONTENTS

VOLUME FOUR

KNICKERBOCKER'S HISTORY OF NEW YORK
VOLUME ONE

(3)

Contents

MISCELLANIES

A HISTORY OF NEW YORK

FROM THE

BEGINNING OF THE WORLD TO THE END OF THE DUTCH DYNASTY

CONTAINING

AMONG MANY SURPRISING AND CURIOUS MATTERS

The Unutterable Ponderings of Walter the Doubter
The Disastrous Projects of William the Testy, and
The Chivalric Achievements of Peter the Headstrong

THE THREE DUTCH GOVERNORS OF NEW AMSTERDAM

BEING THE ONLY AUTHENTIC HISTORY OF THE TIMES THAT EVER HATH
BEEN OR EVER WILL BE PUBLISHED

BY DIEDRICH KNICKERBOCKER

De waarheid die in duister lag,
Die komt met klaarheid aan den dag

ACCOUNT OF THE AUTHOR

It was some time, if I recollect right, in the early part of the autumn of 1808 that a stranger applied for lodgings at the Independent Columbian Hotel in Mulberry Street, of which I am landlord. He was a small, brisk-looking old gentleman, dressed in a rusty black coat, a pair of olive velvet breeches, and a small cocked hat. He had a few gray hairs plaited and clubbed behind, and his beard seemed to be of some eight-and-forty hours' growth. The only piece of finery which he bore about him was a bright pair of square silver shoe-buckles, and all his baggage was contained in a pair of saddle-bags, which he carried under his arm. His whole appearance was something out of the common run; and my wife, who is a very shrewd body, at once set him down for some eminent country schoolmaster.

As the Independent Columbian Hotel is a very small house, I was a little puzzled at first where to put him; but my wife, who seemed taken with his looks, would needs put him in her best chamber, which is genteelly set off with the profiles of the whole family, done in black, by those two great painters, Jarvis and Woods, and commands a very pleasant view of the new grounds on the Collect, together with the rear of the Poor House and Bridewell, and a full front of the Hospital; so that it is the cheerfulest room in the whole house.

During the whole time that he stayed with us we found him a very worthy, good sort of an old gentleman, though a little queer in his ways. He would keep in his room for days together, and if any of the children cried, or made

(9)

noise about his door, he would bounce out in a great passion, with his hands full of papers, and say something about "deranging his ideas"; which made my wife believe sometimes that he was not altogether *compos*. Indeed, there was more than one reason to make her think so, for his room was always covered with scraps of paper and old mouldy books, laying about at sixes and sevens, which he would never let anybody touch; for he said he had laid them all away in their proper places, so that he might know where to find them; though for that matter he was half his time worrying about the house in search of some book or writing which he had carefully put out of the way. I shall never forget what a pother he once made because my wife cleaned out his room when his back was turned, and put everything to rights; for he swore he would never be able to get his papers in order again in a twelvemonth. Upon this my wife ventured to ask him what he did with so many books and papers? and he told her that he was "seeking for immortality"; which made her think more than ever that the poor old gentleman's head was a little cracked.

He was a very inquisitive body, and when not in his room was continually poking about town, hearing all the news, and prying into everything that was going on: this was particularly the case about election time, when he did nothing but bustle about from poll to poll, attending all ward meetings and committee rooms; though I could never find that he took part with either side of the question. On the contrary, he would come home and rail at both parties with great wrath—and plainly proved one day, to the satisfaction of my wife and three old ladies who were drinking tea with her, that the two parties were like two rogues, each tugging at a skirt of the nation; and that in the end they would tear the very coat off its back and expose its nakedness. Indeed, he was an oracle among the neighbors, who would collect around him to hear him talk of an afternoon, as he smoked his pipe on the bench before the door; and I really believe he would have brought over the whole neighborhood to his own side of the question, if they could ever have found out what it was.

He was very much given to argue, or, as he called it, *philosophize*, about the most trifling matter; and to do him justice, I never knew anybody that was a match for him, except it was a grave-looking old gentleman who called now and then to see him, and often posed him in an argument. But this is nothing surprising, as I have since found out this stranger is the city librarian; and, of course, must be a man of great learning: and I have my doubts if he had not some hand in the following history.

As our lodger had been a long time with us, and we had never received any pay, my wife began to be somewhat uneasy, and curious to find out who and what he was. She accordingly made bold to put the question to his friend the librarian, who replied in his dry way that he was one of the *literati*, which she supposed to mean some new party in politics. I scorn to push a lodger for his pay; so I let day after day pass on without dunning the old gentleman for a farthing; but my wife, who always takes these matters on herself, and is, as I said, a shrewd kind of a woman, at last got out of patience, and hinted that she thought it high time "some people should have a sight of some people's money." To which the old gentleman replied, in a mighty touchy manner, that she need not make herself uneasy, for that he had a treasure there (pointing to his saddle-bags) worth her whole house put together. This was the only answer we could ever get from him; and as my wife, by some of those odd ways in which women find out everything, learned that he was of very great connections, being related to the Knickerbockers of Scaghtikoke, and cousin-german to the Congressman of that name, she did not like to treat him uncivilly. What is more, she even offered, merely by way of making things easy, to let him live scot-free if he would teach the children their letters; and to try her best and get her neighbors to send their children also; but the old gentleman took it in such dudgeon, and seemed so affronted at being taken for a schoolmaster, that she never dared speak on the subject again.

About two months ago he went out of a morning with a bundle in his hand—and has never been heard of since. All kinds of inquiries were made after him, but in vain. I wrote to his relations at Scaghtikoke, but they sent for answer that he had not been there since the year before last, when he had a great dispute with the Congressman about politics, and left the place in a huff, and they had neither heard nor seen anything of him from that time to this. I must own I felt very much worried about the poor old gentleman, for I thought something bad must have happened to him, that he should be missing so long, and never return to pay his bill. I therefore advertised him in the newspapers, and though my melancholy advertisement was published by several humane printers, yet I have never been able to learn anything satisfactory about him.

My wife now said it was high time to take care of ourselves, and see if he had left anything behind in his room that would pay us for his board and lodging. We found nothing, however, but some old books and musty writings, and his saddle-bags, which, being opened in the presence of the librarian, contained only a few articles of wornout clothes, and a large bundle of blotted paper. On looking over this, the librarian told us he had no doubt it was the treasure which the old gentleman had spoken about; as it proved to be a most excellent and faithful History of New York, which he advised us by all means to publish: assuring us that it would be so eagerly bought up by a discerning public that he had no doubt it would be enough to pay our arrears ten times over. Upon this we got a very learned schoolmaster, who teaches our children, to prepare it for the press, which he accordingly has done; and has, moreover, added to it a number of valuable notes of his own.

This, therefore, is a true statement of my reasons for having this work printed, without waiting for the consent of the author: and I here declare that if he ever returns (though I

much fear some unhappy accident has befallen him) I stand
ready to account with him like a true and honest man. Which
is all at present,

From the public's humble Serv't,

SETH HANDASIDE.

Independent Columbian Hotel,
New York.

————

THE foregoing account of the author was prefixed to the
first edition of this work. Shortly after its publication a letter was received from him by Mr. Handaside, dated at a
small Dutch village on the banks of the Hudson, whither he
had traveled for the purpose of inspecting certain ancient
records. As this was one of those few and happy villages
into which newspapers never find their way, it is not a matter of surprise that Mr. Knickerbocker should never have
seen the numerous advertisements that were made concerning him; and that he should learn of the publication of his
history by mere accident.

He expressed much concern at its premature appearance,
as thereby he was prevented from making several important
corrections and alterations; as well as from profiting by many
curious hints which he had collected during his travels along
the shores of the Tappaan Sea, and his sojourn at Haverstraw and Esopus.

Finding that there was no longer any immediate necessity for his return to New York, he extended his journey up
to the residence of his relations at Scaghtikoke. On his way
thither, he stopped for some days at Albany, for which city
he is known to have entertained a great partiality. He found
it, however, considerably altered, and was much concerned
at the inroads and improvements which the Yankees were
making, and the consequent decline of the good old Dutch
manners. Indeed, he was informed that these intruders were
making sad innovations in all parts of the State; where they
had given great trouble and vexation to the regular Dutch

settlers, by the introduction of turnpike gates and country schoolhouses. It is said also that Mr. Knickerbocker shook his head sorrowfully at noticing the gradual decay of the great Vander Heyden palace; but was highly indignant at finding that the ancient Dutch church, which stood in the middle of the street, had been pulled down since his last visit.

The fame of Mr. Knickerbocker's history having reached even to Albany, he received much flattering attention from its worthy burghers, some of whom, however, pointed out two or three very great errors he had fallen into, particularly that of suspending a lump of sugar over the Albany tea-tables, which, they assured him, had been discontinued for some years past. Several families, moreover, were somewhat piqued that their ancestors had not been mentioned in his work, and showed great jealousy of their neighbors who had been thus distinguished; while the latter, it must be confessed, plumed themselves vastly thereupon; considering these recordings in the light of letters-patent of nobility, establishing their claims to ancestry—which, in this republican country, is a matter of no little solicitude and vainglory.

It is also said that he enjoyed high favor and countenance from the governor, who once asked him to dinner, and was seen two or three times to shake hands with him, when they met in the street; which certainly was going great lengths, considering that they differed in politics. Indeed, certain of the governor's confidential friends, to whom he could venture to speak his mind freely on such matters, have assured us that he privately entertained a considerable good-will for our author—nay, he even once went so far as to declare, and that openly, too, and at his own table, just after dinner, that "Knickerbocker was a very well-meaning sort of an old gentleman, and no fool." From all which, many have been led to suppose that, had our author been of different politics, and written for the newspapers, instead of wasting his talents on histories, he might have risen to some post of honor and profit; peradventure, to be a notary public, or even a Justice in the Ten Pound Court.

Besides the honors and civilities already mentioned, he was much caressed by the literati of Albany; particularly by Mr. John Cook, who entertained him very hospitably at his circulating library and reading-room, where they used to drink Spa water and talk about the ancients. He found Mr. Cook a man after his own heart—of great literary research, and a curious collector of books. At parting, the latter, in testimony of friendship, made him a present of the two oldest works in his collection; which were the earliest edition of the "Heidelburgh Catechism," and Adrian Vander Donck's famous account of the New Netherlands; by the last of which Mr. Knickerbocker profited greatly in this his second edition.

Having passed some time very agreeably at Albany, our author proceeded to Scaghtikoke; where, it is but justice to say, he was received with open arms. and treated with wonderful loving-kindness. He was much looked up to by the family, being the first historian of the name; and was considered almost as great a man as his cousin the Congressman —with whom, by the bye, he became perfectly reconciled, and contracted a strong friendship.

In spite, however, of the kindness of his relations, and their great attention to his comforts, the old gentleman soon became restless and discontented. His history being published, he had no longer any business to occupy his thoughts, or any scheme to excite his hopes and anticipations. This, to a busy mind like his, was a truly deplorable situation; and, had he not been a man of inflexible morals and regular habits, there would have been great danger of his taking to politics, or drinking—both which pernicious vices we daily see men driven to by mere spleen and idleness.

It is true he sometimes employed himself in preparing a second edition of his history, wherein he endeavored to correct and improve many passages with which he was dissatisfied, and to rectify some mistakes that had crept into it; for he was particularly anxious that his work should be noted for its authenticity, which, indeed, is the very life and soul of history.—But the glow of composition had departed—he had to leave many places untouched which he would fain have altered; and even where he did make alterations, he seemed always in doubt whether they were for the better or the worse.

After a residence of some time at Scaghtikoke, he began to feel a strong desire to return to New York, which he ever regarded with the warmest affection; not merely because it was his native city, but because he really considered it the very best city in the whole world. On his return, he entered into the full enjoyment of the advantages of a literary reputation. He was continually importuned to write advertisements, petitions, hand-bills, and productions of similar import; and, although he never meddled with the public papers, yet had he the credit of writing innumerable essays, and smart things, that appeared on all subjects and all sides of the question; in all which he was clearly detected "by his style."

He contracted, moreover, a considerable debt at the post-office, in consequence of the numerous letters he received from authors and printers soliciting his subscription; and he was applied to by every charitable society for yearly donations, which he gave very cheerfully, considering these applications as so many compliments. He was once invited to a great corporation dinner; and was even twice summoned to attend as a juryman at the court of quarter sessions. Indeed, so renowned did he become that he could no longer pry about, as formerly, in all holes and corners of the city, according to the bent of his humor, unnoticed and uninterrupted; but several times when he has been sauntering the streets, on his usual rambles of observation, equipped with his cane and cocked hat, the little boys at play have been known to cry, "There goes Diedrich!"—at which the old gentleman seemed not a little pleased, looking upon these salutations in the light of the praises of posterity.

In a word, if we take into consideration all these various honors and distinctions, together with an exuberant eulogium, passed on him in the "Port Folio"—(with which, we are told, the old gentleman was so much overpowered that he was sick for two or three days)—it must be confessed that few authors have ever lived to receive such illustrious rewards, or have so completely enjoyed in advance their own immortality.

After his return from Scaghtikoke, Mr. Knickerbocker took up his residence at a little rural retreat, which the Stuyvesants had granted him on the family domain, in gratitude for his honorable mention of their ancestor. It was pleasantly situated on the borders of one of the salt marshes beyond Corlear's Hook: subject, indeed, to be occasionally overflowed, and much infested, in the summer time, with mosquitoes; but otherwise very agreeable, producing abundant crops of salt grass and bull-rushes.

Here, we are sorry to say, the good old gentleman fell dangerously ill of a fever, occasioned by the neighboring marshes. When he found his end approaching, he disposed of his worldly affairs, leaving the bulk of his fortune to the New York Historical Society; his "Heidelburgh Catechism," and Vander Donck's work, to the city library; and his saddle-bags to Mr. Handaside. He forgave all his enemies— that is to say, all who bore any enmity toward him; for as to himself, he declared he died in good-will with all the world. And, after dictating several kind messages to his relations at Scaghtikoke, as well as to certain of our most substantial Dutch citizens, he expired in the arms of his friend the librarian.

His remains were interred, according to his own request, in St. Mark's churchyard, close by the bones of his favorite hero, Peter Stuyvesant: and it is rumored that the Historical Society have it in mind to erect a wooden monument to his memory in the Bowling Green.

TO THE PUBLIC

"To rescue from oblivion the memory of former incidents, and to render a just tribute of renown to the many great and wonderful transactions of our Dutch progenitors, Diedrich Knickerbocker, native of the city of New York, produces this historical essay." * Like the great Father of History, whose words I have just quoted, I treat of times long past, over which the twilight of uncertainty had already thrown its shadows, and the night of forgetfulness was about to descend forever. With great solicitude had I long beheld the early history of this venerable and ancient city gradually slipping from our grasp, trembling on the lips of narrative old age, and day by day dropping piecemeal into the tomb. In a little while, thought I, and those reverend Dutch burghers, who serve as the tottering monuments of good old times, will be gathered to their fathers; their children, engrossed by the empty pleasures or insignificant transactions of the present age, will neglect to treasure up the recollections of the past, and posterity will search in vain for memorials of the days of the Patriarchs. The origin of our city will be buried in eternal oblivion, and even the names and achievements of Wouter Van Twiller, William Kieft, and Peter Stuyvesant, be enveloped in doubt and fiction, like those of Romulus and Remus, of Charlemagne, King Arthur, Rinaldo, and Godfrey of Boulogne.

Determined, therefore, to avert if possible this threatened misfortune, I industriously set myself to work to gather together all the fragments of our infant history which still existed, and, like my revered prototype, Herodotus, where no

---

* Beloe's Herodotus.

written records could be found, I have endeavored to continue the chain of history by well-authenticated traditions.

In this arduous undertaking, which has been the whole business of a long and solitary life, it is incredible the number of learned authors I have consulted, and all but to little purpose. Strange as it may seem, though such multitudes of excellent works have been written about this country, there are none extant which give any full and satisfactory account of the early history of New York, or of its three first Dutch governors. I have, however, gained much valuable and curious matter from an elaborate manuscript written in exceeding pure and classic Low Dutch, excepting a few errors in orthography, which was found in the archives of the Stuyvesant family. Many legends, letters, and other documents have I likewise gleaned, in my researches among the family chests and lumber garrets of our respectable Dutch citizens; and I have gathered a host of well-authenticated traditions from divers excellent old ladies of my acquaintance, who requested that their names might not be mentioned. Nor must I neglect to acknowledge how greatly I have been assisted by that admirable and praiseworthy institution, the New York Historical Society, to which I here publicly return my sincere acknowledgments.

In the conduct of this inestimable work, I have adopted no individual model; but, on the contrary, have simply contented myself with combining and concentrating the excellences of the most approved ancient historians. Like Zenophon, I have maintained the utmost impartiality, and the strictest adherence to truth, thoughout my history. I have enriched it, after the manner of Sallust, with various characters of ancient worthies, drawn at full length and faithfully colored. I have seasoned it with profound political speculations like Thucydides, sweetened it with the graces of sentiment like Tacitus, and infused into the whole the dignity, the grandeur, and magnificence of Livy.

I am aware that I shall incur the censure of numerous very learned and judicious critics, for indulging too fre-

quently in the bold excursive manner of my favorite Herodotus. And to be candid, I have found it impossible always
to resist the allurements of those pleasing episodes, which,
like flowery banks and fragrant bowers, beset the dusty road
of the historian, and entice him to turn aside and refresh
himself from his wayfaring. But I trust it will be found
that I have always resumed my staff, and addressed myself
to my weary journey with renovated spirits, so that both my
readers and myself have been benefited by the relaxation.

Indeed, though it has been my constant wish and uniform endeavor to rival Polybius himself, in observing the
requisite unity of History, yet the loose and unconnected
manner in which many of the facts herein recorded have
come to hand rendered such an attempt extremely difficult.
This difficulty was likewise increased by one of the grand
objects contemplated in my work, which was to trace the
rise of sundry customs and institutions in this best of cities,
and to compare them, when in the germ of infancy, with
what they are in the present old age of knowledge and improvement.

But the chief merit on which I value myself, and found
my hopes for future regard, is that faithful veracity with
which I have compiled this invaluable little work; carefully
winnowing away the chaff of hypothesis, and discarding the
tares of fable, which are too apt to spring up and choke the
seeds of truth and wholesome knowledge.—Had I been anxious to captivate the superficial throng who skim like swallows over the surface of literature, or had I been anxious to
commend my writings to the pampered palates of literary
epicures, I might have availed myself of the obscurity that
overshadows the infant years of our city to introduce a thousand pleasing fictions. But I have scrupulously discarded
many a pithy tale and marvelous adventure, whereby the
drowsy ear of summer indolence might be inthralled; jeal-
ously maintaining that fidelity, gravity and dignity which
should ever distinguish the historian. "For a writer of this
class," observes an elegant critic, "must sustain the char-

acter of a wise man, writing for the instruction of posterity; one who has studied to inform himself well, who has pondered his subject with care, and addresses himself to our judgment rather than to our imagination."

Thrice happy, therefore, is this our renowned city, in having incidents worthy of swelling the theme of history; and doubly thrice happy is it in having such a historian as myself to relate them. For, after all, gentle reader, cities *of themselves*, and, in fact, empires *of themselves*, are nothing without a historian. It is the patient narrator who records their prosperity as they rise—who blazons forth the splendor of their noontide meridian—who props their feeble memorials as they totter to decay—who gathers together their scattered fragments as they rot—and who piously, at length, collects their ashes into the mausoleum of his work, and rears a monument that will transmit their renown to all succeeding ages.

What has been the fate of many fair cities of antiquity, whose nameless ruins encumber the plains of Europe and Asia, and awaken the fruitless inquiry of the traveler? They have sunk into dust and silence—they have perished from remembrance, for want of a historian! The philanthropist may weep over their desolation—the poet may wander among their mouldering arches and broken columns, and indulge the visionary flights of his fancy—but alas! alas! the modern historian, whose pen, like my own, is doomed to confine itself to dull matter of fact, seeks in vain among their oblivious remains for some memorial that may tell the instructive tale of their glory and their ruin.

"Wars, conflagrations, deluges," says Aristotle, "destroy nations, and with them all their monuments, their discoveries, and their vanities.—The torch of science has more than once been extinguished and rekindled—a few individuals, who have escaped by accident, reunite the thread of generations."

The same sad misfortune which has happened to so many ancient cities will happen again, and from the same sad cause, to nine-tenths of those which now flourish on the face

of the globe. With most of them, the time for recording
their early history is gone by; their origin, their foundation,
together with the eventful period of their youth, are forever
buried in the rubbish of years; and the same would have
been the case with this fair portion of the earth, if I had not
snatched it from obscurity in the very nick of time, at the
moment that those matters herein recorded were about entering into the widespread insatiable maw of oblivion—if I had
not dragged them out, as it were, by the very locks, just as
the monster's adamantine, fangs were closing upon them forever! And here have I, as before observed, carefully collected, collated, and arranged them, scrip and scrap, "*punt
en punt, gat en gat*," and commenced, in this little work, a
history to serve as a foundation on which other historians
may hereafter raise a noble superstructure, swelling in process of time, until "Knickerbocker's New York" may be
equally voluminous with "Gibbon's Rome," or "Hume and
Smollett's England"!

And now indulge me for a moment, while I lay down my
pen, skip to some little eminence at the distance of two or three
hundred years ahead; and, casting back a bird's-eye glance
over the waste of years that is to roll between, discover myself—little I!—at this moment the progenitor, prototype, and
precursor of them all, posted at the head of this host of literary worthies, with my book under my arm and New York
on my back, pressing forward, like a gallant commander, to
honor and immortality.

Such are the vainglorious imaginings that will now and
then enter into the brain of the author—that irradiate, as
with celestial light, his solitary chamber, cheering his weary
spirits, and animating him to persevere in his labors. And
I have freely given utterance to these rhapsodies, whenever
they have occurred; not, I trust, from an unusual spirit of
egotism, but merely that the reader may for once have an
idea how an author thinks and feels while he is writing—a
kind of knowledge very rare and curious, and much to be
desired.

A HISTORY OF NEW YORK

BOOK ONE

*CONTAINING DIVERS INGENIOUS THEORIES AND PHILO-
SOPHIC SPECULATIONS, CONCERNING THE CREATION
AND POPULATION OF THE WORLD, AS CONNECTED
WITH THE HISTORY OF NEW YORK*

CHAPTER ONE

DESCRIPTION OF THE WORLD

ACCORDING to the best authorities, the world in which we
dwell is a huge, opaque, reflecting, inanimate mass, floating
in the vast ethereal ocean of infinite space. It has the form
of an orange, being an oblate spheroid, curiously flattened
at opposite parts, for the insertion of two imaginary poles,
which are supposed to penetrate and unite at the center;
thus forming an axis on which the mighty orange turns with
a regular diurnal revolution.

The transitions of light and darkness, whence proceed the
alternations of day and night, are produced by this diurnal
revolution successively presenting the different parts of the
earth to the rays of the sun. The latter is, according to the
best, that is to say, the latest accounts, a luminous or fiery
body, of a prodigious magnitude, from which this world is
driven by a centrifugal or repelling power, and to which it is
drawn by a centripetal or attractive force, otherwise called
the attraction of gravitation; the combination, or rather the
counteraction, of these two opposing impulses producing a
circular and annual revolution. Hence result the different

seasons of the year, viz., spring, summer, autumn, and winter.

This I believe to be the most approved modern theory on the subject—though there be many philosophers who have entertained very different opinions; some, too, of them entitled to much deference from their great antiquity and illustrious characters. Thus it was advanced by some of the ancient sages that the earth was an extended plain, supported by vast pillars; and by others, that it rested on the head of a snake, or the back of a huge tortoise—but as they did not provide a resting-place for either the pillars or the tortoise, the whole theory fell to the ground, for want of proper foundation.

The Brahmins assert that the heavens rest upon the earth, and the sun and moon swim therein like fishes in the water, moving from east to west by day, and gliding along the edge of the horizon to their original stations during the night;* while, according to the pauranicas of India, it is a vast plain, encircled by seven oceans of milk, nectar, and other delicious liquids; that it is studded with seven mountains, and ornamented in the center by a mountainous rock of burnished gold; and that a great dragon occasionally swallows up the moon, which accounts for the phenomena of lunar eclipses.†

Besides these, and many other equally sage opinions, we have the profound conjectures of Aboul-Hassan-Aly, son of Al Khan, son of Aly, son of Abderrahman, son of Abdallah, son of Masoud-el-Had-heli, who is commonly called Masoudi, and surnamed Cothbeddin, but who takes the humble title of Laheb-ar-rasoul, which means the companion of the embassador of God. He has written a universal history, entitled "Mouroudge-ed-dharab, or the Golden Meadows, and the Mines of Precious Stones." ‡ In this valuable work he has

---

* Faria y Souza.   Mick. Lus. note b. 7.
† Sir W. Jones, Diss. Antiq. Ind. Zod.
‡ Mss. Bibliot. Roi. Fr.

related the history of the world, from the creation down to
the moment of writing; which was under the Caliphate of
Mothi Billah, in the month Dgioumadi-el-aoual of the 336th
year of the Hegira or flight of the Prophet. He informs us
that the earth is a huge bird, Mecca and Medina constituting
the head, Persia and India the right wing, the land of Gog
the left wing, and Africa the tail. He informs us, moreover,
that an earth has existed before the present (which he con-
siders as a mere chicken of 7,000 years), that it has undergone divers deluges, and that, according to the opinion of
some well-informed Brahmins of his acquaintance, it will be
renovated every seventy thousandth hazarouam; each hazarouam consisting of 12,000 years.

These are a few of the many contradictory opinions of
philosophers concerning the earth, and we find that the
learned have had equal perplexity as to the nature of the
sun. Some of the ancient philosophers have affirmed that
it is a vast wheel of brilliant fire;* others, that it is merely
a mirror or sphere of transparent crystal;† and a third class,
at the head of whom stands Anaxagoras, maintained that it
was nothing but a huge ignited mass of iron or stone—indeed, he declared the heavens to be merely a vault of stone—
and that the stars were stones whirled upward from the
earth, and set on fire by the velocity of its revolutions.‡ But
I give little attention to the doctrines of this philosopher, the
people of Athens having fully refuted them, by banishing
him from their city; a concise mode of answering unwelcome doctrines much resorted to in former days. Another
sect of philosophers do declare that certain fiery particles
exhale constantly from the earth, which, concentrating in a
single point of the firmament by day, constitute the sun, but

---

* Plutarch de Placitis Philosoph. lib. iii. cap. 20.
† Achill. Tat. Isag. cap. 19. Ap. Petav. t. iii. p. 81. Stob. Eclog.
Phys. lib. i. p. 56. Plut. de Plac. Phi.
‡ Diogenes Laertius in Anaxag. l. ii. sec. 8. Plat. Apol. t. i. p. 26.
Plut. de Plac. Philo. Xenoph. Mem. l. iv. p. 815.

being scattered and rambling about in the dark at night, collect in various points and form stars. These are regularly burned out and extinguished, not unlike to the lamps in our streets, and require a fresh supply of exhalations for the next occasion.*

It is even recorded that at certain remote and obscure periods, in consequence of a great scarcity of fuel, the sun has been completely burned out, and sometimes not rekindled for a month at a time—a most melancholy circumstance, the very idea of which gave vast concern to Heraclitus, that worthy weeping philosopher of antiquity. In addition to these various speculations, it was the opinion of Herschel that the sun is a magnificent, habitable abode; the light it furnishes arising from certain empyreal, luminous or phosphoric clouds, swimming in its transparent atmosphere.†

But we will not enter further at present into the nature of the sun, that being an inquiry not immediately necessary to the development of this history; neither will we embroil ourselves in any more of the endless disputes of philosophers touching the form of this globe, but content ourselves with the theory advanced in the beginning of this chapter, and will proceed to illustrate, by experiment, the complexity of motion therein ascribed to this our rotatory planet.

Professor Von Poddingcoft (or Puddinghead, as the name may by rendered into English) was long celebrated in the University of Leyden, for profound gravity of deportment, and a talent of going to sleep in the midst of examinations, to the infinite relief of his hopeful students, who thereby worked their way through college with great ease and little study. In the course of one of his lectures, the learned professor, seizing a bucket of water, swung it round his head at arms-length. The impulse with which he threw the vessel from him, being a centrifugal force, the retention of his arm

---

* Aristot. Meteor. l. ii. c. 2. Idem. Probl. sec. 15. Stob. Ecl. Phys. l i. p. 55. Bruck. Hist. Phil. t. i. p. 1154, etc.

† Philos. Trans. 1795, p. 72. Idem. 1801, p. 265. Nich. Philos. Journ. i. p. 18.

operating as a centripetal power, and the bucket, which was
a substitute for the earth, describing a circular orbit round
about the globular head and ruby visage of Professor Von
Poddingcoft, which formed no bad representation of the sun.
All of these particulars were duly explained to the class of
gaping students around him. He apprised them, moreover,
that the same principle of gravitation, which retained the
water in the bucket, restrains the ocean from flying from the
earth in its rapid revolutions; and he further informed them,
that should the motion of the earth be suddenly checked, it
would incontinently fall into the sun, through the centripetal
force of gravitation; a most ruinous event to this planet, and
one which would also obscure, though it most probably would
not extinguish, the solar luminary. An unlucky stripling,
one of those vagrant geniuses who seem sent into the world
merely to annoy worthy men of the puddinghead order,
desirous of ascertaining the correctness of the experiment,
suddenly arrested the arm of the professor, just at the moment that the bucket was in its zenith, which immediately
descended with astonishing precision upon the head of the
philosopher. A hollow sound, and a red-hot hiss, attended
the contact; but the theory was in the amplest manner illustrated, for the unfortunate bucket perished in the conflict;
but the blazing countenance of Professor Von Poddingcoft
emerged from amid the waters, glowing fiercer than ever
with unutterable indignation, whereby the students were
marvelously edified, and departed considerably wiser than
before.

It is a mortifying circumstance, which greatly perplexes
many a philosopher, that Nature often refuses to second his
efforts; so that after having invented one of the most ingenious and natural theories imaginable, she will have the
perverseness to act directly in the teeth of it. This is a
manifest and unmerited grievance, since it throws the censure of the vulgar and unlearned entirely upon the philosopher; whereas the fault is to be ascribed to dame Nature,
who, with the proverbial fickleness of her sex, is continually

indulging in coquetries and caprices; and who seems to take pleasure in violating all philosophic rules, and jilting the most learned and indefatigable of her adorers. Thus it happened with respect to the foregoing explanation of the motion of our planet; it appears that the centrifugal force has long since ceased to operate, while its antagonist remains in undiminished potency: the world, therefore, ought, in strict propriety, to tumble into the sun; philosophers were convinced that it would do so, and awaited in anxious impatience the fulfillment of their prognostics. But the untoward planet pertinaciously continued her course, notwithstanding that she had reason, philosophy, and a whole university of learned professors, opposed to her conduct. The philosophers took this in very ill part, and it is thought they would never have pardoned the slight which they conceived put upon them by the world, had not a good-natured professor kindly officiated as a mediator between the parties and effected a reconciliation.

Finding the world would not accommodate itself to the theory, he wisely accommodated the theory to the world: he informed his brother philosophers that the circular motion of the earth round the sun was no sooner engendered by the conflicting impulses above described than it became a regular revolution, independent of the causes which gave it origin. His learned brethren readily joined in the opinion, heartily glad of any explanation that would decently extricate them from their embarrassment—and ever since that era the world has been left to take her own course, and to revolve around the sun in such orbit as she thinks proper.

CHAPTER TWO

COSMOGONY, OR CREATION OF THE WORLD; WITH A MULTI-
TUDE OF EXCELLENT THEORIES BY WHICH THE CREA-
TION OF A WORLD IS SHOWN TO BE NO SUCH DIFFI-
CULT MATTER AS COMMON FOLK WOULD IMAGINE

HAVING thus briefly introduced my reader to the world,
and given him some idea of its form and situation, he will
naturally be curious to know from whence it came, and how
it was created. And, indeed, the clearing up of these points
is absolutely essential to my history, inasmuch as, if this
world had not been formed, it is more than probable that this
renowned island on which is situated the city of New York
would never have had an existence. The regular course of
my history, therefore, requires that I should proceed to notice
the cosmogony, or formation of this our globe.

And now I give my readers fair warning that I am
about to plunge, for a chapter or two, into as complete a
labyrinth as ever historian was perplexed withal; therefore,
I advise them to take fast hold of my skirts, and keep close
at my heels, venturing neither to the right hand nor to the
left, lest they get bemired in a slough of unintelligible learning, or have their brains knocked out by some of those hard
Greek names which will be flying about in all directions.
But should any of them be too indolent or chicken-hearted to
accompany me in this perilous undertaking, they had better
take a short cut round, and wait for me at the beginning of
some smoother chapter.

Of the creation of the world we have a thousand contradictory accounts; and though a very satisfactory one is
furnished us by divine revelation, yet every philosopher feels
himself in honor bound to furnish us with a better. As an
impartial historian, I consider it my duty to notice their

several theories, by which mankind have been so exceedingly
edified and instructed.

Thus it was the opinion of certain ancient sages that the
earth and the whole system of the universe was the deity
himself;* a doctrine most strenuously maintained by Zenoph-
anes and the whole tribe of Eleatics, as also by Strabo and
the sect of peripatetic philosophers. Pythagoras likewise inculcated the famous numerical system of the monad, dyad,
and triad, and by means of his sacred quaternary elucidated
the formation of the world, the arcana of nature, and the
principles both of music and morals.† Other sages adhered
to the mathematical system of squares and triangles; the
cube, the pyramid, and the sphere, the tetrahedron, the oc-
tahedron, the icosahedron, and the dodecahedron.‡ While
others advocated the great elementary theory, which refers
the construction of our globe, and all that it contains, to the
combination of four material elements—air, earth, fire, and
water; with the assistance of a fifth, an immaterial and
vivifying principle.

Nor must I omit to mention the great atomic system,
taught by old Moschus, before the siege of Troy; revived by
Democritus, of laughing memory; improved by Epicurus,
that king of good fellows, and modernized by the fanciful
Descartes.

But I decline inquiring whether the atoms, of which the
earth is said to be composed, are eternal or recent; whether
they are animate or inanimate; whether, agreeably to the
opinion of the atheists, they were fortuitously aggregated,
or, as the theists maintain, were arranged by a supreme
intelligence.§ Whether, in fact, the earth be an insensate

---

* Aristot. ap. Cic. lib. i. cap. 3.

† Aristot. Metaph. lib. i. c. 5. Idem. de Cœlo, I. iii. c. I. Rous-
seau mem. sur. Musique ancien. p. 39. Plutarch de Plac. Philos. lib. i.
cap. 3.

‡ Tim. Locr. ap. Plato, t. iii. p. 90.

§ Aristot. Nat. Auscult. l. ii. cap. 6. Aristoph. Metaph. lib. i.
cap. 3. Cic. de Nat. Deor. lib. i. cap. 10. Justin. Mart. orat. ad gent.
p. 20.

clod, or whether it be animated by a soul;* which opinion
was strenuously maintained by a host of philosophers, at the
head of whom stands the great Plato, that temperate sage,
who threw the cold water of philosophy on the form of sexual
intercourse, and inculcated the doctrine of Platonic love—an
exquisitely refined intercourse, but much better adapted to
the ideal inhabitants of his imaginary island of Atlantis
than to the sturdy race, composed of rebellious flesh and
blood, which populates the little matter-of-fact island we
inhabit.

Beside these systems, we have, moreover, the poetical
theogony of old Hesiod, who generated the whole universe
in the regular mode of procreation; and the plausible opinion
of others, that the earth was hatched from the great egg of
night, which floated in chaos, and was cracked by the horns
of the celestial bull. To illustrate this last doctrine, Burnet,
in his theory of the earth,† has favored us with an accurate
drawing and description, both of the form and texture of this
mundane egg; which is found to bear a marvelous resemblance to that of a goose. Such of my readers as take a proper
interest in the origin of this our planet will be pleased to
learn that the most profound sages of antiquity, among the
Egyptians, Chaldeans, Persians, Greeks, and Latins, have
alternately assisted at the hatching of this strange bird, and
that their cacklings have been caught, and continued in
different tones and inflections, from philosopher to philosopher, unto the present day.

But while briefly noticing long-celebrated systems of
ancient sages, let me not pass over with neglect those of
other philosophers; which, though less universal and renowned, have equal claims to attention, and equal chance
for correctness. Thus it is recorded by the Brahmins, in the
pages of their inspired Shastah, that the angel Bistnoo, trans-
forming himself into a great boar, plunged into the watery

---

* Mosheim in Cudw. lib. i. cap. 4. Tim. de anim. mund ap. Plat.
lib. iii. Mem. de l'Acad. des Belles Lettr. t. xxxii. p. 19, et al.

† Book i. ch. 5.

abyss, and brought up the earth on his tusks. Then issued from him a mighty tortoise and a mighty snake; and Bistnoo placed the snake erect upon the back of the tortoise, and he placed the earth upon the head of the snake.*

The negro philosophers of Congo affirm that the world was made by the hands of angels, excepting their own country, which the Supreme Being constructed himself, that it might be supremely excellent. And he took great pains with the inhabitants, and made them very black and beautiful; and when he had finished the first man, he was well pleased with him and smoothed him over the face; and hence his nose, and the nose of all his descendants, became flat.

The Mohawk philosophers tell us that a pregnant woman fell down from heaven, and that a tortoise took her upon its back, because every place was covered with water; and that the woman, sitting upon the tortoise, paddled with her hands in the water and raked up the earth, whence it finally happened that the earth became higher than the water.†

But I forbear to quote a number more of these ancient and outlandish philosophers, whose deplorable ignorance, in despite of all their erudition, compelled them to write in languages which but few of my readers can understand; and I shall proceed briefly to notice a few more intelligible and fashionable theories of their modern successors.

And, first, I shall mention the great Buffon, who conjectures that this globe was originally a globe of liquid fire, scintillated from the body of the sun, by the percussion of a comet, as a spark is generated by the collision of flint and steel. That at first it was surrounded by gross vapors, which, cooling and condensing in process of time, constituted, according to their densities, earth, water and air; which gradually arranged themselves, according to their respective gravities, round the burning or vitrified mass that formed their center.

---

* Holwell. Gent. Philosophy.
† Johannes Megapolensis, Jun. Account of Maquaas or Mohawk Indians. 1644.

Hutton, on the contrary, supposes that the waters at first were universally paramount; and he terrifies himself with the idea that the earth must be eventually washed away by the force of rain, rivers and mountain torrents, until it is confounded with the ocean, or, in other words, absolutely dissolves into itself.—Sublime idea! far surpassing that of the tender-hearted damsel of antiquity, who wept herself into a fountain; or the good dame of Narbonne in France, who, for a volubility of tongue unusual in her sex, was doomed to peel five hundred thousand and thirty-nine ropes of onions, and actually run out at her eyes before half the hideous task was accomplished.

Whiston, the same ingenious philosopher who rivaled Ditton in his researches after the longitude (for which the mischief-loving Swift discharged on their heads a most savory stanza), has distinguished himself by a very admirable theory respecting the earth. He conjectures that it was originally a *chaotic comet*, which, being selected for the abode of man, was removed from its eccentric orbit, and whirled round the sun in its present regular motion; by which change of direction order succeeded to confusion in the arrangement of its component parts. The philosopher adds, that the deluge was produced by an uncourteous salute from the watery tail of another comet; doubtless through sheer envy of its improved condition: thus furnishing a melancholy proof that jealousy may prevail, even among the heavenly bodies, and discord interrupt that celestial harmony of the spheres so melodiously sung by the poets.

But I pass over a variety of excellent theories, among which are those of Burnet, and Woodward, and Whitehurst; regretting extremely that my time will not suffer me to give them the notice they deserve—and shall conclude with that of the renowned Dr. Darwin. This learned Theban, who is as much distinguished for rhyme as reason, and for good-natured credulity as serious research, and who has recommended himself wonderfully to the good graces of the ladies, by letting them into all the gallantries, amours, intrigues,

and other topics of scandal of the court of Flora, has fallen
upon a theory worthy of his combustible imagination. According to his opinion, the huge mass of chaos took a sudden
occasion to explode, like a barrel of gunpowder, and in that
act exploded the sun—which in its flight, by a similar convulsion, exploded the earth—which in like guise exploded
the moon—and thus, by a concatenation of explosions, the
whole solar system was produced, and set most systematically
in motion!*

By the great variety of theories here alluded to, every one
of which, if thoroughly examined, will be found surprisingly
consistent in all its parts, my unlearned readers will perhaps
be led to conclude that the creation of a world is not so difficult a task as they at first imagined. I have shown at least
a score of ingenious methods in which a world could be
constructed; and I have no doubt that had any of the
philosophers above quoted the use of a good manageable
comet, and the philosophical warehouse *chaos* at his command, he would engage to manufacture a planet as good,
or, if you would take his word for it, better than this we
inhabit.

And here I cannot help noticing the kindness of Providence, in creating comets for the great relief of bewildered
philosophers. By their assistance more sudden evolutions
and transitions are effected in the system of nature than are
wrought in a pantomimic exhibition, by the wonder-working
sword of Harlequin. Should one of our modern sages, in
his theoretical flights among the stars, ever find himself lost
in the clouds, and in danger of tumbling into the abyss of
nonsense and absurdity, he has but to seize a comet by the
beard, mount astride of its tail, and away he gallops in triumph, like an enchanter on his hippogriff, or a Connecticut
witch on her broomstick, "to sweep the cobwebs out of the
sky."

There is an old and vulgar saying about a "beggar on

---

* Darw. Bot. Garden, Part I. Cant. i. l. 105.

horseback" which I would not for the world have applied to
these reverend philosophers; but I must confess that some of
them, when they are mounted on one of those fiery steeds,
are as wild in their curvetings as was Phæton of yore, when
he aspired to manage the chariot of Phœbus.   One drives his
comet at full speed against the sun, and knocks the world
out of him with the mighty concussion; another, more
moderate, makes his comet a mere beast of burden, carrying
the sun a regular supply of food and fagots; a third, of more
combustible disposition, threatens to throw his comet, like a
bombshell, into the world and blow it up like a powder-
magazine; while a fourth, with no great delicacy to this
planet and its inhabitants, insinuates that some day or other
his comet—my modest pen blushes while I write it—shall
absolutely turn tail upon our world and deluge it with water!
—Surely, as I have already observed, comets were intended
by Providence for the benefit of philosophers, to assist them
in manufacturing theories.

And now, having adduced several of the most prominent
theories that occur to my recollection, I leave my judicious
readers at full liberty to choose among them.   They are all
serious speculations of learned men—all differ essentially
from each other—and all have the same title to belief.   It
has ever been the task of one race of philosophers to demolish
the works of their predecessors, and elevate more splendid
fantasies in their stead, which in their turn are demolished
and replaced by the air-castles of a succeeding generation.
Thus it would seem that knowledge and genius, of which we
make such great parade, consist but in detecting the errors
and absurdities of those who have gone before, and devising
new errors and absurdities, to be detected by those who are
to come after us.   Theories are the mighty soap-bubbles
with which the grown-up children of science amuse themselves—while the honest vulgar stand gazing in stupid admiration, and dignify these learned vagaries with the name
of wisdom!—Surely, Socrates was right in his opinion that
philosophers are but a soberer sort of madmen, busying them-

selves in things totally incomprehensible, or which, if they
could be comprehended, would be found not worth the trouble
of discovery.

For my own part, until the learned have come to an
agreement among themselves, I shall content myself with
the account handed down to us by Moses; in which I do but
follow the example of our ingenious neighbors of Connecticut; who at their first settlement proclaimed that the colony
should be governed by the laws of God—until they had time
to make better.

One thing, however, appears certain—from the unanimous
authority of the before-quoted philosophers, supported by the
evidence of our own senses (which, though very apt to deceive us, may be cautiously admitted as additional testimony),
it appears, I say, and I make the assertion deliberately, without fear of contradiction, that this globe really *was created*,
and that it is composed of *land and water*. It further appears that it is curiously divided and parceled out into continents and islands, among which I boldly declare the renowned ISLAND OF NEW YORK will be found by any one
who seeks for it in its proper place.

CHAPTER THREE

HOW THAT FAMOUS NAVIGATOR, NOAH, WAS SHAMEFULLY
NICKNAMED; AND HOW HE COMMITTED AN UNPARDON-
ABLE OVERSIGHT IN NOT HAVING FOUR SONS. WITH THE
GREAT TROUBLE OF PHILOSOPHERS CAUSED THEREBY,
AND THE DISCOVERY OF AMERICA

NOAH, who is the first seafaring man we read of, begat
three sons, Shem, Ham, and Japhet. Authors, it is true,
are not wanting who affirm that the patriarch had a number
of other children. Thus Berosus makes him father of the
gigantic Titans; Methodius gives him a son called Jonithus,

or Jonicus, and others have mentioned a son named Thuis-
con, from whom descended the Teutons or Teutonic, or, in
other words, the Dutch nation.

I regret exceedingly that the nature of my plan will not
permit me to gratify the laudable curiosity of my readers,
by investigating minutely the history of the great Noah. Indeed, such an undertaking would be attended with more
trouble than many people would imagine; for the good old
patriarch seems to have been a great traveler in his day, and
to have passed under a different name in every country that
he visited. The Chaldeans, for instance, give us his history, merely altering his name into Xisuthrus—a trivial alteration, which, to a historian skilled in etymologies, will
appear wholly unimportant. It appears, likewise, that he
had exchanged his tarpaulin and quadrant among the Chaldeans for the gorgeous insignia of royalty, and appears as
a monarch in their annals. The Egyptians celebrate him
under 'the name of Osiris; the Indians, as Menu; the Greek
and Roman writers confound him with Ogyges, and the
Theban with Deucalion and Saturn. But the Chinese, who
deservedly rank among the most extensive and authentic
historians, inasmuch as they have known the world much
longer than any one else, declare that Noah was no other
than Fohi; and what gives this assertion some air of credibility is, that it is a fact admitted by the most enlightened
literati that Noah traveled into China at the time of the
building of the tower of Babel (probably to improve himself
in the study of languages), and the learned Dr. Shuckford
gives us the additional information that the ark rested on a
mountain on the frontiers of China.

From this mass of rational conjectures and sage hypothe-
ses, many satisfactory deductions might be drawn; but I shall
content myself with the simple fact stated in the Bible; viz.,
that Noah begat three sons, Shem, Ham, and Japhet. It is
astonishing on what remote and obscure contingencies the
great affairs of this world depend, and how events the most
distant, and to the common observer unconnected, are inevi-

tably consequent the one to the other. It remains for the
philosopher to discover these mysterious affinities, and it is
the proudest triumph of his skill to detect and drag forth
some latent chain of causation, which at first sight appears
a paradox to the inexperienced observer. Thus many of my
readers will doubtless wonder what connection the family of
Noah can possibly have with this history—and many will
stare when informed that the whole history of this quarter of
the world has taken its character and course from the simple
circumstance of the patriarch's having but three sons—but
to explain:

Noah, we are told by sundry very credible historians, becoming sole surviving heir and proprietor of the earth in fee
simple, after the deluge, like a good father, portioned out his
estate among his children. To Shem he gave Asia; to Ham,
Africa; and to Japhet, Europe. Now it is a thousand times
to be lamented that he had but three sons, for had there been
a fourth, he would doubtless have inherited America; which,
of course, would have been dragged forth from its obscurity
on the occasion; and thus many a hard-working historian
and philosopher would have been spared a prodigious mass of
weary conjecture respecting the first discovery and population of this country. Noah, however, having provided for
his three sons, looked in all probability upon our country as
mere wild unsettled land, and said nothing about it; and to
this unpardonable taciturnity of the patriarch may we ascribe
the misfortune that America did not come into the world as
early as the other quarters of the globe.

It is true, some writers have vindicated him from this
misconduct toward posterity, and asserted that he really did
discover America. Thus it was the opinion of Mark Lescar-
bot, a French writer, possessed of that ponderosity of thought
and profoundness of reflection so peculiar to his nation, that
the immediate descendants of Noah peopled this quarter of
the globe, and that the old patriarch himself, who still retained a passion for the seafaring life, superintended the
transmigration. The pious and enlightened father, Charle-

voix, a French Jesuit, remarkable for his aversion to the
marvelous, common to all great travelers, is conclusively of
the same opinion; nay, he goes still further, and decides
upon the manner in which the discovery was effected, which
was by sea, and under the immediate direction of the great
Noah. "I have already observed," exclaims the good father,
in a tone of becoming indignation, "that it is an arbitrary
supposition that the grandchildren of Noah were not able to
penetrate into the new world, or that they never thought of
it. In effect, I can see no reason that can justify such a notion. Who can seriously believe that Noah and his immediate descendants knew less than we do, and that the builder
and pilot of the greatest ship that ever was, a ship which
was formed to traverse an unbounded ocean, and had so
many shoals and quicksands to guard against, should be
ignorant of, or should not have communicated to his descendants, the art of sailing on the ocean?" Therefore, they did
sail on the ocean—therefore, they sailed to America—therefore, America was discovered by Noah!

Now all this exquisite chain of reasoning, which is so
strikingly characteristic of the good father, being addressed
to the faith, rather than the understanding, is flatly opposed
by Hans de Laert, who declares it a real and most ridiculous
paradox to suppose that Noah ever entertained the thought
of discovering America; and as Hans is a Dutch writer, I
am inclined to believe he must have been much better acquainted with the worthy crew of the ark than his competitors, and of course possessed of more accurate sources of information. It is astonishing how intimate historians do daily
become with the patriarchs and other great men of antiquity.
As intimacy improves with time, and as the learned are particularly inquisitive and familiar in their acquaintance with
the ancients, I should not be surprised if some future writers
should gravely give us a picture of men and manners as they
existed before the flood, far more copious and accurate than
the Bible; and that, in the course of another century, the
log-book of the good Noah should be as current among his-

torians as the voyages of Captain Cook, or the renowned
history of Robinson Crusoe.

I shall not occupy my time by discussing the huge mass
of additional suppositions, conjectures, and probabilities, respecting the first discovery of this country, with which unhappy historians overload themselves, in their endeavors to
satisfy the doubts of an incredulous world. It is painful to
see these laborious wights panting, and toiling, and sweating
under an enormous burden, at the very outset of their works,
which, on being opened, turns out to be nothing but a mighty
bundle of straw. As, however, by unwearied assiduity, they
seem to have established the fact, to the satisfaction of all
the world, that this country *has been discovered*, I shall
avail myself of their useful labors to be extremely brief upon
this point.

I shall not, therefore, stop to inquire whether America
was first discovered by a wandering vessel of that celebrated
Phœnician fleet, which, according to Herodotus, circumnavi-
gated Africa; or by that Carthaginian expedition, which
Pliny, the naturalist, informs us, discovered the Canary Islands; or whether it was settled by a temporary colony from
Tyre, as hinted by Aristotle and Seneca. I shall neither inquire whether it was first discovered by the Chinese, as Vos-
sius with great shrewdness advances; nor by the Norwegians
in 1102, under Biorn; nor by Behem, the German navigator,
as Mr. Otto has endeavored to prove to the savants of the
learned city of Philadelphia.

Nor shall I investigate the more modern claims of the
Welsh, founded on the voyage of Prince Madoc in the
eleventh century, who having never returned, it has since
been wisely concluded that he must have gone to America,
and that for a plain reason—if he did not go there, where
else could he have gone?—a question which most Socratically
shuts out all further dispute.

Laying aside, therefore, all the conjectures above mentioned, with a multitude of others, equally satisfactory, I
shall take for granted the vulgar opinion that America was

discovered on the 12th of October, 1492, by Christovallo Colon,
a Genoese, who has been clumsily nicknamed Columbus, but
for what reason I cannot discern. Of the voyages and adventures of this Colon I shall say nothing, seeing that they
are already sufficiently known. Nor shall I undertake to
prove that this country should have been called Colonia,
after his name, that being notoriously self-evident.

Having thus happily got my readers on this side of the
Atlantic, I picture them to myself, all impatience to enter
upon the enjoyment of the land of promise, and in full expectation that I will immediately deliver it into their possession. But if I do, may I ever forfeit the reputation of a
regular-bred historian! No—no—most curious and thrice
learned readers (for thrice learned ye are, if ye have read
all that has gone before, and nine times learned shall ye be
if ye read that which comes after), we have yet a world of
work before us. Think you the first discoverers of this fair
quarter of the globe had nothing to do but go on shore and
find a country ready laid out and cultivated like a garden,
wherein they might revel at their ease? No such thing—
they had forests to cut down, underwood to grub up, marshes
to drain, and savages to exterminate.

In like manner, I have sundry doubts to clear away,
questions to resolve, and paradoxes to explain, before I permit you to range at random; but these difficulties once overcome, we shall be enabled to jog on right merrily through
the rest of our history. Thus my work shall, in a manner,
echo the nature of the subject, in the same manner as the
sound of poetry has been found by certain shrewd critics to
echo the sense—this being an improvement in history which
I claim the merit of having invented.

CHAPTER FOUR

SHOWING THE GREAT DIFFICULTY PHILOSOPHERS HAVE HAD
IN PEOPLING AMERICA—AND HOW THE ABORIGINES CAME
TO BE BEGOTTON BY ACCIDENT—TO THE GREAT RELIEF
AND SATISFACTION OF THE AUTHOR

THE next inquiry at which we arrive in the regular course
of our history is to ascertain, if possible, how this country
was originally peopled—a point fruitful of incredible embarrassment; for unless we prove that the aborigines did absolutely come from somewhere, it will be immediately asserted
in this age of skepticism that they did not come at all; and
if they did not come at all, then was this country never popu-
lated—a conclusion perfectly agreeable to the rules of logic,
but wholly irreconcilable to every feeling of humanity, inasmuch as it must syllogistically prove fatal to the innumerable
aborigines of this populous region.

To avert so dire a sophism, and to rescue from logical an-
nihilation so many millions of fellow-creatures, how many
wings of geese have been plundered! what oceans of ink
have been benevolently drained! and how many capacious
heads of learned historians have been addled and forever
confounded! I pause with reverential awe when I contemplate the ponderous tomes, in different languages, with which
they have endeavored to solve this question, so important to
the happiness of society, but so involved in clouds of impenetrable obscurity. Historian after historian has engaged in
the endless circle of hypothetical argument, and after leading us a weary chase through octavos, quartos, and folios,
has let us out at the end of his work just as wise as we were
at the beginning. It was doubtless some philosophical wild-
goose chase of the kind that made the old poet Macrobius rail
in such a passion at curiosity, which he anathematizes most

heartily as "an irksome, agonizing care, a superstitious industry about unprofitable things, an itching humor to see
what is not to be seen, and to be doing what signifies nothing
when it is done." But to proceed:

Of the claims of the children of Noah to the original population of this country I shall say nothing, as they have already been touched upon in my last chapter. The claimants
next in celebrity are the descendants of Abraham. Thus
Christoval Colon (vulgarly called Columbus), when he first
discovered the gold mines of Hispaniola, immediately concluded, with a shrewdness that would have done honor to
a philosopher, that he had found the ancient Ophir, from
whence Solomon procured the gold for embellishing the temple at Jerusalem; nay, Colon even imagined that he saw the
remains of furnaces of veritable Hebraic construction, employed in refining the precious ore.

So golden a conjecture, tinctured with such fascinating
extravagance, was too tempting not to be immediately snapped
at by the gudgeons of learning; and, accordingly, there were
divers profound writers ready to swear to its correctness, and
to bring in their usual load of authorities, and wise surmises,
wherewithal to prop it up. Vetablus and Robertus Stephens
declared nothing could be more clear—Arius Montanus, without the least hesitation, asserts that Mexico was the true
Ophir, and the Jews the early settlers of the country. While
Possevin, Becan, and several other sagacious writers, lug in
a *supposed* prophecy of the fourth book of Esdras, which,
being inserted in the mighty hypothesis, like the keystone of
an arch, gives it, in their opinion, perpetual durability.

Scarce, however, have they completed their goodly superstructure than in trudges a phalanx of opposite authors, with
Hans de Laert, the great Dutchman, at their head, and at
one blow tumbles the whole fabric about their ears. Hans,
in fact, contradicts outright all the Israelitish claims to the
first settlement of this country, attributing all those equivocal
symptoms, and traces of Christianity and Judaism, which
have been said to be found in divers provinces of the new

world, to the *Devil*, who has always affected to counterfeit the worship of the true deity. "A remark," says the knowing old Padre d'Acosta, "made by all good authors who have spoken of the religion of nations newly discovered, and founded besides on the authority of the *fathers of the church.*"

Some writers again, among whom it is with great regret I am compelled to mention Lopez de Gomara, and Juan de Leri, insinuate that the Canaanites, being driven from the land of promise by the Jews, were seized with such a panic that they fled without looking behind them, until, stopping to take breath, they found themselves safe in America. As they brought neither their national language, manners, nor features with them, it is supposed they left them behind in the hurry of their flight—I cannot give my faith to this opinion.

I pass over the supposition of the learned Grotius, who being both an embassador and a Dutchman to boot, is entitled to great respect; that North America was peopled by a strolling company of Norwegians, and that Peru was founded by a colony from China—Manco or Mango Capac, the first Inca, being himself a Chinese. Nor shall I more than barely mention that father Kircher ascribes the settlement of America to the Egyptians, Rudbeck to the Scandinavians, Charron to the Gauls, Juffredus Petri to a skating party from Friesland, Milius to the Celtæ, Marinocus the Sicilian to the Romans, Le Compte to the Phœnicians, Postel to the Moors, Martyn d'Angleria to the Abyssinians, together with the sage surmise of De Laert, that England, Ireland and the Orcades may contend for that honor.

Nor will I bestow any more attention or credit to the idea that America is the fairy region of Zipangri, described by that dreaming traveler, Marco Polo, the Venetian; or that it comprises the visionary island of Atlantis, described by Plato. Neither will I stop to investigate the heathenish assertion of Paracelsus, that each hemisphere of the globe was originally furnished with an Adam and Eve—or the more

flattering opinion of Dr. Romayne, supported by many nameless authorities, that Adam was of the Indian race—or the
startling conjecture of Buffon, Helvetius, and Darwin, so
highly honorable to mankind, that the whole human species is
accidentally descended from a remarkable family of monkeys!

This last conjecture, I must own, came upon me very
suddenly and very ungraciously. I have often beheld the
clown in a pantomime, while gazing in stupid wonder at the
extravagant gambols of a harlequin, all at once electrified by
a sudden stroke of the wooden sword across his shoulders.
Little did I think at such times that it would ever fall to my
lot to be treated with equal discourtesy; and that while I
was quietly beholding these grave philosophers, emulating
the eccentric transformations of the hero of pantomime, they
would on a sudden turn upon me and my readers, and with
one hypothetical flourish metamorphose us into beasts! I
determined from that moment not to burn my fingers with
any more of their theories, but content myself with detailing
the different methods by which they transported the descendants of these ancient and respectable monkeys to this great
field of theoretical warfare.

This was done either by migrations by land or transmi-
grations by water. Thus, Padre Joseph d'Acosta enumer-
ates three passages by land—first by the north of Europe,
secondly by the north of Asia, and thirdly by regions south-
ward of the Straits of Magellan. The learned Grotius
marches his Norwegians by a pleasant route across frozen
rivers and arms of the sea, through Iceland, Greenland,
Estotiland, and Naremberga: and various writers, among
whom are Angleria, De Hornn, and Buffon, anxious for the
accommodation of these travelers, have fastened the two
continents together by a strong chain of deductions—by
which means they could pass over dry-shod. But should
even this fail, Pinkerton, that industrious old gentleman
who compiles books and manufactures geographies, has constructed a natural bridge of ice, from continent to continent,
at the distance of four or five miles from Behring's Straits

—for which he is entitled to the grateful thanks of all the
wandering aborigines who ever did or ever will pass over it.

It is an evil much to be lamented that none of the worthy
writers above quoted could ever commence his work without
immediately declaring hostilities against every writer who
had treated of the same subject.   In this particular, authors
may be compared to a certain sagacious bird, which, in building its nest, is sure to pull to pieces the nests of all the birds
in the neighborhood.   This unhappy propensity tends grievously to impede the progress of sound knowledge.   Theories
are at best but brittle productions, and when once committed
to the stream they should take care that, like the notable pots
which were fellow-voyagers, they do not crack each other.

My chief surprise is that, among the many writers I have
noticed, no one has attempted to prove that this country was
peopled from the moon—or that the first inhabitants floated
hither on islands of ice, as white bears cruise about the north-
ern oceans—or that they were conveyed hither by balloons,
as modern aeronauts pass from Dover to Calais—or by witchcraft, as Simon Magus posted among the stars—or after the
manner of the renowned Scythian Abaris, who, like the New
England witches on full-blooded broomsticks, made most unheard-of journeys on the back of a golden arrow, given him
by the Hyperborean Apollo.

But there is still one mode left by which this country could
have been peopled, which I have reserved for the last, because I consider it worth all the rest; it is—*by accident!*
Speaking of the islands of Solomon, New Guinea, and New
Holland, the profound father Charlevoix observes, "in fine,
all these countries are peopled, and *it is possible* some have
been so *by accident.*   Now if it could have happened in that
manner, why might it not have been at the *same time,* and
by the *same means,* with *the other* part of the globe?"   This
ingenious mode of deducing certain conclusions from possible
premises, is an improvement in syllogistic skill, and proves
the good father superior even to Archimedes, for he can turn
the world without anything to rest his lever upon.   It is only

surpassed by the dexterity with which the sturdy old Jesuit, in another place, cuts the gordian knot.—"Nothing," says he, "is more easy. The inhabitants of both hemispheres are certainly the descendants of the same father. The common father of mankind received an express order from Heaven to people the world, and *accordingly it has been peopled*. To bring this about, it was necessary to overcome all difficulties in the way, *and they have also been overcome!*" Pious logician! How does he put all the herd of laborious theorists to the blush, by explaining, in five words, what it has cost them volumes to prove they knew nothing about.

From all the authorities here quoted, and a variety of others which I have consulted, but which are omitted through fear of fatiguing the unlearned reader—I can only draw the following conclusions, which luckily, however, are sufficient for my purpose—First, that this part of the world has actually *been peopled* (Q.E.D.), to support which we have living proofs in the numerous tribes of Indians that inhabit it. Secondly, that it has been peopled in five hundred different ways, as proved by a cloud of authors, who, from the positiveness of their assertions, seem to have been eye-witnesses to the fact. Thirdly, that the people of this country had a *variety of fathers*, which, as it may not be thought much to their credit by the common run of readers, the less we say on the subject the better. The question, therefore, I trust, is forever at rest.

CHAPTER FIVE

IN WHICH THE AUTHOR PUTS A MIGHTY QUESTION TO THE ROUT BY THE ASSISTANCE OF THE MAN IN THE MOON —WHICH NOT ONLY DELIVERS THOUSANDS OF PEOPLE FROM GREAT EMBARRASSMENT, BUT LIKEWISE CONCLUDES THIS INTRODUCTORY BOOK

THE writer of a history may, in some respects, be likened unto an adventurous knight, who, having undertaken a peril-

ous enterprise, by way of establishing his fame, feels bound
in honor and chivalry to turn back for no difficulty nor hardship, and never to shrink or quail, whatever enemy he may
encounter.   Under this impression, I resolutely draw my
pen, and fall to, with might and main, at those doughty
questions and subtle paradoxes, which, like fiery dragons
and bloody giants, beset the entrance to my history, and
would fain repulse me from the very threshold.   And at this
moment a gigantic question has started up, which I must
needs take by the beard and utterly subdue, before I can advance another step in my historic undertaking; but I trust
this will be the last adversary I shall have to contend with,
and that in the next book I shall be enabled to conduct my
readers in triumph into the body of my work.

The question which has thus suddenly arisen is, what
right had the first discoverers of America to land and take
possession of a country, without first gaining the consent of
its inhabitants, or yielding them an adequate compensation
for their territory?—a question which has withstood many
fierce assaults, and has given much distress of mind to multitudes of kind-hearted folk.   And, indeed, until it be totally
vanquished, and put to rest, the worthy people of America
can by no means enjoy the soil they inhabit with clear right
and title, and quiet, unsullied consciences.

The first source of right, by which property is acquired
in a country, is DISCOVERY.   For as all mankind have an
equal right to anything which has never before been appro-
priated, so any nation that discovers an uninhabited country,
and takes possession thereof, is considered as enjoying full
property, and absolute, unquestionable empire therein.*

This proposition being admitted, it follows clearly that
the Europeans who first visited America were the real discoverers of the same; nothing being necessary to the establishment of this fact but simply to prove that it was totally
uninhabited by man.   This would, at first, appear to be a

---

* Grotius Puffendorf, b. v. c. 4.   Vattel, b. i. c. 18, etc.

point of some difficulty, for it is well known that this quarter
of the world abounded with certain animals that walked erect
on two feet, had something of the human countenance, uttered certain unintelligible sounds very much like language;
in short, had a marvelous resemblance to human beings.
But the zealous and enlightened fathers, who accompanied
the discoverers, for the purpose of promoting the kingdom
of heaven by establishing fat monasteries and bishoprics on
earth, soon cleared up this point, greatly to the satisfaction
of his holiness the Pope and of all Christian voyagers and
discoverers.

They plainly proved, and as there were no Indian writers
arose on the other side the fact was considered as fully admitted and established, that the two-legged race of animals
before mentioned were mere cannibals, detestable monsters,
and many of them giants—which last description of vagrants
have, since the time of Gog, Magog, and Goliath, been considered as outlaws, and have received no quarter in either
history, chivalry, or song. Indeed, even the philosophic
Bacon declared the Americans to be people proscribed by
the laws of nature, inasmuch as they had a barbarous custom
of sacrificing men and feeding upon man's flesh.

Nor are these all the proofs of their utter barbarism:
among many other writers of discernment, Ulloa tells us,
"their imbecility is so visible that one can hardly form an
idea of them different from what one has of the brutes.
Nothing disturbs the tranquillity of their souls, equally insen-
sible to disasters and to prosperity. Though half naked, they
are as contented as a monarch in his most splendid array.
Fear makes no impression on them, and respect as little."
All this is furthermore supported by the authority of M. Bou-
guer: "It is not easy," says he, "to describe the degree of
their indifference for wealth and all its advantages. One
does not well know what motives to propose to them, when
one would persuade them to any service. It is vain to offer
them money; they answer that they are not hungry." And
Vanegas confirms the whole, assuring us that "ambition they

*** C

have none, and are more desirous of being thought strong than valiant. The objects of ambition with us—honor, fame, reputation, riches, posts and distinctions—are unknown among them. So that this powerful spring of action, the cause of so much *seeming* good and *real* evil in the world, has no power over them. In a word, these unhappy mortals may be compared to children, in whom the development of reason is not completed."

Now all these peculiarities, although in the unenlightened states of Greece they would have entitled their possessors to immortal honor, as having reduced to practice those rigid and abstemious maxims, the mere talking about which acquired certain old Greeks the reputation of sages and philosophers;—yet, were they clearly proved in the present instance to betoken a most abject and brutified nature, totally beneath the human character. But the benevolent fathers, who had undertaken to turn these unhappy savages into dumb beasts by dint of argument, advanced still stronger proofs; for as certain divines of the sixteenth century, and among the rest, Lullus, affirm—the Americans go naked and have no beards! —"They have nothing," says Lullus, "of the reasonable animal, except the mask."—And even that mask was allowed to avail them but little, for it was soon found that they were of a hideous copper complexion—and being of a copper complexion, it was all the same as if they were negroes—and negroes are black, "and black," said the pious fathers, devoutly crossing themselves, "is the color of the Devil!" Therefore, so far from being able to own property, they had no right even to personal freedom—for liberty is too radiant a deity to inhabit such gloomy temples. All which circumstance plainly convinced the righteous followers of Cortes and Pizarro that these miscreants had no title to the soil that they infested—that they were a perverse, illiterate, dumb, beardless, black-seed—mere wild beasts of the forests, and, like them, should either be subdued or exterminated.

From the foregoing arguments, therefore, and a variety of others equally conclusive, which I forbear to enumerate, it is clearly evident that this fair quarter of the globe, when first visited by Europeans, was a howling wilderness, inhabited by nothing but wild beasts; and that the transatlantic visitors acquired an incontrovertible property therein, by the *right of discovery*.

This right being fully established, we now come to the next, which is the right acquired by *cultivation*. "The cultivation of the soil," we are told, "is an obligation imposed by nature on mankind. The whole world is appointed for the nourishment of its inhabitants: but it would be incapable of doing it, was it uncultivated. Every nation is then obliged by the law of nature to cultivate the ground that has fallen to its share. Those people, like the ancient Germans and modern Tartars, who, having fertile countries, disdain to cultivate the earth and choose to live by rapine, are wanting to themselves, and *deserve to be exterminated as savage and pernicious beasts.*"*

Now it is notorious that the savages knew nothing of agriculture, when first discovered by the Europeans, but lived a most vagabond, disorderly, unrighteous life—rambling from place to place, and prodigally rioting upon the spontaneous luxuries of nature, without tasking her generosity to yield them anything more; whereas it has been most unquestionably shown that Heaven intended the earth should be plowed and sown, and manured, and laid out into cities, and towns, and farms, and country-seats, and pleasure grounds, and public gardens, all which the Indians knew nothing about—therefore, they did not improve the talents Providence had bestowed on them—therefore, they were careless stewards—therefore, they had no right to the soil—therefore, they deserved to be exterminated.

It is true the savages might plead that they drew all the benefits from the land which their simple wants required—they found plenty of game to hunt, which, together with the roots and uncultivated fruits of the earth, furnished a suffi-

---

* Vattel, b. i. ch. 17.

cient variety for their frugal repasts;—and that as Heaven
merely designed the earth to form the abode and satisfy the
wants of man, so long as those purposes were answered the
will of Heaven was accomplished. —But this only proves how
undeserving they were of the blessings around them—they
were so much the more savages for not having more wants;
for knowledge is in some degree an increase of desires, and
it is this superiority, both in the number and magnitude of
his desires, that distinguishes the man from the beast.
Therefore, the Indians, in not having more wants, were very
unreasonable animals; and it was but just that they should
make way for the Europeans, who had a thousand wants to
their one, and, therefore, would turn the earth to more account, and, by cultivating it, more truly fulfill the will of
Heaven. Besides—Grotius and Lauterbach, and Puffen-
dorff, and Titus, and many wise men besides, who have considered the matter properly, have determined that the property of a country cannot be acquired by hunting, cutting
wood, or drawing water in it—nothing but precise demarca-
tion of limits and the intention of cultivation can establish
the possession. Now, as the savages (probably from never
having read the authors above quoted) had never complied
with any of these necessary forms, it plainly followed that
they had no right to the soil, but that it was completely at
the disposal of the first comers, who had more knowledge,
more wants, and more elegant, that is to say artificial, desires than themselves.

In entering upon a newly-discovered, uncultivated country, therefore, the newcomers were but taking possession of
what, according to the aforesaid doctrine, was their own
property—therefore, in opposing them, the savages were invading their just rights, infringing the immutable laws of
Nature, and counteracting the will of Heaven—therefore,
they were guilty of impiety, burglary, and trespass on the
case—therefore, they were hardened offenders against God
and man—therefore, they ought to be exterminated.

But a more irresistible right than either that I have men-

tioned, and one which will be the most readily admitted by
my reader, provided he be blessed with bowels of charity and
philanthropy, is the right acquired by civilization.   All the
world knows the lamentable state in which these poor savages were found—not only deficient in the comforts of life,
but, what is still worse, most piteously and unfortunately
blind to the miseries of their situation.   But no sooner did
the benevolent inhabitants of Europe behold their sad condition than they immediately went to work to meliorate and
improve it.   They introduced among them rum, gin, brandy,
and the other comforts of life—and it is astonishing to read
how soon the poor savages learned to estimate these blessings
—they likewise made known to them a thousand remedies,
by which the most inveterate diseases are alleviated and
healed; and that they might comprehend the benefits and
enjoy the comforts of these medicines, they previously introduced among them the diseases which they were calculated
to cure.   By these and a variety of other methods was the
condition of these poor savages wonderfully improved; they
acquired a thousand wants of which they had before been
ignorant; and as he has most sources of happiness who has
most wants to be gratified, they were doubtlessly rendered a
much happier race of beings.

But the most important branch of civilization, and which
has most strenuously been extolled by the zealous and pious
fathers of the Romish Church, is the introduction of the
Christian faith.   It was truly a sight that might well inspire
horror, to behold these savages stumbling among the dark
mountains of paganism, and guilty of the most horrible ignorance of religion.   It is true they neither stole nor defrauded; they were sober, frugal, continent, and faithful to
their word; but though they acted right habitually, it was
all in vain, unless they acted so from precept.   The newcomers, therefore, used every method to induce them to
embrace and practice the true religion—except indeed that
of setting them the example.

But notwithstanding all these complicated labors for their

good, such was the unparalleled obstinacy of these stubborn
wretches, that they ungratefully refused to acknowledge the
strangers as their benefactors, and persisted in disbelieving
the doctrines they endeavored to inculcate; most insolently
alleging that from their conduct the advocates of Christianity
did not seem to believe in it themselves. Was not this too
much for human patience?—would not one suppose that the
benign visitants from Europe, provoked at their incredulity,
and discouraged by their stiff-necked obstinacy, would forever have abandoned their shores and consigned them to
their original ignorance and misery?—But no—so zealous
were they to effect the temporal comfort and eternal salvation of these pagan infidels, that they even proceeded from
the milder means of persuasion to the more painful and
troublesome one of persecution, let loose among them whole
troops of fiery monks and furious bloodhounds—purified them
by fire and sword, by stake and fagot; in consequence of
which indefatigable measures the cause of Christian love
and charity was so rapidly advanced that in a very few
years not one-fifth of the number of unbelievers existed in
South America that were found there at the time of its
discovery.

What stronger right need the European settlers advance
to the country than this? Have not whole nations of unin-
formed savages been made acquainted with a thousand imperious wants and indispensable comforts, of which they
were before wholly ignorant?—Have they not been literally
hunted and smoked out of the dens and lurking-places of
ignorance and infidelity, and absolutely scourged into the
right path?—Have not the temporal things, the vain baubles
and filthy lucre of this world, which were too apt to engage
their worldly and selfish thoughts, been benevolently taken
from them? and have they not, instead thereof, been taught to
set their affections on things above?—And finally, to use the
words of a reverend Spanish father, in a letter to his superior
in Spain—"Can any one have the presumption to say that
these savage pagans have yielded anything more than an

inconsiderable recompense to their benefactors, in surrender-
ing to them a little pitiful tract of this dirty sublunary planet,
in exchange for a glorious inheritance in the kingdom of
heaven!"

Here, then, are three complete and undeniable sources of
right established, any one of which was more than ample
to establish a property in the newly-discovered regions of
America. Now, so it has happened in certain parts of this
delightful quarter of the globe, that the right of discovery
has been so strenuously asserted—the influence of cultivation
so industriously extended, and the progress of salvation and
civilization so zealously prosecuted that, what with their
attendant wars, persecutions, oppressions, diseases and other
partial evils that often hang on the skirts of great benefits—
the savage aborigines have, somehow or another, been utterly
annihilated—and this all at once brings me to a fourth right,
which is worth all the others put together.—For the original
claimants to the soil being all dead and buried, and no one
remaining to inherit or dispute the soil, the Spaniards, as the
next immediate occupants, entered upon the possession as
clearly as the hangman succeeds to the clothes of the male-
factor—and as they have Blackstone,* and all the learned
expounders of the law on their side, they may set all actions
of ejectment at defiance—and this last right may be entitled
the RIGHT BY EXTERMINATION, or, in other words, the RIGHT
BY GUNPOWDER.

But lest any scruples of conscience should remain on this
head, and to settle the question of right forever, his holiness
Pope Alexander VI. issued a bull, by which he generously
granted the newly-discovered quarter of the globe to the
Spaniards and Portuguese; who, thus having law and gospel
on their side, and being inflamed with great spiritual zeal,
showed the pagan savages neither favor nor affection, but
prosecuted the work of discovery, colonization, civilization
and extermination, with ten times more fury than ever.

---

* Bl. Com. b. ii. c. 1.

Thus were the European worthies who first discovered
America clearly entitled to the soil; and not only entitled to
the soil, but likewise to the eternal thanks of these infidel
savages, for having come so far, endured so many perils by
sea and land, and taken such unwearied pains, for no other
purpose but to improve their forlorn, uncivilized, and heathenish condition—for having made them acquainted with the
comforts of life; for having introduced among them the light
of religion; and, finally, for having hurried them out of the
world, to enjoy its reward!

But as argument is never so well understood by us selfish
mortals as when it comes home to ourselves, and as I am
particularly anxious that this question should be put to rest
forever, I will suppose a parallel case, by way of arousing
the candid attention of my readers.

Let us suppose, then, that the inhabitants of the moon,
by astonishing advancement in science, and by profound insight into that lunar philosophy, the mere flickerings of which
have of late years dazzled the feeble optics and addled the
shallow brains of the good people of our globe—let us suppose, I say, that the inhabitants of the moon, by these means,
had arrived at such a command of their *energies*, such an
enviable state of *perfectibility*, as to control the elements
and navigate the boundless regions of space. Let us suppose
a roving crew of these soaring philosophers, in the course of
an aerial voyage of discovery among the stars, should chance
to alight upon this outlandish planet.

And here I beg my readers will not have the uncharitableness to smile, as is too frequently the fault of volatile readers,
when perusing the grave speculations of philosophers. I am
far from indulging in any sportive vein at present; nor is the
supposition I have been making so wild as many may deem
it. It has long been a very serious and anxious question with
me, and many a time and oft, in the course of my overwhelming cares and contrivances for the welfare and protection of this my native planet, have I lain awake whole nights
debating in my mind whether it were most probable we

should first discover and civilize the moon or the moon discover and civilize our globe. Neither would the prodigy of
sailing in the air and cruising among the stars be a whit
more astonishing and incomprehensible to us, than was the
European mystery of navigating floating castles through the
world of waters to the simple savages. We have already
discovered the art of coasting along the aerial shores of our
planet, by means of balloons, as the savages had of venturing
along their seacoasts in canoes; and the disparity between
the former, and the aerial vehicles of the philosophers from
the moon, might not be greater than that between the bark
canoes of the savages and the mighty ships of their discoverers. I might here pursue an endless chain of similar speculations; but as they would be unimportant to my subject, I
abandon them to my reader, particularly if he be a philosopher, as matters well worthy of his attentive consideration.

To return then to my supposition—let us suppose that the
aerial visitants I have mentioned, possessed of vastly superior
knowledge to ourselves; that is to say, possessed of superior
knowledge in the art of extermination—riding on hippogriffs
—defended with impenetrable armor—armed with concentrated sunbeams, and provided with vast engines, to hurl
enormous moonstones: in short, let us suppose them, if our
vanity will permit the supposition, as superior to us in knowledge, and consequently in power, as the Europeans were to
the Indians, when they first discovered them. All this is
very possible; it is only our self-sufficiency that makes us
think otherwise; and I warrant the poor savages, before they
had any knowledge of the white men, armed in all the terrors
of glittering steel and tremendous gunpowder, were as perfectly convinced that they themselves were the wisest, the
most virtuous, powerful, and perfect of created beings, as
are at this present moment the lordly inhabitants of Old
England, the volatile populace of France, or even the self-
satisfied citizens of this most enlightened republic.

Let us suppose, moreover, that the aerial voyagers, finding this planet to be nothing but a howling wilderness, in-

habited by us, poor savages and wild beasts, shall take
formal possession of it in the name of his most gracious and
philosophic excellency, the man in the moon.   Finding, however, that their numbers are incompetent to hold it in complete subjection, on account of the ferocious barbarity of its
inhabitants, they shall take our worthy President, the King
of England, the Emperor of Hayti, the mighty Bonaparte,
and the great King of Bantam, and returning to their native
planet, shall carry them to court, as were the Indian chiefs
led about as spectacles in the courts of Europe.

Then making such obeisance as the etiquette of the court
requires, they shall address the puissant man in the moon,
in, as near as I can conjecture, the following terms:

"Most serene and mighty Potentate, whose dominions
extend as far as eye can reach, who rideth on the Great
Bear, useth the sun as a looking-glass, and maintaineth un-
rivaled control over tides, madmen and sea-crabs: We, thy
liege subjects, have just returned from a voyage of discovery,
in the course of which we have landed and taken possession
of that obscure little dirty planet which thou beholdest rolling at a distance.   The five uncouth monsters which we have
brought into this august presence were once very important
chiefs among their fellow-savages, who are a race of beings
totally destitute of the common attributes of humanity; and
differing in everything from the inhabitants of the moon,
inasmuch as they carry their heads upon their shoulders,
instead of under their arms—have two eyes instead of one—
are utterly destitute of tails, and of a variety of unseemly
complexions, particularly of a horrible whiteness—instead of
pea-green.

"We have, moreover, found these miserable savages sunk
into a state of the utmost ignorance and depravity, every
man shamelessly living with his own wife, and rearing his
own children, instead of indulging in that community of
wives enjoined by the law of nature, as expounded by the
philosophers of the moon.   In a word, they have scarcely a
gleam of true philosophy among them, but are, in fact, utter

heretics, ignoramuses, and barbarians. Taking compassion, therefore, on the sad condition of these sublunary wretches, we have endeavored, while we remained on their planet, to introduce among them the light of reason—and the comforts of the moon. We have treated them to mouthfuls of moon-shine, and draughts of nitrous oxide, which they swallowed with incredible voracity, particularly the females; and we have likewise endeavored to instil into them the precepts of lunar philosophy. We have insisted upon their renouncing the contemptible shackles of religion and common sense, and adoring the profound, omnipotent, and all-perfect energy, and the ecstatic, immutable, immovable perfection. But such was the unparalleled obstinacy of these wretched sav-ages that they persisted in cleaving to their wives, and ad-hering to their religion, and absolutely set at naught the sub-lime doctrines of the moon—nay, among other abominable heresies, they even went so far as blasphemously to declare that this ineffable planet was made of nothing more nor less than green cheese!"

At these words, the great man in the moon (being a very profound philosopher) shall fall into a terrible passion, and possessing equal authority over things that do not belong to him, as did whilom his holiness the Pope, shall forthwith issue a formidable bull, specifying "That, whereas a certain crew of Lunatics have lately discovered, and taken possession of, a newly discovered planet called *the earth*—and that whereas it is inhabited by none but a race of two-legged ani-mals, that carry their heads on their shoulders instead of under their arms; cannot talk the lunatic language; have two eyes instead of one; are destitute of tails, and of a hor-rible whiteness, instead of pea-green—therefore, and for a variety of other excellent reasons, they are considered in-capable of possessing any property in the planet they infest, and the right and title to it are confirmed to its original dis-coverers.—And furthermore, the colonists who are now about to depart to the aforesaid planet are authorized and com-manded to use every means to convert these infidel savages from the darkness of Christianity, and make them thorough and absolute Lunatics."

In consequence of this benevolent bull, our philosophic benefactors go to work with hearty zeal. They seize upon our fertile territories, scourge us from our rightful possessions, relieve us from our wives, and when we are unreasonable enough to complain, they will turn upon us and say: Miserable barbarians! ungrateful wretches! have we not come thousands of miles to improve your worthless planet? have we not fed you with moonshine? have we not intoxicated you with nitrous oxide? does not our moon give you light every night, and have you the baseness to murmur when we claim a pitiful return for all these benefits? But finding that we not only persist in absolute contempt of their reasoning and disbelief in their philosophy, but even go so far as daringly to defend our property, their patience shall be exhausted, and they shall resort to their superior powers of argument; hunt us with hippogriffs, transfix us with concentrated sunbeams, demolish our cities with moonstones; until having, by main force, converted us to the true faith, they shall graciously permit us to exist in the torrid deserts of Arabia, or the frozen regions of Lapland, there to enjoy the blessings of civilization and the charms of lunar philosophy, in much the same manner as the reformed and enlightened savages of this country are kindly suffered to inhabit the inhospitable forests of the north, or the impenetrable wilderness of South America.

Thus, I hope, I have clearly proved, and strikingly illustrated, the right of the early colonists to the possession of this country; and thus is this gigantic question completely vanquished. So, having manfully surmounted all obstacles, and subdued all opposition, what remains but that I should forthwith conduct my readers into the city which we have been so long in a manner besieging? But hold—before I proceed another step, I must pause to take breath, and recover from the excessive fatigue I have undergone, in preparing to begin this most accurate of histories. And in this

I do but imitate the example of a renowned Dutch tumbler of antiquity, who took a start of three miles for the purpose of jumping over a hill, but having run himself out of breath by the time he reached the foot, sat himself quietly down for a few moments to blow, and then walked over it at his leisure.

BOOK TWO

TREATING OF THE FIRST SETTLEMENT OF THE PROVINCE
OF NIEUW NEDERLANDTS

CHAPTER ONE

IN WHICH ARE CONTAINED DIVERS REASONS WHY A MAN
SHOULD NOT WRITE IN A HURRY; ALSO, OF MASTER HEN-
DRICK HUDSON, HIS DISCOVERY OF A STRANGE COUNTRY—
AND HOW HE WAS MAGNIFICENTLY REWARDED BY THE
MAGNIFICENCE OF THEIR HIGH MIGHTINESSES

MY great-grandfather, by the mother's side, Hermanus Van Clattercop, when employed to build the large stone church at Rotterdam, which stands about three hundred yards to your left after you turn off from the Boomkeys, and which is so conveniently constructed that all the zealous Christians of Rotterdam prefer sleeping through a sermon there to any other church in the city—my great-grandfather, I say, when employed to build that famous church, did, in the first place, send to Delft for a box of long pipes; then, having purchased a new spitting-box and a hundred weight of the best Virginia, he sat himself down and did nothing for the space of three months but smoke most laboriously. Then did he spend full three months more in trudging on foot, and voyaging in trekschuit, from Rotterdam to Amsterdam—to Delft — to Haerlem — to Leyden — to the

Hague, knocking his head and breaking his pipe against every church in his road. Then did he advance gradually nearer and nearer to Rotterdam, until he came in full sight of the identical spot whereon the church was to be built. Then did he spend three months longer in walking round it and round it, contemplating it, first from one point of view, and then from another—now would he be paddled by it on the canal—now would he peep at it through a telescope from the other side of the Meuse, and now would he take a bird's-eye glance at it, from the top of one of those gigantic wind-mills which protect the gates of the city. The good folks of the place were on the tiptoe of expectation and impatience—notwithstanding all the turmoil of my great-grandfather, not a symptom of the church was yet to be seen; they even began to fear it would never be brought into the world, but that its great projector would lie down and die in labor of the mighty plan he had conceived. At length, having occupied twelve good months in puffing and paddling, and talking and walk-ing—having traveled over all Holland, and even taken a peep into France and Germany—having smoked five hundred and ninety-nine pipes, and three hundred weight of the best Virginia tobacco—my great-grandfather gathered together all that knowing and industrious class of citizens who prefer attending to anybody's business sooner than their own, and having pulled off his coat and five pair of breeches, he ad-vanced sturdily up and laid the corner-stone of the church in the presence of the whole multitude—just at the commence-ment of the thirteenth month.

In a similar manner, and with the example of my worthy ancestor full before my eyes, have I proceeded in writing this most authentic history. The honest Rotterdamers no doubt thought my great-grandfather was doing nothing at all to the purpose, while he was making such a world of prefatory bustle about the building of his church—and many of the ingenious inhabitants of this fair city will unquestionably suppose that all the preliminary chapters, with the discovery, population, and final settlement of America, were totally irrelevant and superfluous—and that the main business, the history of New York, is not a jot more advanced than if I had never taken up my pen. Never were wise people more mistaken in their conjectures; in consequence of going to work slowly and deliberately, the church came out of my grandfather's hands one of the most sumptuous, goodly, and glorious edifices in the known world—excepting that, like our magnificent capitol, at Washington, it was begun on so grand a scale that the good folks could not afford to finish more than the wing of it. So, likewise, I trust, if ever I am able to finish this work on the plan I have commenced (of which, in simple truth, I sometimes have my doubts), it will be found that I have pursued the latest rules of my art, as exemplified in the writings of all the great American historians, and wrought a very large history out of a small subject— which nowadays is considered one of the great triumphs of historic skill. To proceed, then, with the thread of my story.

In the ever-memorable year of Our Lord, 1609, on a Saturday morning, the five-and-twentieth day of March, old style, did that "worthy and irrecoverable discoverer (as he has justly been called), Master Henry Hudson," set sail from Holland in a stout vessel called the "Half Moon," being employed by the Dutch East India Company to seek a north-west passage to China.

Henry (or, as the Dutch historians call him, Hendrick) Hudson, was a seafaring man of renown, who had learned to smoke tobacco under Sir Walter Raleigh, and is said to have been the first to introduce it into Holland, which gained him much popularity in that country, and caused him to find great favor in the eyes of their High Mightinesses, the Lords States-General, and also of the honorable West India Company. He was a short, square, brawny old gentleman, with a double chin, a mastiff mouth, and a broad copper nose, which was supposed in those days to have acquired its fiery hue from the constant neighborhood of his tobacco pipe.

He wore a true Andrea Ferrara, tucked in a leathern belt, and a commodore's cocked hat on one side of his head.

He was remarkable for always jerking up his breeches when
he gave out his orders; and his voice sounded not unlike the
brattling of a tin trumpet—owing to the number of hard
northwesters which he had swallowed in the course of his
seafaring.

Such was Hendrick Hudson, of whom we have heard so
much and know so little: and I have been thus particular in
his description, for the benefit of modern painters and statu-
aries, that they may represent him as he was; and not, according to their common custom with modern heroes, make
him look like Cæsar, or Marcus Aurelius, or the Apollo of
Belvidere.

As chief mate and favorite companion, the commodore
chose Master Robert Juet, of Limehouse, in England. By
some his name has been spelled *Chewit*, and ascribed to the
circumstance of his having been the first man that ever
chewed tobacco; but this I believe to be a mere flippancy;
more especially as certain of his progeny are living at this
day, who write their name Juet. He was an old comrade
and early schoolmate of the great Hudson, with whom he
had often played truant and sailed chip boats in a neighboring pond when they were little boys—from whence it is said
the commodore first derived his bias toward a seafaring life.
Certain it is, that the old people about Limehouse declared
Robert Juet to be an unlucky urchin, prone to mischief, that
would one day or other come to the gallows.

He grew up as boys of that kind often grow up, a rambling, heedless varlet, tossed about in all quarters of the world
—meeting with more perils and wonders than did Sindbad the
Sailor, without growing a whit more wise, prudent, or ill-
natured. Under every misfortune, he comforted himself
with a quid of tobacco, and the truly philosophic maxim
that "it will be all the same thing a hundred years hence."
He was skilled in the art of carving anchors and true-lovers'
knots on the bulkheads and quarter-railings, and was considered a great wit on board ship, in consequence of his playing pranks on everybody around, and now and then even

making a wry face at old Hendrick when his back was turned.

To this universal genius are we indebted for many particulars concerning this voyage; of which he wrote a history at the request of the commodore, who had an unconquerable aversion to writing himself, from having received so many floggings about it when at school. To supply the deficiencies of Master Juet's journal, which is written with true log-book brevity, I have availed myself of divers family traditions, handed down from my great-great-grandfather, who accompanied the expedition in the capacity of cabin-boy.

From all that I can learn, few incidents worthy of remark happened in the voyage; and it mortifies me exceedingly that I have to admit so noted an expedition into my work without making any more of it.

Suffice it to say the voyage was prosperous and tranquil —the crew, being a patient people, much given to slumber and vacuity, and but little troubled with the disease of thinking—a malady of the mind which is the sure breeder of discontent. Hudson had laid in abundance of gin and sauerkraut, and every man was allowed to sleep quietly at his post unless the wind blew. True it is, some slight dissatisfaction was shown on two or three occasions, at certain unreasonable conduct of Commodore Hudson. Thus, for instance, he forbore to shorten sail when the wind was light, and the weather serene, which was considered, among the most experienced Dutch seamen, as certain *weather-breeders*, or prognostics, that the weather would change for the worse. He acted, moreover, in direct contradiction to that ancient and sage rule of the Dutch navigators, who always took in sail at night—put the helm a-port, and turned in— by which precaution they had a good night's rest—were sure of knowing where they were the next morning, and stood but little chance of running down a continent in the dark. He likewise prohibited the seamen from wearing more than five jackets and six pair of breeches, under pretense of rendering them more alert; and no man was permitted to go aloft and hand in sails with a pipe in his mouth, as is the invariable Dutch custom at the present day. All these grievances, though they might ruffle for a moment the constitutional tranquillity of the honest Dutch tars, made but transient impression; they eat hugely, drank profusely, and slept immeasurably, and being under the especial guidance of Providence, the ship was safely conducted to the coast of America; where, after sundry unimportant touchings and standing off and on, she at length, on the fourth day of September, entered that majestic bay which at this day expands its ample bosom before the city of New York, and which had never before been visited by any European.*

It has been traditionary in our family that when the great

* True it is—and I am not ignorant of the fact, that in a certain apocryphal book of voyages, compiled by one Hakluyt, is to be found a letter written to Francis the First, by one Giovanne, or John Verazzani, on which some writers are inclined to found a belief that this delightful bay had been visited nearly a century previous to the voyage of the enterprising Hudson. Now this (albeit it has met with the countenance of certain very judicious and learned men) I hold in utter disbelief, and that for various good and substantial reasons: *First,* Because on strict examination it will be found that the description given by this Verazzani applies about as well to the bay of New York as it does to my night-cap. *Secondly,* Because that this John Verazzani, for whom I already begin to feel a most bitter enmity, is a native of Florence; and everybody knows the crafty wiles of these losel Florentines, by which they filched away the laurels from the brows of the immortal Colon (vulgarly called Columbus), and bestowed them on their officious townsman, Amerigo Vespucci; and I make no doubt they are equally ready to rob the illustrious Hudson of the credit of discovering this beautiful island, adorned by the city of New York, and placing it beside their usurped discovery of South America. And, *thirdly,* I award my decision in favor of the pretensions of Hendrick Hudson, inasmuch as his expedition sailed from Holland, being truly and absolutely a Dutch enterprise—and though all the proofs of the world were introduced on the other side, I would set them at naught, as undeserving my attention. If these three reasons be not sufficient to satisfy every burgher of this ancient city—all I can say is, they are degenerate descendants from their venerable Dutch ancestors, and totally unworthy the trouble of convincing. Thus, therefore, the title of Hendrick Hudson to his renowned discovery is fully vindicated.

navigator was first blessed with a view of this enchanting island, he was observed, for the first and only time in his life, to exhibit strong symptoms of astonishment and admiration. He is said to have turned to Master Juet, and uttered these remarkable words, while he pointed toward this paradise of the new world—"See! there!"—and thereupon, as was always his way when he was uncommonly pleased, he did puff out such clouds of dense tobacco-smoke that in one minute the vessel was out of sight of land, and Master Juet was fain to wait until the winds dispersed this impenetrable fog.

It was indeed—as my great-great-grandfather used to say —though in truth I never heard him, for he died, as might be expected, before I was born—"It was indeed a spot on which the eye might have reveled forever, in ever new and never-ending beauties." The island of Manna-hata spread wide before them, like some sweet vision of fancy, or some fair creation of industrious magic. Its hills of smiling green swelled gently one above another, crowned with lofty trees of luxuriant growth; some pointing their tapering foliage toward the clouds, which were gloriously transparent; and others loaded with a verdant burden of clambering vines, bowing their branches to the earth, that was covered with flowers. On the gentle declivities of the hills were scattered, in gay profusion, the dog-wood, the sumach, and the wild brier, whose scarlet berries and white blossoms glowed brightly among the deep green of the surrounding foliage; and here and there a curling column of smoke rising from the little glens that opened along the shore seemed to promise the weary voyagers a welcome at the hands of their fellow-creatures. As they stood gazing with entranced attention on the scene before them, a red man, crowned with feathers, issued from one of these glens, and after contemplating in silent wonder the gallant ship, as she sat like a stately swan swimming on a silver lake, sounded the war-whoop, and bounded into the woods like a wild deer, to the utter astonishment of the phlegmatic Dutchmen, who had never heard such a noise, or witnessed such a caper, in their whole lives.

Of the transactions of our adventurers with the savages, and how the latter smoked copper pipes, and ate dried currants; how they brought great store of tobacco and oysters; how they shot one of the ship's crew, and how he was buried, I shall say nothing; being that I consider them unimportant to my history. After tarrying a few days in the bay, in order to refresh themselves after their seafaring, our voyagers weighed anchor to explore a mighty river which emptied into the bay. This river, it is said, was known among the savages by the name of the Shatemuck; though we are assured, in an excellent little history published in 1674, by John Josselyn, Gent., that it was called the Mohegan,* and Master Richard Bloome, who wrote some time afterward, asserts the same—so that I very much incline in favor of the opinion of these two honest gentlemen. Be this as it may, up this river did the adventurous Hendrick proceed, little doubting but it would turn out to be the much-looked-for passage to China!

The journal goes on to make mention of divers interviews between the crew and the natives in the voyage up the river; but as they would be impertinent to my history, I shall pass over them in silence, except the following dry joke, played off by the old commodore and his schoolfellow, Robert Juet, which does such vast credit to their experimental philosophy that I cannot refrain from inserting it. "Our master and his mate determined to try some of the chiefe men of the countrey, whether they had any treacherie in them. So they tooke them downe into the cabin and gave them so much wine and aqua vitæ that they were all merrie; and one of them had his wife with him, which sate so modestly as any of our countrey women would do in a strange place. In the end one of them was drunke, which had been aboarde of our

---

* This river is likewise laid down in Ogilvy's map as Manhattan—Noordt—Montaigne and Mauritius river.

ship all the time that we had been there, and that was strange
to them, for they could not tell how to take it." *

Having satisfied himself by this ingenious experiment that
the natives were an honest, social race of jolly roisterers, who
had no objection to a drinking bout, and were very merry in
their cups, the old commodore chuckled hugely to himself,
and thrusting a double quid of tobacco in his cheek, directed
Master Juet to have it carefully recorded, for the satisfaction of all the natural philosophers of the University of Leyden—which done, he proceeded on his voyage, with great
self-complacency. After sailing, however, above a hundred
miles up the river, he found the watery world around him
began to grow more shallow and confined, the current more
rapid, and perfectly fresh—phenomena not uncommon in the
ascent of rivers, but which puzzled the honest Dutchmen
prodigiously. A consultation was therefore called, and having deliberated full six hours, they were brought to a determination, by the ship's running aground—whereupon they
unanimously concluded that there was but little chance of
getting to China in this direction. A boat, however, was
dispatched to explore higher up the river, which, on its return, confirmed the opinion—upon this the ship was warped
off and put about, with great difficulty, being, like most of
her sex, exceedingly hard to govern; and the adventurous
Hudson, according to the account of my great-great-grandfather, returned down the river—with a prodigious flea in
his ear!

Being satisfied that there was little likelihood of getting
to China, unless, like the blind man, he returned from whence
he set out, and took a fresh start, he forthwith recrossed the
sea to Holland, where he was received with great welcome
by the honorable East India Company, who were very much
rejoiced to see him come back safe—with their ship; and at
a large and respectable meeting of the first merchants and
burgomasters of Amsterdam it was unanimously determined

* Juet's Journ. Purch. Pil.

that, as a munificent reward for the eminent services he had
performed, and the important discovery he had made, the
great river Mohegan should be called after his name!—and
it continues to be called Hudson River unto this very day.

CHAPTER TWO

CONTAINING AN ACCOUNT OF A MIGHTY ARK, WHICH FLOAT-
ED, UNDER THE PROTECTION OF ST. NICHOLAS, FROM
HOLLAND TO GIBBET ISLAND—THE DESCENT OF THE
STRANGE ANIMALS THEREFROM — A GREAT VICTORY,
AND A DESCRIPTION OF THE ANCIENT VILLAGE OF
COMMUNIPAW

THE delectable accounts given by the great Hudson, and
Master Juet, of the country they had discovered, excited not
a little talk and speculation among the good people of Holland.   Letters-patent were granted by government to an association of merchants called the West India Company, for
the exclusive trade on Hudson River, on which they erected
a trading house called Fort Aurania or Orange, from whence
did spring the great city of Albany.   But I forbear to dwell
on the various commercial and colonizing enterprises which
took place; among which was that of Mynheer Adrian Block,
who discovered and gave a name to Block Island, since famous for its cheese—and shall barely confine myself to that
which gave birth to this renowned city.

It was some three or four years after the return of the
immortal Hendrick that a crew of honest, Low Dutch colonists set sail from the city of Amsterdam for the shores of
America.   It is an irreparable loss to history, and a great
proof of the darkness of the age and the lamentable neglect
of the noble art of book-making, since so industriously cultivated by knowing sea-captains and learned supercargoes,
that an expedition so interesting and important in its results
should be passed over in utter silence.   To my great-great-

grandfather am I again indebted for the few facts I am enabled to give concerning it—he having once more embarked
for this country, with a full determination, as he said, of ending his days here—and of begetting a race of Knickerbockers
that should rise to be great men in the land.

The ship in which these illustrious adventurers set sail
was called the "Goede Vrouw" or good woman, in compliment to the wife of the President of the West India Company, who was allowed by everybody (except her husband)
to be a sweet-tempered lady—when not in liquor. It was in
truth a most gallant vessel, of the most approved Dutch construction, and made by the ablest ship-carpenters of Amsterdam, who, it is well known, always model their ships after
the fair forms of their countrywomen. Accordingly, it had
one hundred feet in the beam, one hundred feet in the keel,
and one hundred feet from the bottom of the stern-post to
the taffrail. Like the beauteous model, who was declared
to be the greatest belle in Amsterdam, it was full in the bows,
with a pair of enormous catheads, a copper bottom, and,
withal, a most prodigious poop!

The architect, who was somewhat of a religious man, far
from decorating the ship with pagan idols, such as Jupiter,
Neptune, or Hercules (which heathenish abominations, I
have no doubt, occasion the misfortunes and shipwreck of
many a noble vessel), he, I say, on the contrary, did laud-
ably erect for a head a goodly image of St. Nicholas,
equipped with a low, broad-brimmed hat, a huge pair of
Flemish trunk-hose, and a pipe that reached to the end of
the bowsprit. Thus gallantly furnished, the stanch ship
floated sidewise, like a majestic goose, out of the harbor of
the great city of Amsterdam, and all the bells, that were not
otherwise engaged, rang a triple bobmajor on the joyful
occasion.

My great-great-grandfather remarks that the voyage was
uncommonly prosperous, for, being under the especial care
of the ever-revered St. Nicholas, the "Goede Vrouw" seemed
to be endowed with qualities unknown to common vessels.

Thus she made as much leeway as headway, could get along
very nearly as fast with the wind ahead as when it was apoop
—and was particularly great in a calm; in consequence of
which singular advantages she made out to accomplish her
voyage in a very few months, and came to anchor at the
mouth of the Hudson, a little to the east of Gibbet Island.

Here lifting up their eyes they beheld, on what is at present called the Jersey shore, a small Indian village, pleasantly
embowered in a grove of spreading elms, and the natives all
collected on the beach, gazing in stupid admiration at the
"Goede Vrouw." A boat was immediately dispatched to
enter into a treaty with them, and, approaching the shore,
hailed them through a trumpet in the most friendly terms;
but so horribly confounded were these poor savages at the
tremendous and uncouth sound of the Low Dutch language
that they one and all took to their heels and scampered over
the Bergen hills; nor did they stop until they had buried
themselves, head and ears, in the marshes on the other side,
where they all miserably perished to a man—and their bones
being collected and decently covered by the Tammany Society of that day, formed that singular mound called Rattle-
snake Hill, which rises out of the center of the salt marshes,
a little to the east of the Newark Causeway.

Animated by this unlooked-for victory, our valiant heroes
sprang ashore in triumph, took possession of the soil as conquerors in the name of their High Mightinesses the Lords
States-General; and marching fearlessly forward, carried the
village of Communipaw by storm, notwithstanding that it was
vigorously defended by some half-a-score of old squaws and
papooses. On looking about them, they were so transported
with the excellences of the place that they had very little
doubt the blessed St. Nicholas had guided them thither, as
the very spot whereon to settle their colony. The softness
of the soil was wonderfully adapted to the driving of piles;
the swamps and marshes around them afforded ample opportunities for the constructing of dikes and dams; the shallow-
ness of the shore was peculiarly favorable to the building of

docks—in a word, this spot abounded with all the requisites for the foundation of a great Dutch city. On making a faithful report, therefore, to the crew of the "Goede Vrouw," they one and all determined that this was the destined end of their voyage. Accordingly they descended from the "Goede Vrouw," men, women, and children, in goodly groups, as did the animals of yore from the ark, and formed themselves into a thriving settlement, which they called by the Indian name Communipaw.

As all the world is doubtless perfectly acquainted with Communipaw, it may seem somewhat superfluous to treat of it in the present work; but my readers will please to recollect that, notwithstanding it is my chief desire to satisfy the present age, yet I write likewise for posterity, and have to consult the understanding and curiosity of some half a score of centuries yet to come; by which time, perhaps, were it not for this invaluable history, the great Communipaw, like Babylon, Carthage, Nineveh, and other great cities, might be perfectly extinct—sunk and forgotten in its own mud—its inhabitants turned into oysters,* and even its situation a fertile subject of learned controversy and hard-headed investigation among indefatigable historians. Let me then piously rescue from oblivion the humble relics of a place which was the egg from whence was hatched the mighty city of New York!

Communipaw is at present but a small village pleasantly situated among rural scenery, on that beauteous part of the Jersey shore which was known in ancient legends by the name of Pavonia,† and commands a grand prospect of the superb Bay of New York. It is within but half an hour's sail of the latter place, provided you have a fair wind, and may be distinctly seen from the city. Nay, it is a well-known fact, which I can testify from my own experience,

---

* Men by inaction degenerate into oysters.—*Kaimes.*

† Pavonia, in the ancient maps, is given to a tract of country extending from about Hoboken to Amboy.

*** D

that on a clear still summer evening you may hear, from the Battery of New York, the obstreperous peals of broad-mouthed laughter of the Dutch negroes at Communipaw, who, like most other negroes, are famous for their risible powers. This is peculiarly the case on Sunday evenings, when, it is remarked by an ingenious and observant philosopher, who has made great discoveries in the neighborhood of this city, that they always laugh loudest—which he attributes to the circumstance of their having their holiday clothes on.

These negroes, in fact, like the monks in the dark ages, engross all the knowledge of the place, and being infinitely more adventurous and more knowing than their masters, carry on all the foreign trade; making frequent voyages to town in canoes loaded with oysters, buttermilk, and cabbages. They are great astrologers, predicting the different changes of weather almost as accurately as an almanac—they are moreover exquisite performers on three-stringed fiddles: in whistling, they almost boast the far-famed powers of Orpheus's lyre, for not a horse or an ox in the place, when at the plow or before the wagon, will budge a foot until he hears the well-known whistle of his black driver and companion.—And from their amazing skill at casting up accounts upon their fingers they are regarded with as much veneration as were the disciples of Pythagoras of yore, when initiated into the sacred quaternary of numbers.

As to the honest burghers of Communipaw, like wise men and sound philosophers, they never look beyond their pipes, nor trouble their heads about any affairs out of their immediate neighborhood; so that they live in profound and enviable ignorance of all the troubles, anxieties, and revolutions of this distracted planet. I am even told that many among them do verily believe that Holland, of which they have heard so much from tradition, is situated somewhere on Long Island—that *Spiking-devil* and *the Narrows* are the two ends of the world—that the country is still under the dominion of their High Mightinesses, and that the city of New

York still goes by the name of Nieuw Amsterdam. They meet every Saturday afternoon at the only tavern in the place, which bears as a sign a square-headed likeness of the Prince of Orange, where they smoke a silent pipe, by way of promoting social conviviality, and invariably drink a mug of cider to the success of Admiral Van Tromp, who they imagine is still sweeping the British channel, with a broom at his masthead.

Communipaw, in short, is one of the numerous little villages in the vicinity of this most beautiful of cities, which are so many strongholds and fastnesses, whither the primitive manners of our Dutch forefathers have retreated, and where they are cherished with devout and scrupulous strictness. The dress of the original settlers is handed down inviolate, from father to son—the identical broad-brimmed hat, broad-skirted coat, and broad-bottomed breeches continue from generation to generation; and several gigantic knee-buckles of massy silver are still in wear that made gallant display in the days of the patriarchs of Communipaw. The language likewise continues unadulterated by barbarous innovations; and so critically correct is the village schoolmaster in his dialect that his reading of a Low Dutch psalm has much the same effect on the nerves as the filing of a handsaw.

CHAPTER THREE

IN WHICH IS SET FORTH THE TRUE ART OF MAKING A BARGAIN—TOGETHER WITH THE MIRACULOUS ESCAPE OF A GREAT METROPOLIS IN A FOG—AND THE BIOGRAPHY OF CERTAIN HEROES OF COMMUNIPAW

HAVING, in the trifling digression which concluded the last chapter, discharged the filial duty which the city of New York owed to Communipaw, as being the mother settlement, and having given a faithful picture of it as it stands at present, I return with a soothing sentiment of self-approbation to dwell upon its early history. The crew of the "Goede Vrouw" being soon re-enforced by fresh importations from Holland, the settlement went jollily on, increasing in magnitude and prosperity. The neighboring Indians in a short time became accustomed to the uncouth sound of the Dutch language, and an intercourse gradually took place between them and the newcomers. The Indians were much given to long talks, and the Dutch to long silence—in this particular, therefore, they accommodated each other completely. The chiefs would make long speeches about the big bull, the wabash, and the great spirit, to which the others would listen very attentively, smoke their pipes, and grunt *yah myn-her*—whereat the poor savages were wondrously delighted. They instructed the new settlers in the best art of curing and smoking tobacco, while the latter in return made them drunk with true Hollands—and then taught them the art of making bargains.

A brisk trade for furs was soon opened: the Dutch traders were scrupulously honest in their dealings, and purchased by weight, establishing it as an invariable table of avoirdupois that the hand of a Dutchman weighed one pound, and his foot two pounds. It is true, the simple Indians were often puzzled by the great disproportion between bulk and weight, for let them place a bundle of furs, never so large, in one scale, and a Dutchman put his hand or foot in the other, the bundle was sure to kick the beam—never was a package of furs known to weigh more than two pounds in the market of Communipaw!

This is a singular fact—but I have it direct from my great-great-grandfather, who had risen to considerable importance in the colony, being promoted to the office of weighmaster on account of the uncommon heaviness of his foot.

The Dutch possessions in this part of the globe began now to assume a very thriving appearance, and were comprehended under the general title of Nieuw Nederlandts, on account, as the sage Vander Donck observes, of their great resemblance to the Dutch Netherlands—which indeed was

truly remarkable, excepting that the former were rugged
and mountainous, and the latter level and marshy. About
this time the tranquillity of the Dutch colonists was doomed
to suffer a temporary interruption. In 1614, Captain Sir
Samuel Argal, sailing under a commission from Dale, governor of Virginia, visited the Dutch settlements on Hudson
River, and demanded their submission to the English crown
and Virginian dominion.—To this arrogant demand, as they
were in no condition to resist it, they submitted for the time
like discreet and reasonable men.

It does not appear that the valiant Argal molested the
settlement of Communipaw; on the contrary, I am told that
when his vessel first hove in sight the worthy burghers were
seized with such a panic that they fell to smoking their pipes
with astonishing vehemence; insomuch that they quickly
raised a cloud, which, combining with the surrounding
woods and marshes, completely enveloped and concealed
their beloved village, and overhung the fair regions of Pavonia; so that the terrible Captain Argal passed on, totally
unsuspicious that a sturdy little Dutch settlement lay snugly
couched in the mud, under cover of all this pestilent vapor.
In commemoration of this fortunate escape, the worthy inhabitants have continued to smoke, almost without intermis-
sion, unto this very day; which is said to be the cause of the
remarkable fog that often hangs over Communipaw of a
clear afternoon.

Upon the departure of the enemy, our magnanimous ancestors took full six months to recover their wind, having
been exceedingly discomposed by the consternation and hurry
of affairs. They then called a council of safety to smoke
over the state of the province. After six months more of
mature deliberation, during which nearly five hundred words
were spoken, and almost as much tobacco was smoked as
would have served a certain modern general through a whole
winter's campaign of hard drinking, it was determined to fit
out an armament of canoes, and dispatch them on a voyage
of discovery; to search if, peradventure, some more sure

and formidable position might not be found where the colony would be less subject to vexatious visitations.

This perilous enterprise was intrusted to the superintendence of Mynheers Oloffe Van Kortlandt, Abraham Hardenbroeck, Jacobus Van Zandt, and Winant Ten Broeck—four indubitably great men, but of whose history, although I have made diligent inquiry, I can learn but little previous to their leaving Holland. Nor need this occasion much surprise; for adventurers, like prophets, though they make great noise abroad, have seldom much celebrity in their own countries; but this much is certain, that the overflowings and offscourings of a country are invariably composed of the richest parts of the soil. And here I cannot help remarking how convenient it would be to many of our great men and great families of doubtful origin could they have the privilege of the heroes of yore, who, whenever their origin was involved in obscurity, modestly announced themselves descended from a god— and who never visited a foreign country but what they told some cock-and-bull stories about their being kings and princes at home. This venal trespass on the truth, though it has occasionally been played off by some pseudo marquis, baronet, and other illustrious foreigner, in our land of good-natured credulity, has been completely discountenanced in this skeptical matter-of-fact age—and I even question whether any tender virgin, who was accidentally and unaccountably enriched with a bantling, would save her character at parlor firesides and evening tea-parties by ascribing the phenomenon to a swan, a shower of gold, or a river-god.

Thus being denied the benefit of mythology and classic fable, I should have been completely at a loss as to the early biography of my heroes had not a gleam of light been thrown upon their origin from their names.

By this simple means have I been enabled to gather some particulars concerning the adventurers in question. Van Kortlandt, for instance, was one of those peripatetic philosophers who tax Providence for a livelihood, and, like Diogenes, enjoy a free and unencumbered estate in sunshine.

He was usually arrayed in garments suitable to his fortune, being curiously fringed and fangled by the hand of time; and was helmeted with an old fragment of a hat, which had acquired the shape of a sugar-loaf; and so far did he carry his contempt for the adventitious distinction of dress that it is said the remnant of a shirt, which covered his back, and dangled like a pocket-handkerchief out of a hole in his breeches, was never washed except by the bountiful showers of heaven. In this garb was he usually to be seen, sunning himself at noonday, with a herd of philosophers of the same sect, on the side of the great canal of Amsterdam. Like your nobility of Europe, he took his name of *Kortlandt* (or *lackland*) from his landed estate, which lay somewhere in terra incognita.

Of the next of our worthies, might I have had the benefit of mythological assistance, the want of which I have just lamented, I should have made honorable mention, as boasting equally illustrious pedigree with the proudest hero of antiquity. His name of *Van Zandt*, which, being freely translated, signifies *from the dirt*, meaning, beyond a doubt, that, like Triptolemus, Themis, the Cyclops and the Titans, he sprang from dame Terra, or the earth! This supposition is strongly corroborated by his size, for it is well known that all the progeny of mother earth were of a gigantic stature; and Van Zandt, we are told, was a tall, raw-boned man, above six feet high—with an astonishing hard head. Nor is this origin of the illustrious Van Zandt a whit more improbable or repugnant to belief than what is related and universally admitted of certain of our greatest, or rather richest men; who, we are told with the utmost gravity, did originally spring from a dunghill!

Of the third hero but a faint description has reached to this time, which mentions that he was a sturdy, obstinate, burly, bustling little man: and from being usually equipped with an old pair of buckskins was familiarly dubbed Harden Broeck, or *Tough Breeches*.

Ten Broeck completed this junto of adventurers. It is a

singular but ludicrous fact which, were I not scrupulous in
recording the whole truth, I should almost be tempted to
pass over in silence, as incompatible with the gravity and
dignity of history, that this worthy gentleman should likewise have been nicknamed from the most whimsical part of
his dress. In fact, the small-clothes seems to have been a
very important garment in the eyes of our venerated ancestors, owing in all probability to its really being the largest
article of raiment among them. The name of Ten Broeck
or Tin Broeck is indifferently translated into Ten Breeches
and Tin Breeches—the High Dutch commentators incline to
the former opinion; and ascribe it to his being the first who
introduced into the settlement the ancient Dutch fashion of
wearing ten pair of breeches. But the most elegant and ingenious writers on the subject declare in favor of Tin, or
rather *Thin* Breeches; from whence they infer that he was
a poor but merry rogue, whose galligaskins were none of the
soundest, and who was the identical author of that truly
philosophical stanza:

> "Then why should we quarrel for riches,
>   Or any such glittering toys?
> A light heart and *thin pair of breeches*,
>   Will go through the world, my brave boys!"

Such was the gallant junto chosen to conduct this voyage
into unknown realms; and the whole was put under the su-
perintending care and direction of Oloffe Van Kortlandt,
who was held in great reverence among the sages of Communipaw, for the variety and darkness of his knowledge.
Having, as I before observed, passed a great part of his life
in the open air, among the peripatetic philosophers of Amsterdam, he had become amazingly well acquainted with the
aspect of the heavens, and could as accurately determine
when a storm was brewing, or a squall rising, as a dutiful
husband can foresee, from the brow of his spouse, when a
tempest is gathering about his ears. He was moreover
a great seer of ghosts and goblins, and a firm believer in
omens; but what especially recommended him to public con-

fidence was his marvelous talent at dreaming, for there never was anything of consequence happened at Communipaw but what he declared he had previously dreamed it; being one of those infallible prophets who always predict events after they have come to pass.

This supernatural gift was as highly valued among the burghers of Pavonia as it was among the enlightened nations of antiquity. The wise Ulysses was more indebted to his sleeping than his waking moments for all his subtle achievements, and seldom undertook any great exploit without first soundly sleeping upon it; and the same may be truly said of the good Van Kortlandt, who was thence aptly denominated Oloffe the Dreamer.

This cautious commander, having chosen the crews that should accompany him in the proposed expedition, exhorted them to repair to their homes, take a good night's rest, settle all family affairs, and make their wills, before departing on this voyage into unknown realms. And indeed this last was a precaution always taken by our forefathers, even in after times, when they became more adventurous, and voyaged to Haverstraw, or Kaatskill, or Groodt Esopus, or any other far country that lay beyond the great waters of the Tappaan Zee.

CHAPTER FOUR

HOW THE HEROES OF COMMUNIPAW VOYAGED TO HELL-GATE, AND HOW THEY WERE RECEIVED THERE

AND now the rosy blush of morn began to mantle in the east, and soon the rising sun, emerging from amid golden and purple clouds, shed his blithesome rays on the tin weathercocks of Communipaw. It was that delicious season of the year when nature, breaking from the chilling thralldom of old winter, like a blooming damsel from the tyranny of a sordid old father, threw herself, blushing with ten thousand charms, into the arms of youthful spring. Every tufted

copse and blooming grove resounded with the notes of hy-
meneal love. The very insects, as they sipped the dew that
gemmed the tender grass of the meadows, joined in the
joyous epithalamium—the virgin bud timidly put forth its
blushes, "the voice of the turtle was heard in the land,"
and the heart of man dissolved away in tenderness. Oh!
sweet Theocritus! had I thine oaten reed, wherewith thou
erst didst charm the gay Sicilian plains.—Or oh! gentle Bion!
thy pastoral pipe, wherein the happy swains of the Lesbian
isle so much delighted, then might I attempt to sing, in soft
Bucolic or negligent Idyllium, the rural beauties of the scene
—but having nothing, save this jaded goose-quill, wherewith
to wing my flight, I must fain resign all poetic disportings of
the fancy, and pursue my narrative in humble prose; comforting myself with the hope that though it may not steal so
sweetly upon the imagination of my reader, yet may it commend itself, with virgin modesty, to his better judgment,
clothed in the chaste and simple garb of truth.

No sooner did the first rays of cheerful Phœbus dart into
the windows of Communipaw than the little settlement was
all in motion. Forth issued from his castle the sage Van
Kortlandt, and, seizing a conch-shell, blew a far-resounding
blast that soon summoned all his lusty followers. Then did
they trudge resolutely down to the waterside, escorted by a
multitude of relatives and friends, who all went down, as
the common phrase expresses it, "to see them off." And
this shows the antiquity of those long family processions
often seen in our city, composed of all ages, sizes, and sexes,
laden with bundles and bandboxes, escorting some bevy of
country cousins about to depart for home in a market-boat.

The good Oloffe bestowed his forces in a squadron of three
canoes, and hoisted his flag on board a little round Dutch
boat, shaped not unlike a tub, which had formerly been the
jolly-boat of the "Goede Vrouw." And now, all being embarked, they bade farewell to the gazing throng upon the
beach, who continued shouting after them, even when out of
hearing, wishing them a happy voyage, advising them to

take good care of themselves, and not to get drowned—with
an abundance other of those sage and invaluable cautions,
generally given by landsmen to such as go down to the sea
in ships, and adventure upon the deep waters. In the meanwhile, the voyagers cheerily urged their course across the
crystal bosom of the bay, and soon left behind them the green
shores of ancient Pavonia.

And first they touched at two small islands which lie
nearly opposite Communipaw, and which are said to have
been brought into existence about the time of the great irruption of the Hudson, when it broke through the Highlands
and made its way to the ocean.* For in this tremendous uproar of the waters, we are told that many huge fragments of
rock and land were rent from the mountains and swept down
by this runaway river for sixty or seventy miles; where some
of them ran aground on the shoals just opposite Communipaw, and formed the identical islands in question, while
others drifted out to sea and were never heard of more. A
sufficient proof of the fact is that the rock which forms the
bases of these islands is exactly similar to that of the Highlands, and, moreover, one of our philosophers, who has diligently compared the agreement of their respective surfaces,
has even gone so far as to assure me, in confidence, that Gibbet Island was originally nothing more nor less than a wart
on Anthony's Nose.†

---

* It is a matter long since established by certain of our philosophers—that is to say, having been often advanced, and never contradicted, it has grown to be pretty nigh equal to a settled fact—that the
Hudson was originally a lake, dammed up by the mountains of the
Highlands. In process of time, however, becoming very mighty and
obstreperous, and the mountains waxing pursy, dropsical, and weak in
the back, by reason of their extreme old age, it suddenly rose upon
them, and after a violent struggle effected its escape. This is said to
have come to pass in very remote time; probably before that rivers
had lost the art of running up hill. The foregoing is a theory in which
I do not pretend to be skilled, notwithstanding that I do fully give it
my belief.

† A promontory in the Highlands.

Leaving these wonderful little isles, they next coasted by
Governor's Island, since terrible from its frowning fortress
and grinning batteries. They would by no means, however,
land upon this island, since they doubted much it might be
the abode of demons and spirits, which in those days did
greatly abound throughout this savage and pagan country.

Just at this time a shoal of jolly porpoises came rolling
and tumbling by, turning up their sleek sides to the sun, and
spouting up the briny element in sparkling showers. No
sooner did the sage Oloffe mark this than he was greatly rejoiced. "This," exclaimed he, "if I mistake not, augurs
well—the porpoise is a fat, well-conditioned fish—a burgomaster among fishes—his looks betoken ease, plenty, and
prosperity—I greatly admire this round, fat fish, and doubt
not but this is a happy omen of the success of our undertaking." So saying, he directed his squadron to steer in the
track of these alderman fishes.

Turning, therefore, directly to the left, they swept up the
strait vulgarly called the East River. And here the rapid
tide which courses through this strait, seizing on the gallant
tub in which Commodore Van Kortlandt had embarked, hurried it forward with a velocity unparalleled in a Dutch boat,
navigated by Dutchmen; insomuch that the good commodore, who had all his life long been accustomed only to the
drowsy navigation of canals, was more than ever convinced
that they were in the hands of some supernatural power,
and that the jolly porpoises were towing them to some fair
haven that was to fulfill all their wishes and expectations.

Thus borne away by the resistless current, they doubled
that boisterous point of land since called Corlear's Hook,*
and leaving to the right the rich winding cove of the Wallabout, they drifted into a magnificent expanse of water, surrounded by pleasant shores, whose verdure was exceedingly
refreshing to the eye. While the voyagers were looking
around them, on what they conceived to be a serene and

* Properly spelled *hoeck* (*i.e.*, a point of land).

sunny lake, they beheld at a distance a crew of painted savages, busily employed in fishing, who seemed more like the genii of this romantic region—their slender canoe lightly balanced like a feather on the undulating surface of the bay.

At sight of these, the hearts of the heroes of Communipaw were not a little troubled. But as good fortune would have it, at the bow of the commodore's boat was stationed a very valiant man named Hendrick Kip (which, being interpreted, means *chicken;* a name given him in token of his courage). No sooner did he behold these varlet heathens than he trembled with excessive valor, and, although a good half mile distant, he seized a musquetoon that lay at hand, and turning away his head, fired it most intrepidly in the face of the blessed sun. The blundering weapon recoiled and gave the valiant Kip an ignominious kick that laid him prostrate with uplifted heels in the bottom of the boat. But such was the effect of this tremendous fire that the wild men of the woods, struck with consternation, seized hastily upon their paddles, and shot away into one of the deep inlets of the Long Island shore.

This signal victory gave new spirits to the hardy voyagers, and in honor of the achievement they gave the name of the valiant Kip to the surrounding bay, and it has continued to be called Kip's Bay from that time to the present. The heart of the good Van Kortlandt—who, having no land of his own, was a great admirer of other people's—expanded at the sumptuous prospect of rich, unsettled country around him, and falling into a delicious reverie, he straightway began to riot in the possession of vast meadows of salt marsh and interminable patches of cabbages. From this delectable vision he was all at once awakened by the sudden turning of the tide, which would soon have hurried him from this land of promise, had not the discreet navigator given signal to steer for shore; where they accordingly landed hard by the rocky heights of Bellevue—that happy retreat, where our jolly aldermen eat for the good of the city, and fatten the turtle that are sacrificed on civic solemnities.

Here, seated on the greensward, by the side of a small
stream that ran sparkling among the grass, they refreshed
themselves after the toils of the seas, by feasting lustily on
the ample stores which they had provided for this perilous
voyage. Thus having well fortified their deliberative powers,
they fell into an earnest consultation what was further to be
done. This was the first council dinner ever eaten at Bellevue by Christian burghers, and here, as tradition relates, did
originate the great family feud between the Hardenbroecks
and the Tenbroecks, which afterward had a singular influence on the building of the city. The sturdy Hardenbroeck,
whose eyes had been wondrously delighted with the salt
marshes that spread their reeking bosoms along the coast, at
the bottom of Kip's Bay, counseled by all means to return
thither and found the intended city. This was strenuously
opposed by the unbending Ten Broeck, and many testy
arguments passed between them. The particulars of the
controversy have not reached us, which is ever to be lamented;
this much is certain, that the sage Oloffe put an end to the dispute by determining to explore still further in the route which
the mysterious porpoises had so clearly pointed out—whereupon the sturdy Tough Breeches abandoned the expedition,
took possession of a neighboring hill, and in a fit of great
wrath peopled all that tract of country, which has continued
to be inhabited by the Hardenbroecks unto this very day.

By this time the jolly Phœbus, like some wanton urchin
sporting on the side of a green hill, began to roll down the
declivity of the heavens; and now, the tide having once
more turned in their favor, the resolute Pavonians again
committed themselves to its discretion, and coasting along
the western shores, were borne toward the straits of Blackwell's Island.

And here the capricious wanderings of the current occasioned not a little marvel and perplexity to these illustrious
mariners. Now would they be caught by the wanton eddies,
and, sweeping round a jutting point, would wind deep into
some romantic little cove, that indented the fair island of

Manna-hata; now were they hurried narrowly by the very
bases of impending rocks, mantled with the flaunting grape-
vine, and crowned with groves that threw a broad shade on
the waves beneath; and anon they were borne away into the
mid-channel, and wafted along with a rapidity that very
much discomposed the sage Van Kortlandt, who, as he saw
the land swiftly receding on either side, began exceedingly
to doubt that terra firma was giving them the slip.

Wherever the voyagers turned their eyes, a new creation
seemed to bloom around. No signs of human thrift appeared
to check the delicious wildness of nature, who here reveled
in all her luxuriant variety. Those hills, now bristled, like
the fretful porcupine, with rows of poplars (vain upstart
plants! minions of wealth and fashion!), were then adorned
with the vigorous natives of the soil; the lordly oak, the
generous chestnut, the graceful elm—while here and there
the tulip-tree reared his majestic head, the giant of the forest.
—Where now are seen the gay retreats of luxury—villas
half buried in twilight bowers, whence the amorous flute oft
breathes the sighings of some city swain—there the fish-
hawk built his solitary nest, on some dry trees that overlooked his watery domain. The timid deer fed undisturbed
along those shores now hallowed by the lover's moonlight
walk and printed by the slender foot of beauty; and a
savage solitude extended over those happy regions where
now are reared the stately towers of the Jones's, the Schermerhornes, and the Rhinelanders.

Thus gliding in silent wonder through these new and
unknown scenes, the gallant squadron of Pavonia swept by
the foot of a promontory that strutted forth boldly into the
waves, and seemed to frown upon them as they brawled
against its base. This is the bluff well known to modern
mariners by the name of Gracie's Point, from the fair castle
which, like an elephant, it carries upon its back. And here
broke upon their view a wild and varied prospect, where land
and water were beauteously intermingled, as though they had
combined to heighten and set off each other's charms. To

their right lay the sedgy point of Blackwell's Island, dressed
in the fresh garniture of living green—beyond it stretched
the pleasant coast of Sundswick, and the small harbor well
known by the name of Hallet's Cove—a place infamous in
latter days, by reason of its being the haunt of pirates who
infest these seas, robbing orchards and watermelon patches,
and insulting gentlemen navigators when voyaging in their
pleasure-boats. To the left a deep bay, or rather creek,
gracefully receded between shores fringed with forests, and
forming a kind of vista through which were beheld the sylvan
regions of Haerlem, Morrisania, and East Chester. Here
the eye reposed with delight on a richly-wooded country,
diversified by tufted knolls, shadowy intervals, and waving
lines of upland swelling above each other; while over the
whole the purple mists of spring diffused a hue of soft voluptuousness.

Just before them the grand course of the stream, making
a sudden bend, wound among embowered promontories and
shores of emerald verdure, that seemed to melt into the wave.
A character of gentleness and mild fertility prevailed around.
The sun had just descended, and the thin haze of twilight,
like a transparent veil drawn over the bosom of virgin beauty,
heightened the charms which it half concealed.

Ah! witching scenes of foul delusion! Ah! hapless voyagers, gazing with simple wonder on these Circean shores!
Such, alas! are they, poor easy souls, who listen to the se-
ductions of a wicked world—treacherous are its smiles! fatal
its caresses! He who yields to its enticements launches upon
a whelming tide and trusts his feeble bark among the dimpling eddies of a whirlpool! And thus it fared with the
worthies of Pavonia, who, little mistrusting the guileful scene
before them, drifted quietly on, until they were aroused by
an uncommon tossing and agitation of their vessels. For
now the late dimpling current began to brawl around them,
and the waves to boil and foam with horrific fury. Awakened as if from a dream, the astonished Oloffe bawled aloud
to put about, but his words were lost amid the roaring of the

waters. And now ensued a scene of direful consternation—at one time they were borne with dreadful velocity among tumultuous breakers; at another hurried down boisterous rapids. Now they were nearly dashed upon the Hen and Chickens (infamous rocks!—more voracious than Scylla and her whelps); and anon they seemed sinking into yawning gulfs, that threatened to entomb them beneath the waves. All the elements combined to produce a hideous confusion. The waters raged—the winds howled—and as they were hurried along, several of the astonished mariners beheld the rocks and trees of the neighboring shores driving through the air!

At length the mighty tub of Commodore Van Kortlandt was drawn into the vortex of that tremendous whirlpool called the Pot, where it was whirled about in giddy mazes, until the senses of the good commander and his crew were overpowered by the horror of the scene and the strangeness of the revolution.

How the gallant squadron of Pavonia was snatched from the jaws of this modern Charybdis has never been truly made known; for so many survived to tell the tale, and, what is still more wonderful, told it in so many different ways, that there has ever prevailed a great variety of opinions on the subject.

As to the commodore and his crew, when they came to their senses they found themselves stranded on the Long Island shore. The worthy commodore, indeed, used to relate many and wonderful stories of his adventures in this time of peril; how that he saw specters flying in the air, and heard the yelling of hobgoblins, and put his hand into the Pot when they were whirled around and found the water scalding hot, and beheld several uncouth-looking beings seated on rocks and skimming it with huge ladles—but particularly he declared, with great exultation, that he saw the losel porpoises, which had betrayed them into this peril, some broiling on the Gridiron and others hissing in the Frying-pan!

These, however, were considered by many as mere phantasies of the commodore's imagination while he lay in a trance; especially as he was known to be given to dreaming; and the truth of them has never been clearly ascertained. It is certain, however, that to the accounts of Oloffe and his followers may be traced the various traditions handed down of this marvelous strait—as how the devil has been seen there, sitting astride of the Hog's Back and playing on the fiddle— how he broils fish there before a storm; and many other stories, in which we must be cautious of putting too much faith. In consequence of all these terrific circumstances, the Pavonian commander gave this pass the name of *Helle-gat*, or, as it has been interpreted, *Hell-gate;** which it continues to bear at the present day.

CHAPTER FIVE

HOW THE HEROES OF COMMUNIPAW RETURNED SOMEWHAT WISER THAN THEY WENT—AND HOW THE SAGE OLOFFE DREAMED A DREAM—AND THE DREAM THAT HE DREAMED

THE darkness of night had closed upon this disastrous day, and a doleful night was it to the shipwrecked Pavonians, whose ears were incessantly assailed with the raging of the

---

* This is a narrow strait in the Sound, at the distance of six miles above New York. It is dangerous to shipping, unless under the care of skillful pilots, by reason of numerous rocks, shelves, and whirlpools. These have received sundry appellations, such as the Gridiron, Frying-pan, Hog's Back, Pot, etc., and are very violent and turbulent at certain times of the tide. Certain wise men who instruct these modern days have softened the above characteristic name into *Hurl-gate*, which means nothing. I leave them to give their own etymology. The name as given by our author is supported by the map in Vander Donck's history, published in 1656; by Ogilvie's history of America, 1671; as also by a journal still extant, written in the 16th century, and to be found in Hazard's State Papers. And an old MS., written in French, speaking of various alterations in names about this city, observes, "De *Helle-gat* trou d'Enfer, ils ont fait *Hell-gate*. Porte d'Enfer."

elements and the howling of the hobgoblins that infested
this perfidious strait. But when the morning dawned, the
horrors of the preceding evening had passed away; rapids,
breakers, and whirlpools had disappeared; the stream again
ran smooth and dimpling, and having changed its tide rolled
gently back toward the quarter where lay their much-re-
gretted home.

The woe-begone heroes of Communipaw eyed each other
with rueful countenances; their squadron had been totally
dispersed by the late disaster. Some were cast upon the
western shore, where, headed by one Ruleff Hopper, they
took possession of all the country lying about the six-mile
stone; which is held by the Hoppers at this present writing.

The Waldrons were driven by stress of weather to a distant coast, where, having with them a jug of genuine Hollands, they were enabled to conciliate the savages, setting
up a kind of tavern; from whence, it is said, did spring the
fair town of Haerlem, in which their descendants have ever
since continued to be reputable publicans. As to the Suy-
dams, they were thrown upon the Long Island coast, and
may still be found in those parts. But the most singular
luck attended the great Ten Broeck, who, falling overboard,
was miraculously preserved from sinking by the multitude
of his nether garments. Thus buoyed up, he floated on the
waves, like a merman, or like the cork float of an angler,
until he landed safely on a rock, where he was found the
next morning busily drying his many breeches in the sunshine.

I forbear to treat of the long consultation of our adventurers—how they determined that it would not do to found
a city in this diabolical neighborhood—and how at length,
with fear and trembling, they ventured once more upon the
briny element, and steered their course back for Communipaw. Suffice it, in simple brevity, to say, that after toiling
back through the scenes of their yesterday's voyage, they at
length opened the southern point of Manna-hata, and gained
a distant view of their beloved Communipaw.

And here they were opposed by an obstinate eddy, that resisted all the efforts of the exhausted mariners. Weary and dispirited, they could no longer make head against the power of the tide, or rather, as some will have it, of old Neptune, who, anxious to guide them to a spot whereon should be founded his stronghold in this western world, sent half a score of potent billows, that rolled the tub of Commodore Van Kortlandt high and dry on the shores of Mannahata.

Having thus in a manner been guided by supernatural power to this delightful island, their first care was to light a fire at the foot of a large tree that stood upon the point at present called the Battery. Then gathering together great store of oysters which abounded on the shore, and emptying the contents of their wallets, they prepared and made a sumptuous council repast. The worthy Van Kortlandt was observed to be particularly zealous in his devotions to the trencher; for having the cares of the expedition especially committed to his care, he deemed it incumbent on him to eat profoundly for the public good. In proportion as he filled himself to the very brim with the dainty viands before him did the heart of this excellent burgher rise up toward his throat, until he seemed crammed and almost choked with good eating and good nature. And at such times it is, when a man's heart is in his throat, that he may more truly be said to speak from it, and his speeches abound with kindness and good-fellowship. Thus the worthy Oloffe, having swallowed the last possible morsel, and washed it down with a fervent potation, felt his heart yearning and his whole frame in a manner dilating with unbounded benevolence. Everything around him seemed excellent and delightful; and, laying his hands on each side of his capacious periphery, and rolling his half-closed eyes around on the beautiful diversity of land and water before him, he exclaimed, in a fat half-smothered voice, "What a charming prospect!" The words died away in his throat—he seemed to ponder on the fair scene for a moment—his eyelids heavily closed over their orbs—his head drooped upon his bosom—he slowly sunk upon the green turf, and a deep sleep stole gradually upon him.

And the sage Oloffe dreamed a dream—and lo! the good St. Nicholas came riding over the tops of the trees, in that self-same wagon wherein he brings his yearly presents to children, and he came and descended hard by where the heroes of Communipaw had made their late repast. And the shrewd Van Kortlandt knew him by his broad hat, his long pipe, and the resemblance which he bore to the figure on the bow of the "Goede Vrouw." And he lighted his pipe by the fire and sat himself down and smoked; and as he smoked the smoke from his pipe ascended into the air, and spread like a cloud overhead. And Oloffe bethought him, and he hastened and climbed up to the top of one of the tallest trees, and saw that the smoke spread over a great extent of country— and as he considered it more attentively, he fancied that the great volume of smoke assumed a variety of marvelous forms, where in dim obscurity he saw shadowed out palaces and domes and lofty spires, all of which lasted but a moment and then faded away, until the whole rolled off, and nothing but the green woods were left. And when St. Nicholas had smoked his pipe, he twisted it in his hat-band, and laying his finger beside his nose, gave the astonished Van Kortlandt a very significant wink, then, mounting his wagon, he returned over the tree-tops and disappeared.

And Van Kortlandt awoke from his sleep greatly instructed, and he aroused his companions and related to them his dream, and interpreted it, that it was the will of St. Nicholas that they should settle down and build the city here. And that the smoke of the pipe was a type how vast should be the extent of the city; inasmuch as the volumes of its smoke should spread over a wide extent of country. And they all, with one voice, assented to this interpretation, excepting Mynheer Ten Broeck, who declared the meaning to be that it should be a city wherein a little fire should occasion a great smoke, or in other words, a very vaporing little city—both which interpretations have strangely come to pass!

The great object of their perilous expedition, therefore, being thus happily accomplished, the voyagers returned merrily to Communipaw, where they were received with great rejoicings. And here, calling a general meeting of all the wise men and the dignitaries of Pavonia, they related the whole history of their voyage and of the dream of Oloffe Van Kortlandt. And the people lifted up their voices and blessed the good St. Nicholas, and from that time forth the sage Van Kortlandt was held more in honor than ever, for his great talent at dreaming, and was pronounced a most useful citizen and a right good man—when he was asleep.

CHAPTER SIX

CONTAINING AN ATTEMPT AT ETYMOLOGY—AND OF THE FOUNDING OF THE GREAT CITY OF NEW AMSTERDAM

THE original name of the island wherein the squadron of Communipaw was thus propitiously thrown is a matter of some dispute, and has already undergone considerable vitiation—a melancholy proof of the instability of all sublunary things, and the vanity of all our hopes of lasting fame! for who can expect his name will live to posterity when even the names of mighty islands are thus soon lost in contradiction and uncertainty?

The name most current at the present day, and which is likewise countenanced by the great historian Vander Donck, is MANHATTAN; which is said to have originated in a custom among the squaws, in the early settlement, of wearing men's hats, as is still done among many tribes. "Hence," as we are told by an old governor who was somewhat of a wag, and flourished almost a century since, and had paid a visit to the wits of Philadelphia, "hence arose the appellation of man-hat-on, first given to the Indians, and afterward to the island"—a stupid joke!—but well enough for a governor.

Among the more venerable sources of information on this subject is that valuable history of the American possessions, written by Master Richard Bloome in 1687, wherein it is called Manhadaes and Manahanent; nor must I forget the excellent little book, full of precious matter, of that authentic historian, John Josselyn, Gent., who expressly calls it Manadaes.

Another etymology still more ancient, and sanctioned by the countenance of our ever-to-be-lamented Dutch ancestors, is that found in certain letters still extant,* which passed between the early governors and their neighboring powers, wherein it is called indifferently Monhattoes, Munhatos, and Manhattoes, which are evidently unimportant variations of the same name; for our wise forefathers set little store by those niceties either in orthography or orthoepy which form the sole study and ambition of many learned men and women of this hypercritical age. This last name is said to be derived from the great Indian spirit Manetho, who was supposed to make this island his favorite abode, on account of its uncommon delights. For the Indian traditions affirm that the bay was once a translucid lake, filled with silver and golden fish, in the midst of which lay this beautiful island, covered with every variety of fruits and flowers; but that the sudden irruption of the Hudson laid waste these blissful scenes, and Manetho took his flight beyond the great waters of Ontario.

These, however, are fabulous legends to which very cautious credence must be given; and although I am willing to admit the last quoted orthography of the name, as very suitable for prose, yet is there another one founded on still more ancient and indisputable authority, which I particularly delight in, seeing that it is at once poetical, melodious, and significant—and this is recorded in the before-mentioned voyage of the great Hudson, written by Master Juet; who clearly and correctly calls it MANNA-HATA—that is to say, the island

* Vide Hazard's Col. State Papers.

of Manna, or, in other words—"a land flowing with milk and honey!"

It having been solemnly resolved that the seat of empire should be transferred from the green shores of Pavonia to this delectable island, a vast multitude embarked, and migrated across the mouth of the Hudson, under the guidance of Oloffe the Dreamer, who was appointed protector or patron to the new settlement.

And here let me bear testimony to the matchless honesty and magnanimity of our worthy forefathers, who purchased the soil of the native Indians before erecting a single roof— a circumstance singular and almost incredible in the annals of discovery and colonization.

The first settlement was made on the southwest point of the island, on the very spot where the good St. Nicholas had appeared in the dream. Here they built a mighty and impregnable fort and trading house, called FORT AMSTERDAM, which stood on that eminence at present occupied by the custom-house, with the open space now called the Bowling Green in front.

Around this potent fortress was soon seen a numerous progeny of little Dutch houses, with tiled roofs, all which seemed most lovingly to nestle under its walls, like a brood of half-fledged chickens sheltered under the wings of the mother hen. The whole was surrounded by an inclosure of strong palisadoes, to guard against any sudden irruption of the savages, who wandered in hordes about the swamps and forests that extended over those tracts of country at present called Broadway, Wall Street, William Street, and Pearl Street.

No sooner was the colony once planted than it took root and throve amazingly; for it would seem that this thrice-favored island is like a munificent dunghill, where every foreign weed finds kindly nourishment, and soon shoots up and expands to greatness.

And now, the infant settlement having advanced in age and stature, it was thought high time it should receive an

honest Christian name, and it was accordingly called NEW
AMSTERDAM. It is true, there were some advocates for the
original Indian name, and many of the best writers of the
province did long continue to call it by the title of "Manhattoes"; but this was discountenanced by the authorities,
as being heathenish and savage. Besides, it was considered
an excellent and praiseworthy measure to name it after a
great city of the old world; as by that means it was induced
to emulate the greatness and renown of its namesake—in the
manner that little sniveling urchins are called after great
statesmen, saints, and worthies and renowned generals of
yore, upon which they all industriously copy their examples
and come to be very mighty men in their day and generation.

The thriving state of the settlement and the rapid increase
of houses gradually awakened the good Oloffe from a deep
lethargy, into which he had fallen after the building of the
fort. He now began to think it was time some plan should
be devised on which the increasing town should be built.
Summoning, therefore, his counselors and coadjutors together, they took pipe in mouth and forthwith sunk into a
very sound deliberation on the subject.

At the very outset of the business an unexpected difference of opinion arose, and I mention it with much sorrowing,
as being the first altercation on record in the councils of New
Amsterdam. It was a breaking forth of the grudge and
heartburning that had existed between those two eminent
burghers, Mynheers Tenbroeck and Hardenbroeck, ever since
their unhappy altercation on the coast of Bellevue. The
great Hardenbroeck had waxed very wealthy and powerful
from his domains, which embraced the whole chain of
Apulean mountains that stretched along the gulf of Kip's
Bay, and from part of which his descendants have been
expelled in latter age; by the powerful clans of the Jones's
and the Schermerhornes.

An ingenious plan for the city was offered by Mynheer
Tenbroeck, who proposed that it should be cut up and inter-
sected by canals, after the manner of the most admired cities

in Holland. To this Mynheer Hardenbroeck was diametrically opposed, suggesting, in place thereof, that they should run out docks and wharfs, by means of piles driven into the bottom of the river, on which the town should be built. By these means, said he triumphantly, shall we rescue a considerable space of territory from these immense rivers, and build a city that shall rival Amsterdam, Venice, or any amphibious city in Europe. To this proposition, Ten Broeck (or Ten Breeches) replied with a look of as much scorn as he could possibly assume. He cast the utmost censure upon the plan of his antagonist as being preposterous and against the very order of things, as he would leave to every true Hollander. "For what," said he, "is a town without canals? —it is a body without veins and arteries and must perish for want of a free circulation of the vital fluid."—Tough Breeches, on the contrary, retorted with a sarcasm upon his antagonist, who was somewhat of an arid, dry-boned habit; he remarked, that as to the circulation of the blood being necessary to existence, Mynheer Ten Breeches was a living contradiction to his own assertion; for everybody knew there had not a drop of blood circulated through his wind-dried carcass for good ten years, and yet there was not a greater busybody in the whole colony. Personalities have seldom much effect in making converts in argument—nor have I ever seen a man convinced of error by being convicted of deformity. At least such was not the case at present. Ten Breeches was very acrimonious in reply, and Tough Breeches, who was a sturdy little man and never gave up the last word, rejoined with increasing spirit—Ten Breeches had the advantage of the greatest volubility, but Tough Breeches had that invaluable coat of mail in argument called obstinacy—Ten Breeches had, therefore, the most mettle, but Tough Breeches the best bottom—so that though Ten Breeches made a dreadful clattering about his ears and battered and belabored him with hard words and sound arguments, yet Tough Breeches hung on most resolutely to the last. They parted, therefore, as is usual in all arguments where both parties are in the right, without coming to any conclusion—but they hated each other most heartily forever after, and a similar breach with that between the houses of Capulet and Montague did ensue between the families of Ten Breeches and Tough Breeches.

I would not fatigue my reader with these dull matters of fact, but that my duty as a faithful historian requires that I should be particular—and, in truth, as I am now treating of the critical period when our city, like a young twig, first received the twists and turns that have since contributed to give it the present picturesque irregularity for which it is celebrated, I cannot be too minute in detailing their first causes.

After the unhappy altercation I have just mentioned, I do not find that anything further was said on the subject worthy of being recorded. The council, consisting of the largest and oldest heads in the community, met regularly once a week, to ponder on this momentous subject. But either they were deterred by the war of words they had witnessed, or they were naturally averse to the exercise of the tongue and the consequent exercise of the brains—certain it is, the most profound silence was maintained—the question as usual lay on the table—the members quietly smoked their pipes, making but few laws, without ever enforcing any, and in the meantime the affairs of the settlement went on—as it pleased God.

As most of the council were but little skilled in the mystery of combining pot-hooks and hangers, they determined most judiciously not to puzzle either themselves or posterity with voluminous records. The secretary, however, kept the minutes of the council with tolerable precision, in a large vellum folio, fastened with massy brass clasps; the journal of each meeting consisted but of two lines, stating in Dutch that "the council sat this day, and smoked twelve pipes, on the affairs of the colony."—By which it appears that the first settlers did not regulate their time by hours, but pipes, in the same manner as they measure distances in Holland at this very time; an admirably exact measurement, as a pipe in the mouth of a true-born Dutchman is never liable to those accidents and irregularities that are continually putting our clocks out of order. It is said, moreover, that a regular smoker was appointed as council clock, whose duty was to sit at the elbow of the president and smoke incessantly; every puff marked a division of time as exactly as a second-hand, and t e knocking out of the ashes of his pipe was equivalent to striking the hour.

In this manner did the profound council of New Amsterdam smoke, and doze, and ponder, from week to week, month to month, and year to year, in what manner they should construct their infant settlement; meanwhile, the town took care of itself, and like a sturdy brat which is suffered to run about wild, unshackled by clouts and bandages, and other abominations by which your notable nurses and sage old women cripple and disfigure the children of men, increased so rapidly in strength and magnitude, that before the honest burgomasters had determined upon a plan, it was too late to put it in execution—whereupon they wisely abandoned the subject altogether.

CHAPTER SEVEN

HOW THE CITY OF NEW AMSTERDAM WAXED GREAT UNDER THE PROTECTION OF OLOFFE THE DREAMER

THERE is something exceedingly delusive in thus looking back, through the long vista of departed years, and catching a glimpse of the fairy realms of antiquity that lie beyond. Like some goodly landscape melting into distance, they receive a thousand charms from their very obscurity, and the fancy delights to fill up their outlines with graces and excellences of its own creation. Thus beam on my imagination those happier days of our city, when as yet New Amsterdam

was a mere pastoral town, shrouded in groves of sycamore
and willows, and surrounded by trackless forests and widespreading waters, that seemed to shut out all the cares and
vanities of a wicked world.

In those days did this embyro city present the rare and
noble spectacle of a community governed without laws; and
thus being left to its own course, and the fostering care of
Providence, increased as rapidly as though it had been bur-
dened with a dozen panniers-full of those sage laws that are
usually heaped on the backs of young cities—in order to
make them grow. And in this particular I greatly admire
the wisdom and sound knowledge of human nature displayed
by the sage Oloffe the Dreamer and his fellow-legislators.
For my part, I have not so bad an opinion of mankind as
many of my brother philosophers. I do not think poor
human nature so sorry a piece of workmanship as they would
make it out to be; and as far as I have observed, I am fully
satisfied that man, if left to himself, would about as readily
go right as wrong. It is only this eternally sounding in his
ears that it is his duty to go right that makes him go the
very reverse. The noble independence of his nature revolts
at this intolerable tyranny of law, and the perpetual inter-
ference of officious morality, which is ever besetting his path
with finger-posts and directions to "keep to the right, as the
law directs"; and, like a spirited urchin, he turns directly
contrary, and gallops through mud and mire, over hedges
and ditches, merely to show that he is a lad of spirit and out
of his leading-strings. And these opinions are amply sub-
stantiated by what I have above said of our worthy ancestors; who, never being be-preached and be-lectured, and
guided and governed by statutes and laws and by-laws, as
are their more enlightened descendants, did one and all de-
mean themselves honestly and peaceably, out of pure ignorance, or, in other words, because they knew no better.

Nor must I omit to record one of the earliest measures of
this infant settlement, inasmuch as it shows the piety of our
forefathers, and that, like good Christians, they were always

ready to serve God, after they had first served themselves.
Thus, having quietly settled themselves down, and provided
for their own comfort, they bethought themselves of testifying
their gratitude to the great and good St. Nicholas, for his
protecting care in guiding them to this delectable abode.   To
this end they built a fair and goodly chapel within the fort,
which they consecrated to his name; whereupon he immediately took the town of New Amsterdam under his peculiar
patronage, and he has ever since been, and I devoutly hope
will ever be, the tutelar saint of this excellent city.

I am moreover told that there is a little legendary book,
somewhere extant, written in Low Dutch, which says that the
image of this renowned saint, which whilom graced the bowsprit of the "Goede Vrouw," was elevated in front of this
chapel, in the very center of what, in modern days, is called
the Bowling Green.   And the legend further treats of divers
miracles wrought by the mighty pipe which the saint held
in his mouth; a whiff of which was a sovereign cure for an
indigestion—an invaluable relic in this colony of brave
trenchermen.   As, however, in spite of the most diligent
search, I cannot lay my hands upon this little book, I must
confess that I entertain considerable doubt on the subject.

Thus benignly fostered by the good St. Nicholas, the
burghers of New Amsterdam beheld their settlement increase
in magnitude and population, and soon become the metropolis
of divers settlements, and an extensive territory.   Already
had the disastrous pride of colonies and dependencies, those
banes of a sound-hearted empire, entered into their imaginations; and Fort Aurania on the Hudson, Fort Nassau on the
Delaware, and Fort Goede Hoep on the Connecticut River,
seemed to be the darling offspring of the venerable council.*

---

* The province about this time extended on the north to Fort
Aurania, or Orange (now the city of Albany), situated about 160 miles
up the Hudson River.   Indeed, the province claimed quite to the river
St. Lawrence; but this claim was not much insisted on at the time, as
the country beyond Fort Aurania was a perfect wilderness.   On the
south, the province reached to Fort Nassau, on the South River, since

Thus prosperously, to all appearance, did the province of New Netherlands advance in power; and the early history of its metropolis presents a fair page, unsullied by crime or calamity.

Hordes of painted savages still lurked about the tangled forests and rich bottoms of the unsettled part of the island— the hunter pitched his rude bower of skins and bark beside the rills that ran through the cool and shady glens; while here and there might be seen, on some sunny knoll, a group of Indian wigwams, whose smoke rose above the neighboring trees and floated in the transparent atmosphere. By degrees a mutual good-will had grown up between these wandering beings and the burghers of New Amsterdam. Our benevolent forefathers endeavored as much as possible to meliorate their situation, by giving them gin, rum, and glass beads, in exchange for their peltries; for it seems the kind-hearted Dutchmen had conceived a great friendship for their savage neighbors on account of their being pleasant men to trade with and little skilled in the art of making a bargain.

Now and then a crew of these half-human sons of the forest would make their appearance in the streets of New Amsterdam, fantastically painted and decorated with beads and flaunting feathers, sauntering about with an air of listless indifference—sometimes in the market-place, instructing the little Dutch boys in the use of the bow and arrow—at other times, inflamed with liquor, swaggering and whooping and yelling about the town like so many fiends, to the great dismay of all the good wives, who would hurry their children into the house, fasten the doors, and throw water upon the enemy from the garret-windows. It is worthy of mention here, that our forefathers were very particular in holding

---

called the Delaware; and on the east, it extended to the Varshe (or fresh) River, now the Connecticut. On this last frontier was likewise erected a fort or trading house, much about the spot where at present is situated the pleasant town of Hartford. This was called Fort Goede Hoep (or Good Hope), and was intended as well for the purposes of trade as of defense.

up these wild men as excellent domestic examples—and for reasons that may be gathered from the history of Master Ogilby, who tells us that "for the least offense the bridegroom soundly beats his wife and turns her out of doors, and marries another, insomuch that some of them have every year a new wife." Whether this awful example had any influence or not history does not mention; but it is certain that our grandmothers were miracles of fidelity and obedience.

True it is that the good understanding between our ancestors and their savage neighbors was liable to occasional interruptions; and I have heard my grandmother, who was a very wise old woman, and well versed in the history of these parts, tell a long story, of a winter's evening, about a battle between the New Amsterdamers and the Indians, which was known by the name of the *Peach War*, and which took place near a peach orchard, in a dark glen which for a long while went by the name of the Murderer's Valley.

The legend of this sylvan war was long current among the nurses, old wives, and other ancient chroniclers of the place; but time and improvement have almost obliterated both the tradition and the scene of battle; for what was once the blood-stained valley is now in the center of this populous city, and known by the name of *Dey Street*.

The accumulating wealth and consequence of New Amsterdam and its dependencies at length awakened the tender solicitude of the mother country; who, finding it a thriving and opulent colony, and that it promised to yield great profit and no trouble, all at once became wonderfully anxious about its safety, and began to load it with tokens of regard, in the same manner that your knowing people are sure to overwhelm rich relations with their affection and lovingkindness.

The usual marks of protection shown by mother countries to wealthy colonies were forthwith manifested—the first care always being to send rulers to the new settlement, with orders to squeeze as much revenue from it as it will yield.

Accordingly, in the year of Our Lord 1629, Mynheer
WOUTER VAN TWILLER was appointed governor of the
province of Nieuw Nederlandts, under the commission and
control of their High Mightinesses, the Lords States-General
of the United Netherlands, and the privileged West India
Company.

This renowned old gentleman arrived at New Amsterdam
in the merry month of June, the sweetest month in all the
year; when Dan Apollo seems to dance up the transparent
firmanent—when the robin, the thrush, and a thousand other
wanton songsters make the woods to resound with amorous
ditties, and the luxurious little boblincoln revels among the
clover blossoms of the meadows—all which happy coincidence
persuaded the old dames of New Amsterdam, who were
skilled in the art of foretelling events, that this was to be a
happy and prosperous administration.

But as it would be derogatory to the consequence of the
first Dutch governor of the great province of Nieuw Nederlandts, to be thus scurvily introduced at the end of the
chapter, I will put an end to this second book of my history,
that I may usher him in with more dignity in the beginning
of my next.

BOOK THREE

IN WHICH IS RECORDED THE GOLDEN REIGN OF WOUTER VAN TWILLER

CHAPTER ONE

OF THE RENOWNED WALTER VAN TWILLER—HIS UNPARAL-
LELED VIRTUES—AND LIKEWISE HIS UNUTTERABLE WIS-
DOM IN THE LAW-CASE OF WANDLE SCHOONHOVEN AND
BARENT BLEECKER—AND THE GREAT ADMIRATION OF
THE PUBLIC THEREAT

GRIEVOUS and very much to be commiserated is the task
of the feeling historian who writes the history of his native
land. If it fall to his lot to be the sad recorder of calamity
or crime, the mournful page is watered with his tears; nor
can he recall the most prosperous and blissful era without a
melancholy sigh at the reflection that it has passed away forever! I know not whether it be owing to an immoderate
love for the simplicity of former times, or to that certain tenderness of heart incident to all sentimental historians, but I
candidly confess that I cannot look back on the happier days
of our city, which I now describe, without a sad dejection of
the spirits. With a faltering hand do I withdraw the curtain of oblivion that veils the modest merit of our venerable
ancestors, and as their figures rise to my mental vision, humble myself before the mighty shades.

Such are my feelings when I revisit the family mansion
of the Knickerbockers, and spend a lonely hour in the chamber where hang the portraits of my forefathers, shrouded in
dust, like the forms they represent. With pious reverence
do I gaze on the countenances of those renowned burghers,

who have preceded me in the steady march of existence—
whose sober and temperate blood now meanders through my
veins, flowing slower and slower in its feeble conduits, until
its current shall soon be stopped forever!

These, say I to myself, are but frail memorials of the
mighty men who flourished in the days of the patriarchs;
but who, alas! have long since mouldered in that tomb toward which my steps are insensibly and irresistibly hastening! As I pace the darkened chamber, and lose myself in
melancholy musings, the shadowy images around me almost
seem to steal once more into existence—their countenances
to assume the animation of life—their eyes to pursue me in
every movement! Carried away by the delusions of fancy,
I almost imagine myself surrounded by the shades of the departed, and holding sweet converse with the worthies of antiquity! Ah, hapless Diedrich! born in a degenerate age,
abandoned to the buffetings of fortune—a stranger and a
weary pilgrim in thy native land—blest with no weeping
wife, nor family of helpless children; but doomed to wander
neglected through those crowded streets, and elbowed by foreign upstarts from those fair abodes where once thine ancestors held sovereign empire!

Let me not, however, lose the historian in the man, nor
suffer the doting recollections of age to overcome me, while
dwelling with fond garrulity on the virtuous days of the patriarchs—on those sweet days of simplicity and ease which
never more will dawn on the lovely island of Manna-hata!

The renowned Wouter (or Walter) Van Twiller was descended from a long line of Dutch burgomasters, who had
successively dozed away their lives and grown fat upon the
bench of magistracy in Rotterdam; and who had comported
themselves with such singular wisdom and propriety that
they were never either heard or talked of—which, next to
being universally applauded, should be the object of ambition of all sage magistrates and rulers.

The surname of Twiller is said to be a corruption of the
original *Twijfler*, which in English means *doubter;* a name

admirably descriptive of his deliberative habits. For, though he was a man shut up within himself like an oyster, and of such a profoundly reflective turn that he scarcely ever spoke except in monosyllables, yet did he never make up his mind on any doubtful point. This was clearly accounted for by his adherents, who affirmed that he always conceived every object on so comprehensive a scale that he had not room in his head to turn it over and examine both sides of it, so that he always remained in doubt, merely in consequence of the astonishing magnitude of his ideas!

There are two opposite ways by which some men get into notice—one by talking a vast deal and thinking a little, and the other by holding their tongues and not thinking at all. By the first, many a vaporing, superficial pretender acquires the reputation of a man of quick parts; by the other, many a vacant dunderpate, like the owl, the stupidest of birds, comes to be complimented by a discerning world with all the attributes of wisdom. This, by the way, is a mere casual remark, which I would not for the universe have it thought I apply to Governor Van Twiller. On the contrary, he was a very wise Dutchman, for he never said a foolish thing— and of such invincible gravity that he was never known to laugh, or even to smile, through the course of a long and prosperous life. Certain, however, it is, there never was a matter proposed, however simple, and on which your common narrow-minded mortals would rashly determine at the first glance, but what the renowned Wouter put on a mighty, mysterious, vacant kind of look, shook his capacious head, and, having smoked for five minutes with redoubled earnestness, sagely observed that "he had his doubts about the matter"—which in process of time gained him the character of a man slow in belief, and not easily imposed on.

The person of this illustrious old gentleman was as regularly formed, and nobly proportioned, as though it had been molded by the hands of some cunning Dutch statuary, as a model of majesty and lordly grandeur. He was exactly five feet six inches in height and six feet five inches in circum-

ference. His head was a perfect sphere, and of such stupendous dimensions that Dame Nature, with all her sex's ingenuity, would have been puzzled to construct a neck capable of
supporting it; wherefore she wisely declined the attempt,
and settled it firmly on the top of his backbone, just between
the shoulders. His body was of an oblong form, particularly
capacious at bottom; which was wisely ordered by Providence, seeing that he was a man of sedentary habits, and
very averse to the idle labor of walking. His legs, though
exceeding short, were sturdy in proportion to the weight they
had to sustain; so that when erect he had not a little the appearance of a robustious beer-barrel, standing on skids. His
face, that infallible index of the mind, presented a vast expanse, perfectly unfurrowed or deformed by any of those
lines and angles which disfigure the human countenance
with what is termed expression. Two small gray eyes
twinkled feebly in the midst, like two stars of lesser magnitude in the hazy firmament; and his full-fed cheeks, which
seemed to have taken toll of everything that went into his
mouth, were curiously mottled and streaked with dusty red,
like a Spitzenberg apple.

His habits were as regular as his person. He daily took
his four stated meals, appropriating exactly an hour to each;
he smoked and doubted eight hours, and he slept the remaining twelve of the four-and-twenty. Such was the renowned
Wouter Van Twiller—a true philosopher, for his mind was
either elevated above, or tranquilly settled below, the cares
and perplexities of this world. He had lived in it for years
without feeling the least curiosity to know whether the sun
revolved round it, or it round the sun; and he had watched,
for at least half a century, the smoke curling from his pipe
to the ceiling, without once troubling his head with any of
those numerous theories, by which a philosopher would have
perplexed his brain, in accounting for its rising above the
surrounding atmosphere.

In his council he presided with great state and solemnity.
He sat in a huge chair of solid oak, hewn in the celebrated

forest of the Hague, fabricated by an experienced timmer-man of Amsterdam, and curiously carved about the arms and feet into exact imitations of gigantic eagle's claws. Instead of a scepter, he swayed a long Turkish pipe, wrought with jasmin and amber, which had been presented to a Stadt-holder of Holland at the conclusion of a treaty with one of the petty Barbary powers. In this stately chair would he sit, and this magnificent pipe would he smoke, shaking his right knee with a constant motion, and fixing his eye for hours together upon a little print of Amsterdam which hung in a black frame against the opposite wall of the council chamber. Nay, it has even been said that when any deliberation of extraordinary length and intricacy was on the carpet, the renowned Wouter would absolutely shut his eyes for full two hours at a time, that he might not be disturbed by external objects—and at such times the internal commotion of his mind was evinced by certain regular guttural sounds, which his admirers declared were merely the noise of conflict made by his contending doubts and opinions.

It is with infinite difficulty I have been enabled to collect these biographical anecdotes of the great man under consideration. The facts respecting him were so scattered and vague, and divers of them so questionable in point of authenticity, that I have had to give up the search after many, and decline the admission of still more, which would have tended to heighten the coloring of his portrait.

I have been the more anxious to delineate fully the person and habits of the renowned Van Twiller, from the consideration that he was not only the first but also the best governor that ever presided over this ancient and respectable province; and so tranquil and benevolent was his reign that I do not find throughout the whole of it a single instance of any offender being brought to punishment—a most indubitable sign of a merciful governor, and a case unparalleled, excepting in the reign of the illustrious King Log, from whom, it is hinted, the renowned Van Twiller was a lineal descendant.

The very outset of the career of this excellent magistrate

was distinguished by an example of legal acumen that gave
flattering presage of a wise and equitable administration.
The morning after he had been solemnly installed in office,
and at the moment that he was making his breakfast, from
a prodigious earthen dish, filled with milk and Indian pudding, he was suddenly interrupted by the appearance of one
Wandle Schoonhoven, a very important old burgher of New
Amsterdam, who complained bitterly of one Barent Bleecker,
inasmuch as he fraudulently refused to come to a settlement
of accounts, seeing that there was a heavy balance in favor
of the said Wandle. Governor Van Twiller, as I have already observed, was a man of few words; he was likewise a
mortal enemy to multiplying writings—or being disturbed at
his breakfast. Having listened attentively to the statement
of Wandle Schoonhoven, giving an occasional grunt, as he
shoveled a spoonful of Indian pudding into his mouth—either
as a sign that he relished the dish or comprehended the story
—he called unto him his constable, and pulling out of his
breeches pocket a huge jack-knife, dispatched it after the de-
fendant as a summons, accompanied by his tobacco-box as a
warrant.

This summary process was as effectual in those simple
days as was the seal-ring of the great Haroun Alraschid
among the true believers. The two parties being confronted
before him, each produced a book of accounts written in a
language and character that would have puzzled any but a
High Dutch commentator, or a learned decipherer of Egyptian
obelisks, to understand. The sage Wouter took them one
after the other, and having poised them in his hands, and attentively counted over the number of leaves, fell straightway
into a very great doubt, and smoked for half an hour without
saying a word; at length, laying his finger beside his nose,
and shutting his eyes for a moment, with the air of a man
who has just caught a subtle idea by the tail, he slowly took
his pipe from his mouth, puffed forth a column of tobacco-
smoke, and with marvelous gravity and solemnity pronounced
—that having carefully counted over the leaves and weighed

the books, it was found that one was just as thick and as heavy as the other—therefore it was the final opinion of the court that the accounts were equally balanced—therefore Wandle should give Barent a receipt, and Barent should give Wandle a receipt—and the constable should pay the costs.

This decision being straightway made known diffused general joy throughout New Amsterdam, for the people immediately perceived that they had a very wise and equitable magistrate to rule over them. But its happiest effect was that not another lawsuit took place throughout the whole of his administration—and the office of constable fell into such decay that there was not one of those losel scouts known in the province for many years. I am the more particular in dwelling on this transaction, not only because I deem it one of the most sage and righteous judgments on record, and well worthy the attention of modern magistrates, but because it was a miraculous event in the history of the renowned Wouter —being the only time he was ever known to come to a decision in the whole course of his life.

CHAPTER TWO

CONTAINING SOME ACCOUNT OF THE GRAND COUNCIL OF NEW AMSTERDAM, AS ALSO DIVERS ESPECIAL GOOD PHILOSOPHICAL REASONS WHY AN ALDERMAN SHOULD BE FAT—WITH OTHER PARTICULARS TOUCHING THE STATE OF THE PROVINCE

IN treating of the early governors of the province, I must caution my readers against confounding them, in point of dignity and power, with those worthy gentlemen who are whimsically denominated governors in this enlightened republic—a set of unhappy victims of popularity, who are in fact the most dependent, henpecked beings in the community: doomed to bear the secret goadings and corrections of

their own party, and the sneers and revilings of the whole
world besides—set up, like geese at Christmas holidays, to
be pelted and shot at by every whipster and vagabond in the
land. On the contrary, the Dutch governors enjoyed that
uncontrolled authority vested in all commanders of distant
colonies or territories. They were in a manner absolute des-
pots in their little domains, lording it, if so disposed, over
both law and gospel, and accountable to none but the mother
country; which it is well known is astonishingly deaf to all
complaints against its governors, provided they discharge the
main duty of their station—squeezing out a good revenue.
This hint will be of importance, to prevent my readers from
being seized with doubt and incredulity, whenever, in the
course of this authentic history, they encounter the uncommon circumstance of a governor acting with independence,
and in opposition to the opinions of the multitude.

To assist the doubtful Wouter in the arduous business of
legislation, a board of magistrates was appointed, which presided immediately over the police. This potent body consisted of a schout or bailiff, with powers between those of the
present mayor and sheriff—five burgermeesters, who were
equivalent to aldermen, and five schepens, who officiated as
scrubs, subdevils or bottle-holders to the burgermeesters, in
the same manner as do assistant aldermen to their principals
at the present day; it being their duty to fill the pipes of the
lordly burgermeesters—hunt the markets for delicacies for
corporation dinners, and to discharge such other little offices
of kindness as were occasionally required. It was, moreover, tactily understood, though not specifically enjoined,
that they should consider themselves as butts for the blunt
wits of the burgermeesters, and should laugh most heartily
at all their jokes; but this last was a duty as rarely called in
action in those days as it is at present, and was shortly re-
mitted, in consequence of the tragical death of a fat little
schepen—who actually died of suffocation, in an unsuccessful effort to force a laugh at one of the burgermeester Van
Zandt's best jokes.

In return for these humble services, they were permitted
to say *yes* and *no* at the council board, and to have that enviable privilege, the run of the public kitchen—being graciously permitted to eat, and drink, and smoke, at all those
snug junketings and public gormandizings for which the ancient magistrates were equally famous with their modern
successors. The post of schepen, therefore, like that of assistant alderman, was eagerly coveted by all your burghers
of a certain description, who have a huge relish for good
feeding, and a humble ambition to be great men in a small
way—who thirst after a little brief authority that shall render them the terror of the almshouse and the bridewell—that
shall enable them to lord it over obsequious poverty, vagrant
vice, outcast prostitution, and hunger-driven dishonesty—
that shall give to their beck a hound-like pack of catch-poles
and bum-bailiffs—tenfold greater rogues than the culprits
they hunt down!—My readers will excuse this sudden
warmth, which I confess is unbecoming of a grave historian; but I have a mortal antipathy to catch-poles, bum-
bailiffs, and little great men.

The ancient magistrates of this city corresponded with
those of the present time no less in form, magnitude, and intellect, than in prerogative and privilege. The burgomasters, like our aldermen, were generally chosen by weight—
and not only the weight of the body, but likewise the weight
of the head. It is a maxim practically observed in all honest, plain-thinking, regular cities, that an alderman should
be fat—and the wisdom of this can be proved to a certainty.
That the body is in some measure an image of the mind, or
rather that the mind is molded to the body, like melted lead
to the clay in which it is cast, has been insisted on by many
philosophers, who have made human nature their peculiar
study; for, as a learned gentleman of our own city observes,
"There is a constant relation between the moral character of
all intelligent creatures and their physical constitution—between their habits and the structure of their bodies." Thus
we see that a lean, spare, diminutive body is generally ac-

companied by a petulant, restless, meddling mind—either
the mind wears down the body by its continual motion; or
else the body, not affording the mind sufficient house-room,
keeps it continually in a state of fretfulness, tossing and
worrying about from the uneasiness of its situation. Whereas
your round, sleek, fat, unwieldy periphery is ever attended
by a mind like itself, tranquil, torpid, and at ease; and we
may always observe that your well-fed, robustious burghers
are in general very tenacious of their ease and comfort; being great enemies to noise, discord, and disturbance—and
surely none are more likely to study the public tranquillity
than those who are so careful of their own. Who ever hears
of fat men heading a riot, or herding together in turbulent
mobs?—no—no—it is your lean, hungry men who are continually worrying society, and setting the whole community
by the ears.

The divine Plato, whose doctrines are not sufficiently attended to by philosophers of the present age, allows to every
man three souls—one immortal and rational, seated in the
brain, that it may overlook and regulate the body—a second
consisting of the surly and irascible passions, which, like belligerent powers, lie encamped around the heart—a third mortal and sensual, destitute of reason, gross and brutal in its
propensities, and enchained in the belly, that it may not disturb the divine soul by its ravenous howlings. Now, according to this excellent theory, what can be more clear than that
your fat alderman is most likely to have the most regular
and well-conditioned mind. His head is like a huge, spheri-
cal chamber, containing a prodigious mass of soft brains,
whereon the rational soul lies softly and snugly couched, as
on a feather bed; and the eyes, which are the windows of the
bedchamber, are usually half closed, that its slumberings
may not be disturbed by external objects. A mind thus
comfortably lodged, and protected from disturbance, is mani-
festly most likely to perform its functions with regularity and
ease. By dint of good feeding, moreover, the mortal and
malignant soul, which is confined in the belly, and which,

by its raging and roaring, puts the irritable soul in the neighborhood of the heart in an intolerable passion, and thus renders men crusty and quarrelsome when hungry, is completely pacified, silenced, and put to rest—whereupon a host of honest good-fellow qualities and kind-hearted affections, which had lain perdue, slyly peeping out of the loop-holes of the heart, finding this Cerberus asleep, do pluck up their spirits, turn out one and all in their holiday suits, and gambol up and down the diaphragm—disposing their possessor to laughter, good-humor, and a thousand friendly offices toward his fellow-mortals.

As a board of magistrates, formed on this model, think but very little, they are the less likely to differ and wrangle about favorite opinions—and as they generally transact business upon a hearty dinner, they are naturally disposed to be lenient and indulgent in the administration of their duties. Charlemagne was conscious of this, and, therefore (a pitiful measure, for which I can never forgive him), ordered in his cartularies that no judge should hold a court of justice, except in the morning, on an empty stomach—a rule which, I warrant, bore hard upon all the poor culprits in his kingdom. The more enlightened and humane generation of the present day have taken an opposite course, and have so managed that the aldermen are the best-fed men in the community; feasting lustily on the fat things of the land, and gorging so heartily oysters and turtles that in process of time they acquire the activity of the one, and the form, the waddle, and the green fat of the other. The consequence is, as I have just said, these luxurious feastings do produce such a dulcet equanimity and repose of the soul, rational and irrational, that their transactions are proverbial for unvarying monotony—and the profound laws which they enact in their dozing moments, amid the labors of digestion, are quietly suffered to remain as dead-letters, and never enforced, when awake. In a word, your fair, round-bellied burgomaster, like a full-fed mastiff, dozes quietly at the house-door, always at home, and always at hand to watch over its safety—but as to electing a lean, meddling candidate to the office, as has now and then been done, I would as lief put a greyhound to watch the house, or a racehorse to drag an ox-wagon.

The burgomasters then, as I have already mentioned, were wisely chosen by weight, and the schepens, or assistant aldermen, were appointed to attend upon them, and help them eat; but the latter, in the course of time, when they had been fed and fattened into sufficient bulk of body and drowsiness of brain, became very eligible candidates for the burgomasters' chairs, having fairly eaten themselves into office as a mouse eats his way into a comfortable lodgment in a goodly, blue-nosed, skimmed-milk, New England cheese.

Nothing could equal the profound deliberations that took place between the renowned Wouter and these his worthy compeers, unless it be the sage divans of some of our modern corporations. They would sit for hours smoking and dozing over public affairs, without speaking a word to interrupt that perfect stillness so necessary to deep reflection. Under the sober sway of Wouter Van Twiller, and these his worthy co-adjutors, the infant settlement waxed vigorous apace, gradually emerging from the swamps and forests, and exhibiting that mingled appearance of town and country customary in new cities, and which at this day may be witnessed in the city of Washington—that immense metropolis which makes so glorious an appearance on paper.

It was a pleasing sight, in those times, to behold the honest burgher, like a patriarch of yore, seated on the bench at the door of his whitewashed house, under the shade of some gigantic sycamore or overhanging willow. Here would he smoke his pipe of a sultry afternoon, enjoying the soft southern breeze, and listening with silent gratulation to the clucking of his hens, the cackling of his geese, and the sonorous grunting of his swine; that combination of farmyard melody which may truly be said to have a silver sound, inasmuch as it conveys a certain assurance of profitable marketing.

The modern spectator, who wanders through the streets of this populous city, can scarcely form an idea of the differ-

ent appearance they presented in the primitive days of the
Doubter. The busy hum of multitudes, the shouts of revelry, the rumbling equipages of fashion, the rattling of ac-
cursed carts, and all the spirit-grieving sounds of brawling
commerce, were unknown in the settlement of New Amsterdam. The grass grew quietly in the highways—the bleating
sheep and frolicsome calves sported about the verdant ridge
where now the Broadway loungers take their morning stroll
—the cunning fox or ravenous wolf skulked in the woods
where now are to be seen the dens of Gomez and his righteous fraternity of money-brokers—and flocks of vociferous
geese cackled about the fields where now the great Tammany wigwam and the patriotic tavern of Martling echo
with the wranglings of the mob.

In these good times did a true and enviable equality of
rank and property prevail, equally removed from the arrogance of wealth and the servility and heart-burnings of re-
pining poverty—and what in my mind is still more conducive
to tranquillity and harmony among friends, a happy equality
of intellect was likewise to be seen. The minds of the good
burghers of New Amsterdam seemed all to have been cast
in one mold, and to be those honest, blunt minds which,
like certain manufactures, are made by the gross, and considered as exceedingly good for common use.

Thus it happens that your true dull minds are generally
preferred for public employ, and especially promoted to city
honors; your keen intellects, like razors, being considered
too sharp for common service. I know that it is common to
rail at the unequal distribution of riches as the great source
of jealousies, broils, and heart-breakings; whereas, for my
part, I verily believe it is the sad inequality of intellect that
prevails that embroils communities more than anything else;
and I have remarked that your knowing people, who are so
much wiser than anybody else, are eternally keeping society
in a ferment. Happily for New Amsterdam, nothing of the
kind was known within its walls—the very words of learning, education, taste, and talents were unheard of—a bright

genius was an animal unknown, and a blue-stocking lady would have been regarded with as much wonder as a horned frog or a fiery dragon. No man, in fact, seemed to know more than his neighbor, nor any man to know more than an honest man ought to know, who has nobody's business to mind but his own; the parson and the council clerk were the only men that could read in the community, and the sage Van Twiller always signed his name with a cross.

Thrice happy and ever to be envied little burgh! existing in all the security of harmless insignificance—unnoticed and unenvied by the world, without ambition, without vainglory, without riches, without learning, and all their train of carking cares—and as of yore, in the better days of man, the deities were wont to visit him on earth and bless his rural habitations, so we are told, in the sylvan days of New Amsterdam, the good St. Nicholas would often make his appearance in his beloved city, of a holiday afternoon, riding jollily among the treetops, or over the roofs of the houses, now and then drawing forth magnificent presents from his breeches pockets, and dropping them down the chimneys of his favorites. Whereas in these degenerate days of iron and brass he never shows us the light of his countenance, nor ever visits us, save one night in the year; when he rattles down the chimneys of the descendants of the patriarchs, confining his presents merely to the children, in token of the degeneracy of the parents.

Such are the comfortable and thriving effects of a fat government. The province of the New Netherlands, destitute of wealth, possessed a sweet tranquillity that wealth could never purchase. There were neither public commotions nor private quarrels; neither parties, nor sects, nor schisms; neither persecutions, nor trials, nor punishments; nor were there counselors, attorneys, catch-poles, or hangmen. Every man attended to what little business he was lucky enough to have, or neglected it if he pleased, without asking the opinion of his neighbor. In those days nobody meddled with concerns above his comprehension, nor thrust his nose into other people's affairs; nor neglected to correct his own conduct, and reform his own character, in his zeal to pull to pieces the characters of others—but, in a word, every respectable citizen eat when he was not hungry, drank when he was not thirsty, and went regularly to bed when the sun set, and the fowls went to roost, whether he were sleepy or not; all which tended so remarkably to the population of the settlement, that I am told every dutiful wife throughout New Amsterdam made a point of enriching her husband with at least one child a year, and very often a brace—this superabundance of good things clearly constituting the true luxury of life, according to the favorite Dutch maxim that "More than enough constitutes a feast." Everything, therefore, went on exactly as it should do; and in the usual words employed by historians to express the welfare of a country, "The profoundest *tranquillity* and *repose* reigned throughout the province."

CHAPTER THREE

HOW THE TOWN OF NEW AMSTERDAM AROSE OUT OF MUD, AND CAME TO BE MARVELOUSLY POLISHED AND POLITE —TOGETHER WITH A PICTURE OF THE MANNERS OF OUR GREAT-GREAT-GRANDFATHERS

MANIFOLD are the tastes and dispositions of the enlightened literati who turn over the pages of history. Some there be whose hearts are brimful of the yeast of courage, and whose bosoms do work, and swell, and foam with untried valor, like a barrel of new cider, or a train-band captain fresh from under the hands of his tailor. This doughty class of readers can be satisfied with nothing but bloody battles and horrible encounters; they must be continually storming forts, sacking cities, springing mines, marching up to the muzzles of cannon, charging bayonet through every page, and reveling in gunpowder and carnage. Others, who are of a less martial but equally ardent imagination, and who, withal, are a little given to the marvelous, will dwell with wondrous satisfaction on descriptions of prodigies, unheard-of events, hairbreadth escapes, hardy adventures, and all those astonishing narrations that just amble along the boundary line of possibility. A third class, who, not to speak slightly of them, are of a lighter turn, and skim over the records of past times as they do over the edifying pages of a novel, merely for relaxation and innocent amusement, do singularly delight in treasons, executions, Sabine rapes, Tarquin outrages, conflagrations, murders, and all the other catalogue of hideous crimes, that, like cayenne in cookery, do give a pungency and flavor to the dull detail of history—while a fourth class, of more philosophic habits, do diligently pore over the musty chronicles of time, to investigate the operations of the human kind, and watch the gradual changes in men and manners, effected by the progress of knowledge, the vicissitudes of events, or the influence of situation.

If the three first classes find but little wherewithal to solace themselves in the tranquil reign of Wouter Van Twiller, I entreat them to exert their patience for a while, and bear with the tedious picture of happiness, prosperity, and peace, which my duty as a faithful historian obliges me to draw; and I promise them that as soon as I can possibly light upon anything horrible, uncommon, or impossible, it shall go hard, but I will make it afford them entertainment. This being promised I turn with great complacency to the fourth class of my readers, who are men, or, if possible, women, after my own heart; grave, philosophical, and investigating; fond of analyzing characters, of taking a start from first causes, and so hunting a nation down, through all the mazes of innovation and improvement. Such will naturally be anxious to witness the first development of the newly-hatched colony, and the primitive manners and customs prevalent among its inhabitants, during the halcyon reign of Van Twiller, or the Doubter.

I will not grieve their patience, however, by describing

*** F

minutely the increase and improvement of New Amsterdam. Their own imaginations will doubtless present to them the good burghers, like so many painstaking and persevering beavers, slowly and surely pursuing their labors—they will behold the prosperous transformation from the rude log-hut to the stately Dutch mansion, with brick front, glazed windows, and tiled roof—from the tangled thicket to the luxuriant cabbage garden; and from the skulking Indian to the ponderous burgomaster. In a word, they will picture to themselves the steady, silent, and undeviating march to prosperity, incident to a city destitute of pride or ambition, cherished by a fat government, and whose citizens do nothing in a hurry.

The sage council, as has been mentioned in a preceding chapter, not being able to determine upon any plan for the building of their city—the cows, in a laudable fit of patriotism, took it under their peculiar charge, and as they went to and from pasture, established paths through the bushes, on each side of which the good folks built their houses; which is one cause of the rambling and picturesque turns and labyrinths which distinguish certain streets of New York at this very day.

The houses of the higher class were generally constructed of wood, excepting the gable end, which was of small black and yellow Dutch bricks, and always faced on the street, as our ancestors, like their descendants, were very much given to outward show, and were noted for putting the best leg foremost. The house was always furnished with abundance of large doors and small windows on every floor; the date of its erection was curiously designated by iron figures on the front; and on the top of the roof was perched a fierce little weathercock, to let the family into the important secret which way the wind blew. These, like the weathercocks on the tops of our steeples, pointed so many different ways that every man could have a wind to his mind. The most stanch and loyal citizens, however, always went according to the weathercock on the top of the governor's house, which was certainly the most correct, as he had a trusty servant employed every morning to climb up and set it to the right quarter.

In those good days of simplicity and sunshine, a passion for cleanliness was the leading principle in domestic economy and the universal test of an able housewife—a character which formed the utmost ambition of our unenlightened grandmothers. The front door was never opened except on marriages, funerals, new-years' days, the festival of St. Nicholas, or some such great occasion. It was ornamented with a gorgeous brass knocker, curiously wrought, sometimes in the device of a dog, and sometimes of a lion's head, and was daily burnished with such religious zeal that it was ofttimes worn out by the very precautions taken for its preservation. The whole house was constantly in a state of inundation, under the discipline of mops and brooms and scrubbing-brushes; and the good housewives of those days were a kind of amphibious animal, delighting exceedingly to be dabbling in water—insomuch that a historian of the day gravely tells us that many of his townswomen grew to have webbed fingers like unto a duck; and some of them, he had little doubt, could the matter be examined into, would be found to have the tails of mermaids—but this I look upon to be a mere sport of fancy, or what is worse, a willful misrepresentation.

The grand parlor was the sanctum sanctorum, where the passion for cleaning was indulged without control. In this sacred apartment no one was permitted to enter, excepting the mistress and her confidential maid, who visited it once a week, for the purpose of giving it a thorough cleaning, and putting things to rights—always taking the precaution of leaving their shoes at the door, and entering devoutly in their stocking-feet. After scrubbing the floor, sprinkling it with fine white sand, which was curiously stroked into angles, and curves, and rhomboids, with a broom—after washing the windows, rubbing and polishing the furniture, and putting a new bunch of evergreens in the fireplace—the window-shutters were again closed to keep out the flies, and the room carefully locked up until the revolution of time brought round the weekly cleaning day.

As to the family, they always entered in at the gate, and most generally lived in the kitchen. To have seen a numerous household assembled around the fire one would have imagined that he was transported back to those happy days of primeval simplicity which float before our imaginations like golden visions. The fireplaces were of a truly patriarchal magnitude, where the whole family, old and young, master and servant, black and white, nay, even the very cat and dog, enjoyed a community of privilege, and had each a right to a corner. Here the old burgher would sit in perfect silence, puffing his pipe, looking in the fire with half-shut eyes, and thinking of nothing for hours together; the goede vrouw on the opposite side would employ herself diligently in spinning yarn or knitting stockings. The young folks would crowd around the hearth, listening with breathless attention to some old crone of a negro, who was the oracle of the family, and who, perched like a raven in a corner of the chimney, would croak forth for a long winter afternoon a string of incredible stories about New England witches, grisly ghosts, horses without heads, and hairbreadth escapes and bloody encounters among the Indians.

In those happy days a well-regulated family always rose with the dawn, dined at eleven, and went to bed at sundown. Dinner was invariably a private meal, and the fat old burghers showed incontestible symptoms of disapprobation and uneasiness at being surprised by a visit from a neighbor on such occasions. But though our worthy ancestors were thus singularly averse to giving dinners, yet they kept up the social bands of intimacy by occasional banquetings called tea-parties.

These fashionable parties were generally confined to the higher classes or noblesse, that is to say, such as kept their own cows and drove their own wagons. The company commonly assembled at three o'clock, and went away about six, unless it was in winter-time, when the fashionable hours were a little earlier, that the ladies might get home before dark. The tea-table was crowned with a huge earthen dish, well stored with slices of fat pork, fried brown, cut up into morsels, and swimming in gravy. The company being seated around the genial board, and each furnished with a fork, evinced their dexterity in lanching at the fattest pieces in this mighty dish—in much the same manner as sailors harpoon porpoises at sea, or our Indians spear salmon in the lakes. Sometimes the table was graced with immense apple pies, or saucers full of preserved peaches and pears; but it was always sure to boast an enormous dish of balls of sweetened dough, fried in hog's fat, and called doughnuts or oly-koeks—a delicious kind of cake, at present scarce known in this city, excepting in genuine Dutch families.

The tea was served out of a majestic delft teapot, ornamented with paintings of fat little Dutch shepherds and shepherdesses tending pigs—with boats sailing in the air, and houses built in the clouds, and sundry other ingenious Dutch fantasies. The beaux distinguished themselves by their adroitness in replenishing this pot from a huge copper tea-kettle, which would have made the pigmy macaronies of these degenerate days sweat merely to look at it. To sweeten the beverage, a lump of sugar was laid beside each cup—and the company alternately nibbled and sipped with great decorum, until an improvement was introduced by a shrewd and economic old lady, which was to suspend a large lump directly over the tea-table, by a string from the ceiling, so that it could be swung from mouth to mouth—an ingenious expedient which is still kept up by some families in Albany; but which prevails without exception in Communipaw, Bergen, Flatbush, and all our uncontaminated Dutch villages.

At these primitive tea-parties the utmost propriety and dignity of deportment prevailed. No flirting nor coquetting —no gambling of old ladies, nor hoyden chattering and romping of young ones—no self-satisfied struttings of wealthy gentlemen, with their brains in their pockets—nor amusing

conceits and monkey divertisements of smart young gentlemen with no brains at all. On the contrary, the young
ladies seated themselves demurely in their rush-bottomed
chairs, and knit their own woolen stockings; nor ever
opened their lips, excepting to say, *yaw Mynher*, or *yah
yah Vrouw*, to any question that was asked them; behav‹
ing, in all things, like decent, well-educated damsels. As
to the gentlemen, each of them tranquilly smoked his pipe,
and seemed lost in contemplation of the blue and white tiles
with which the fireplaces were decorated; wherein sundry
passages of Scripture were piously portrayed—Tobit and his
dog figured to great advantage; Haman swung conspicuously
on his gibbet; and Jonah appeared most manfully bouncing
out of the whale, like Harlequin through a barrel of fire.

The parties broke up without noise and without confusion.
They were carried home by their own carriages, that is to
say, by the vehicles Nature had provided them, excepting
such of the wealthy as could afford to keep a wagon. The
gentlemen gallantly attended their fair ones to their respective
abodes, and took leave of them with a hearty smack at the
door; which, as it was an established piece of etiquette, done
in perfect simplicity and honesty of heart, occasioned no
scandal at that time, nor should it at the present—if our
great-grandfathers approved of the custom, it would argue
a great want of reverence in their descendants to say a
word against it.

<hr />

CHAPTER FOUR

CONTAINING FURTHER PARTICULARS OF THE GOLDEN AGE, AND WHAT CONSTITUTED A FINE LADY AND GENTLEMAN IN THE DAYS OF WALTER THE DOUBTER

In this dulcet period of my history, when the beauteous
island of Manna-hata presented a scene the very counterpart
of those glowing pictures drawn of the golden reign of
Saturn, there was, as I have before observed, a happy igno-

rance, an honest simplicity, prevalent among its inhabitants, which, were I even able to depict, would be but little understood by the degenerate age for which I am doomed to write. Even the female sex, those arch innovators upon the tranquillity, the honesty, and gray-beard customs of society, seemed for a while to conduct themselves with incredible sobriety and comeliness.

Their hair, untortured by the abominations of art, was scrupulously pomatumed back from their foreheads with a candle, and covered with a little cap of quilted calico, which fitted exactly to their heads. Their petticoats of linsey-woolsey were striped with a variety of gorgeous dyes—though I must confess these gallant garments were rather short, scarce reaching below the knee; but then they made up in the number, which generally equaled that of the gentlemen's smallclothes; and what is still more praiseworthy, they were all of their own manufacture—of which circumstance, as may well be supposed, they were not a little vain.

These were the honest days in which every woman stayed at home, read the Bible, and wore pockets—ay, and that too of a goodly size, fashioned with patchwork into many curious devices, and ostentatiously worn on the outside. These, in fact, were convenient receptacles, where all good housewives carefully stowed away such things as they wished to have at hand; by which means they often came to be incredibly crammed—and I remember there was a story current when I was a boy, that the lady of Wouter Van Twiller once had occasion to empty her right pocket in search of a wooden ladle, and the utensil was discovered lying among some rubbish in one corner—but we must not give too much faith to all these stories; the anecdotes of those remote periods being very subject to exaggeration.

Besides these notable pockets, they likewise wore scissors and pincushions suspended from their girdles by red ribbons, or, among the more opulent and showy classes, by brass, and even silver chains, indubitable tokens of thrifty housewives and industrious spinsters. I cannot say much in vindication

of the shortness of the petticoats; it doubtless was introduced
for the purpose of giving the stockings a chance to be seen,
which were generally of blue worsted, with magnificent red
clocks—or perhaps to display a well-turned ankle, and a
neat, though serviceable foot, set off by a high-heeled leathern
shoe, with a large and splendid silver buckle.   Thus we find
that the gentle sex in all ages have shown the same disposition to infringe a little upon the laws of decorum, in order to
betray a lurking beauty or gratify an innocent love of finery.

From the sketch here given, it will be seen that our good
grandmothers differed considerably in their ideas of a fine
figure from their scantily-dressed descendants of the present
day.   A fine lady, in those times, waddled under more
clothes, even on a fair summer's day, than would have clad
the whole bevy of a modern ball-room.   Nor were they the
less admired by the gentlemen in consequence thereof.   On
the contrary, the greatness of a lover's passion seemed to
increase in proportion to the magnitude of its object—and a
voluminous damsel, arrayed in a dozen of petticoats, was
declared by a Low Dutch sonneteer of the province to be
radiant as a sunflower and luxuriant as a full-blown cabbage.   Certain it is, that in those days the heart of a lover
could not contain more than one lady at a time; whereas the
heart of a modern gallant has often room enough to accommodate half-a-dozen.   The reason of which I conclude to be,
that either the hearts of the gentlemen have grown larger,
or the persons of the ladies smaller—this, however, is a
question for physiologists to determine.

But there was a secret charm in these petticoats, which
no doubt entered into the consideration of the prudent gallants.   The wardrobe of a lady was in those days her only
fortune; and she who had a good stock of petticoats and
stockings was as absolutely an heiress as is a Kamtschatka
damsel with a store of bear-skins, or a Lapland belle with a
plenty of reindeer.   The ladies, therefore, were very anxious
to display these powerful attractions to the greatest advantage; and the best rooms in the house, instead of being

adorned with caricatures of Dame Nature, in water-colors and needle-work, were always hung round with abundance of home-spun garments, the manufacture and the property of the females—a piece of laudable ostentation that still prevails among the heiresses of our Dutch villages.

The gentlemen, in fact, who figured in the circles of the gay world in these ancient times, corresponded, in most particulars, with the beauteous damsels whose smiles they were ambitious to deserve. True it is, their merits would make but a very inconsiderable impression upon the heart of a modern fair; they neither drove their curricles nor sported their tandems, for as yet those gaudy vehicles were not even dreamed of—neither did they distinguish themselves by their brilliancy at the table and their consequent rencounters with watchmen, for our forefathers were of too pacific a disposition to need those guardians of the night, every soul throughout the town being sound asleep before nine o'clock. Neither did they establish their claims to gentility at the expense of their tailors—for as yet those offenders against the pockets of society and the tranquillity of all aspiring young gentlemen were unknown in New Amsterdam; every good housewife made the clothes of her husband and family, and even the goede vrouw of Van Twiller himself thought it no disparagement to cut out her husband's linsey-woolsey galligaskins.

Not but what there were some two or three youngsters who manifested the first dawnings of what is called fire and spirit—who held all labor in contempt; skulked about docks and market-places; loitered in the sunshine; squandered what little money they could procure at hustle-cap and chuck-farthing; swore, boxed, fought cocks, and raced their neighbors' horses—in short, who promised to be the wonder, the talk, and abomination of the town, had not their stylish career been unfortunately cut short by an affair of honor with a whipping-post.

Far other, however, was the truly fashionable gentleman of those days—his dress, which served for both morning and evening, street and drawing-room, was a linsey-woolsey coat,

made, perhaps, by the fair hands of the mistress of his affections, and gallantly bedecked with abundance of large brass
buttons—half a score of breeches heightened the proportions
of his figure—his shoes were decorated by enormous copper
buckles—a low-crowned, broad-brimmed hat overshadowed
his burly visage, and his hair dangled down his back in a
prodigious queue of eel-skin.

Thus equipped, he would manfully sally forth with pipe
in mouth, to besiege some fair damsel's obdurate heart—not
such a pipe, good reader, as that which Acis did sweetly
tune in praise of his Galatea, but one of true delft manufacture, and furnished with a charge of fragrant tobacco. With
this would he resolutely set himself down before the fortress,
and rarely failed, in the process of time, to smoke the fair
enemy into a surrender, upon honorable terms.

Such was the happy reign of Wouter Van Twiller, celebrated in many a long-forgotten song as the real golden age,
the rest being nothing but counterfeit copper-washed coin.
In that delightful period a sweet and holy calm reigned over
the whole province. The burgomaster smoked his pipe in
peace—the substantial solace of his domestic cares, after her
daily toils were done, sat soberly at the door, with her arms
crossed over her apron of snowy white, without being insulted
by ribald street-walkers, or vagabond boys—those unlucky
urchin, who do so infest our streets, displaying under the
roses of youth the thorns and briers of iniquity. Then it
was that the lover with ten breeches, and the damsel with
petticoats of half a score, indulged in all the innocent endear-
ments of virtuous love, without fear and without reproach;
for what had that virtue to fear which was defended by a
shield of good linsey-woolseys, equal at least to the seven
bull-hides of the invincible Ajax?

Ah! blissful, and never-to-be-forgotten age! when everything was better than it has ever been since, or ever will be
again—when Buttermilk Channel was quite dry at low water
—when the shad in the Hudson were all salmon, and when
the moon shone with a pure and resplendent whiteness, in-

stead of that melancholy yellow light which is the consequence of her sickening at the abominations she every night
witnesses in this degenerate city!

Happy would it have been for New Amsterdam could it
always have existed in this state of blissful ignorance and
lowly simplicity—but, alas! the days of childhood are too
sweet to last! Cities, like men, grow out of them in time,
and are doomed alike to grow into the bustle, the cares, and
miseries of the world. Let no man congratulate himself
when he beholds the child of his bosom or the city of his
birth increasing in magnitude and importance—let the history of his own life teach him the dangers of the one, and
this excellent little history of Manna-hata convince him of
the calamities of the other.

CHAPTER FIVE

IN WHICH THE READER IS BEGUILED INTO A DELECTABLE
WALK WHICH ENDS VERY DIFFERENTLY FROM WHAT
IT COMMENCED

IN the year of Our Lord one thousand eight hundred and
four, on a fine afternoon in the glowing month of September,
I took my customary walk upon the Battery, which is at
once the pride and bulwark of this ancient and impregnable
city of New York. The ground on which I trod was hallowed by recollections of the past, and as I slowly wandered
through the long alley of poplars, which like so many birch-
brooms standing on end diffused a melancholy and lugubrious shade, my imagination drew a contrast between the
surrounding scenery and what it was in the classic days of
our forefathers. Where the government-house by name, but
the custom-house by occupation, proudly reared its brick
walls and wooden pillars, there whilom stood the low but
substantial red-tiled mansion of the renowned Wouter Van
Twiller. Around it the mighty bulwarks of Fort Amsterdam
frowned defiance to every absent foe; but, like many a whis-

kered warrior and gallant militia captain, confined their mar
tial deeds to frowns alone. The mud breastworks had long
been leveled with the earth, and their site converted into the
green lawns and leafy alleys of the Battery; where the gay
apprentice sported his Sunday coat, and the laborious me-
chanic, relieved from the dirt and drudgery of the week,
poured his weekly tale of love into the half-averted ear of
the sentimental chambermaid. The capacious bay still presented the same expansive sheet of water, studded with
islands, sprinkled with fishing-boats, and bounded with shores
of picturesque beauty. But the dark forests which once
clothed these shores had been violated by the savage hand of
cultivation; and their tangled mazes and impenetrable thickets had degenerated into teeming orchards and waving fields
of grain. Even Governor's Island, once a smiling garden,
appertaining to the sovereigns of the province, was now covered with fortifications, inclosing a tremendous blockhouse—
so that this once peaceful island resembled a fierce little warrior in a big cocked hat, breathing gunpowder and defiance
to the world!

For some time did I indulge in this pensive train of
thought; contrasting, in sober sadness, the present day with
the hallowed years behind the mountains; lamenting the
melancholy progress of improvement, and praising the zeal
with which our worthy burghers endeavored to preserve the
wrecks of venerable customs, prejudices, and errors, from
the overwhelming tide of modern innovation—when by degrees my ideas took a different turn, and I insensibly awakened to an enjoyment of the beauties around me.

It was one of those rich autumnal days, which Heaven
particularly bestows upon the beauteous island of Manna-
hata and its vicinity—not a floating cloud obscured the azure
firmament—the sun, rolling in glorious splendor through
his ethereal course, seemed to expand his honest Dutch countenance into an unusual expression of benevolence, as he
smiled his evening salutation upon a city which he delights
to visit with his most bounteous beams—the very winds

seemed to hold in their breaths in mute attention, lest they should ruffle the tranquillity of the hour—and the waveless bosom of the bay presented a polished mirror in which Nature beheld herself and smiled. The standard of our city, reserved, like a choice handkerchief, for days of gala, hung motionless on the flagstaff, which forms the handle to a gigantic churn; and even the tremulous leaves of the poplar and the aspen ceased to vibrate to the breath of heaven. Everything seemed to acquiesce in the profound repose of nature. The formidable eighteen pounders slept in the embrasures of the wooden batteries, seemingly gathering fresh strength to fight the battles of their country on the next fourth of July—the solitary drum on Governor's Island forgot to call the garrison to their *shovels*—the evening gun had not yet sounded its signal for all the regular, well-meaning poultry throughout the country to go to roost; and the fleet of canoes, at anchor between Gibbet Island and Communipaw, slumbered on their rakes, and suffered the innocent oysters to lie for a while unmolested in the soft mud of their native bank!—My own feelings sympathized with the contagious tranquillity, and I should infallibly have dozed upon one of those fragments of benches, which our benevolent magistrates have provided for the benefit of convalescent loungers, had not the extraordinary inconvenience of the couch set all repose at defiance.

In the midst of this slumber of the soul, my attention was attracted to a black speck, peering above the western horizon, just in the rear of Bergen steeple—gradually it augments, and overhangs the would-be cities of Jersey, Harsimus, and Hoboken, which, like three jockies, are starting on the course of existence, and jostling each other at the commencement of the race. Now it skirts the long shore of ancient Pavonia, spreading its wide shadows from the high settlements at Weehawk quite to the lazaretto and quarantine, erected by the sagacity of our police for the embarrassment of commerce —now it climbs the serene vault of heaven, cloud rolling over cloud, shrouding the orb of day, darkening the vast expanse, and bearing thunder and hail and tempest in its bosom. The earth seems agitated at the confusion of the heavens—the late waveless mirror is lashed into furious waves that roll in hollow murmurs to the shore—the oyster-boats that erst sported in the placid vicinity of Gibbet Island now hurry affrighted to the land—the poplar writhes and twists and whistles in the blast—torrents of drenching rain and sounding hail deluge the Battery walks—the gates are thronged by apprentices, servant-maids, and little Frenchmen, with pocket-handkerchiefs over their hats, scampering from the storm—the late beauteous prospect presents one scene of anarchy and wild uproar, as though old Chaos had resumed his reign, and was hurling back into one vast turmoil the conflicting elements of nature.

Whether I fled from the fury of the storm, or remained boldly at my post, as our gallant train-band captains who march their soldiers through the rain without flinching, are points which I leave to the conjecture of the reader. It is possible he may be a little perplexed also to know the reason why I introduced this tremendous tempest to disturb the serenity of my work. On this latter point I will gratuitously instruct his ignorance. The panorama view of the Battery was given merely to gratify the reader with a correct description of that celebrated place, and the parts adjacent—secondly, the storm was played off partly to give a little bustle and life to this tranquil part of my work, and to keep my drowsy readers from falling asleep—and partly to serve as an overture to the tempestuous times that are about to assail the pacific province of Nieuw Nederlandts—and that overhang the slumberous administration of the renowned Wouter Van Twiller. It is thus the experienced playwright puts all the fiddles, the French horns, the kettledrums and trumpets of his orchestra in requisition, to usher in one of those horrible and brimstone uproars called melodramas—and it is thus he discharges his thunder, his lightning, his rosin, and saltpeter, preparatory to the rising of a ghost or the murdering of a hero.—We will now proceed with our history.

Whatever may be advanced by philosophers to the contrary, I am of opinion that, as to nations, the old maxim, that "honesty is the best policy," is a sheer and ruinous mistake. It might have answered well enough in the honest times when it was made, but in these degenerate days, if a nation pretends to rely merely upon the justice of its dealings it will fare something like an honest man among thieves, who, unless he have something more than his honesty to depend upon, stands but a poor chance of profiting by his company. Such at least was the case with the guileless government of the New Netherlands; which, like a worthy unsuspicious old burgher, quietly settled itself down into the city of New Amsterdam, as into a snug elbow-chair—and fell into a comfortable nap—while, in the meantime, its cunning neighbors stepped in and picked its pockets. Thus may we ascribe the commencement of all the woes of this great province, and its magnificent metropolis, to the tranquil security, or, to speak more accurately, to the unfortunate honesty, of its government. But as I dislike to begin an important part of my history toward the end of a chapter; and as my readers, like myself, must doubtless be exceedingly fatigued with the long walk we have taken, and the tempest we have sustained—I hold it meet we shut up the book, smoke a pipe, and having thus refreshed our spirits, take a fair start in the next chapter.

CHAPTER SIX

FAITHFULLY DESCRIBING THE INGENIOUS PEOPLE OF CONNECTICUT AND THEREABOUTS — SHOWING, MOREOVER, THE TRUE MEANING OF LIBERTY OF CONSCIENCE, AND A CURIOUS DEVICE AMONG THESE STURDY BARBARIANS TO KEEP UP A HARMONY OF INTERCOURSE, AND PROMOTE POPULATION

THAT my readers may the more fully comprehend the extent of the calamity at this very moment impending over

the honest, unsuspecting province of Nieuw Nederlandts, and
its dubious governor, it is necessary that I should give some
account of a horde of strange barbarians bordering upon
the eastern frontier.

Now so it came to pass that, many years previous to the
time of which we are treating, the sage cabinet of England
had adopted a certain national creed, a kind of public walk
of faith, or rather a religious turnpike, in which every loyal
subject was directed to travel to Zion—taking care to pay the
toll-gatherers by the way.

Albeit, a certain shrewd race of men, being very much
given to indulge their own opinions on all manner of subjects (a propensity exceedingly offensive to your free governments of Europe), did most presumptuously dare to think for
themselves in matters of religion, exercising what they considered a natural and inextinguishable right—the liberty of
conscience.

As, however, they possessed that ingenious habit of mind
which always thinks aloud, which rides cock-a-hoop on the
tongue, and is forever galloping into other people's ears, it
naturally followed that their liberty of conscience likewise
implied *liberty of speech*, which, being freely indulged, soon
put the country in a hubbub and aroused the pious indignation of the vigilant fathers of the church.

The usual methods were adopted to reclaim them that in
those days were considered so efficacious in bringing back
stray sheep to the fold; that is to say, they were coaxed, they
were admonished, they were menaced, they were buffeted—
line upon line, precept upon precept, lash upon lash, here a
little and there a great deal, were exhausted without mercy
and without success; until at length the worthy pastors of
the church, wearied out by their unparalleled stubbornness,
were driven, in the excess of their tender mercy, to adopt the
Scripture text, and literally "heaped live embers on their
heads."

Nothing, however, could subdue that invincible spirit of
independence which has ever distinguished this singular race

of people, so that rather than submit to such horrible tyranny they one and all embarked for the wilderness of America, where they might enjoy, unmolested, the inestimable luxury of talking. No sooner did they land on this loquacious soil than, as if they had caught the disease from the climate, they all lifted up their voices at once, and for the space of one whole year did keep up such a joyful clamor that we are told they frightened every bird and beast out of the neighborhood, and so completely dumfounded certain fish, which abound on their coast, that they have been called *dumb-fish* ever since.

From this simple circumstance, unimporatnt as it may seem, did first originate that renowned privilege so loudly boasted of throughout this country—which is so eloquently exercised in newspapers, pamphlets, ward meetings, pot-house committees, and congressional deliberations—which established the right of talking without ideas and without information—of misrepresenting public affairs—of decrying public measures—of aspersing great characters, and destroy-ing little ones; in short, that grand palladium of our country, the *liberty of speech.*

The simple aborigines of the land for a while contem-plated these strange folk in utter astonishment, but discover-ing that they wielded harmless though noisy weapons, and were a lively, ingenious, good-humored race of men, they became very friendly and sociable, and gave them the name of *Yanokies,* which in the Mais-Tchusaeg (or Massachusett) language signifies *silent men*—a waggish appellation, since shortened into the familiar epithet of YANKEES, which they retain unto the present day.

True it is, and my fidelity as a historian will not allow me to pass it over in silence, that the zeal of these good people, to maintain their rights and privileges unimpaired, did for a while betray them into errors which it is easier to pardon than defend. Having served a regular apprenticeship in the school of persecution, it behooved them to show that they had became proficients in the art. They accordingly employed their leisure hours in banishing, scourging or hanging divers heretical Papists, Quakers, and Anabaptists, for daring to abuse the *liberty of conscience:* which they now clearly proved to imply nothing more than that every man should think as he pleased in matters of religion—*provided* he thought *right;* for otherwise it would be giving a latitude to damnable heresies. Now as they (the majority) were perfectly convinced that *they alone* thought right, it consequently followed that whoever thought different from them thought wrong—and whoever thought wrong, and obstinately persisted in not being convinced and converted, was a flagrant violator of the inestimable liberty of conscience, and a corrupt and infectious member of the body politic, and deserved to be lopped off and cast into the fire.

Now I'll warrant there are hosts of my readers ready at once to lift up their hands and eyes, with that virtuous indignation with which we always contemplate the faults and errors of our neighbors, and to exclaim at these well-meaning, but mistaken people, for inflicting on others the injuries they had suffered themselves—for indulging the preposterous idea of convincing the mind by tormenting the body, and establishing the doctrine of charity and forbearance by intolerant persecution. But, in simple truth, what are we doing at this very day, and in this very enlightened nation, but acting upon the very same principle in our political controversies? Have we not, within but a few years, released ourselves from the shackles of a government which cruelly denied us the privilege of governing ourselves, and using in full latitude that invaluable member, the tongue? and are we not at this very moment striving our best to tyrannize over the opinions, tie up the tongues, or ruin the fortunes of one another? What are our great political societies, but mere political inquisitions—our pot-house committees, but little tribunals of denunciatian—our newspapers, but mere whipping-posts and pillories, where unfortunate individuals are pelted with rotten eggs—and our council of appointment, but a grand *auto da fe,* where culprits are annually sacrificed for their political heresies?

Where, then, is the difference in principle between our measures and those you are so ready to condemn among the people I am treating of? There is none; the difference is merely circumstantial. Thus we *denounce*, instead of banishing—we *libel*, instead of scourging—we *turn out of office*, instead of hanging—and where they burned an offender in *propria persona*, we either tar and feather or *burn him in effigy*—this political persecution being, somehow or other, the grand palladium of our liberties, and an incontrovertible proof that this is *a free country!*

But, notwithstanding the fervent zeal with which this holy war was prosecuted against the whole race of unbelievers, we do not find that the population of this new colony was in any wise hindered thereby; on the contrary, they multiplied to a degree which would be incredible to any man unacquainted with the marvelous fecundity of this growing country.

This amazing increase may, indeed, be partly ascribed to a singular custom prevalent among them, commonly known by the name of *bundling*—a superstitious rite observed by the young people of both sexes, with which they usually terminated their festivities; and which was kept up with religious strictness by the more bigoted and vulgar part of the community. This ceremony was likewise, in those primitive times, considered as an indispensable preliminary to matrimony; their courtships commencing where ours usually finish—by which means they acquired that intimate acquaintance with each other's good qualities before marriage which has been pronounced by philosophers the sure basis of a happy union. Thus early did this cunning and ingenious people display a shrewdness at making a bargain which has ever since distinguished them—and a strict adherence to the good old vulgar maxim about "buying a pig in a poke."

To this sagacious custom, therefore, do I chiefly attribute the unparalleled increase of the Yanokie or Yankee tribe; for it is a certain fact, well authenticated by court records and parish registers, that wherever the practice of bundling prevailed there was an amazing number of sturdy brats annually born unto the State, without the license of the law or the benefit of clergy. Neither did the irregularity of their birth operate in the least to their disparagement. On the contrary, they grew up a long-sided, raw-boned, hardy race of whoreson whalers, wood-cutters, fishermen, and peddlers, and strapping corn-fed wenches; who by their united efforts tended marvelously toward populating those notable tracts of country called Nantucket, Piscataway, and Cape Cod.

CHAPTER SEVEN

HOW THESE SINGULAR BARBARIANS TURNED OUT TO BE NOTORIOUS SQUATTERS—HOW THEY BUILT AIR CASTLES, AND ATTEMPTED TO INITIATE THE NEDERLANDERS IN THE MYSTERY OF BUNDLING

IN the last chapter I have given a faithful and unprejudiced account of the origin of that singular race of people inhabiting the country eastward of the Nieuw Nederlandts; but I have yet to mention certain peculiar habits which rendered them exceedingly obnoxious to our ever-honored Dutch ancestors.

The most prominent of these was a certain rambling propensity, with which, like the sons of Ishmael, they seem to have been gifted by Heaven, and which continually goads them on, to shift their residence from place to place, so that a Yankee farmer is in a constant state of migration; *tarrying* occasionally here and there; clearing lands for other people to enjoy, building houses for others to inhabit, and in a manner may be considered the wandering Arab of America.

His first thought, on coming to the years of manhood, is to *settle* himself in the world—which means nothing more nor less than to begin his rambles. To this end he takes unto himself for a wife some buxom country heiress, passing rich in red ribbons, glass beads, and mock tortoise-shell combs, with a white gown and morocco shoes for Sunday, and deeply skilled in the mystery of making apple sweet-meats, long sauce, and pumpkin pie.

Having thus provided himself, like a peddler, with a heavy knapsack, wherewith to regale his shoulders through the journey of life, he literally sets out on the peregrination. His whole family, household furniture, and farming utensils, are hoisted into a covered cart; his own and his wife's ward-robe packed up in a firkin—which done, he shoulders his ax, takes staff in hand, whistles "Yankee Doodle," and trudges off to the woods, as confident of the protection of Providence, and relying as cheerfully upon his own resources, as did ever a patriarch of yore when he journeyed into a strange coun-try of the Gentiles. Having buried himself in the wilder-ness, he builds himself a log hut, clears away a cornfield and potato-patch, and, Providence smiling upon his labors, is soon surrounded by a snug farm and some half a score of flaxen-headed urchins, who, by their size, seem to have sprung all at once out of the earth, like a crop of toadstools.

But it is not the nature of this most indefatigable of spec-ulators to rest contented with any state of sublunary enjoy-ment—*improvement* is his darling passion, and having thus improved his lands, the next care is to provide a mansion worthy the residence of a landholder. A huge palace of pine boards immediately springs up in the midst of the wil-derness, large enough for a parish church, and furnished with windows of all dimensions, but so rickety and flimsy withal that every blast gives it a fit of the ague.

By the time the outside of this mighty air castle is com-pleted either the funds or the zeal of our adventurer are ex-hausted, so that he barely manages to half finish one room within, where the whole family burrow together—while the rest of the house is devoted to the curing of pumpkins, or storing of carrots and potatoes, and is decorated with fan-ciful festoons of dried apples and peaches. The outside remaining unpainted, grows venerably black with time; the family wardrobe is laid under contribution for old hats, pet-

ticoats, and breeches, to stuff into the broken windows, while
the four winds of heaven keep up a whistling and howling
about this aerial palace, and play as many unruly gambols
as they did of yore in the cave of old Æolus.

The humble log hut, which whilom nestled this *improving* family snugly within its narrow but comfortable
walls, stands hard by, in ignominious contrast, degraded
into a cow-house or pig-sty; and the whole scene reminds
one forcibly of a fable, which I am surprised has never been
recorded, of an aspiring snail, who abandoned his humble
habitation, which he had long filled with great respectabil-
ity, to crawl into the empty shell of a lobster—where he
would no doubt have resided with great style and splendor,
the envy and hate of all the painstaking snails in his neighborhood, had he not accidentally perished with cold in one
corner of his stupendous mansion.

Being thus completely settled, and, to use his own words,
"to rights," one would imagine that he would begin to enjoy
the comforts of his situation, to read newspapers, talk politics, neglect his own business, and attend to the affairs of
the nation, like a useful and patriotic citizen; but now it is
that his wayward disposition begins again to operate. He
soon grows tired of a spot where there is no longer any room
for improvement—sells his farm, air castle, petticoat windows and all, reloads his cart, shoulders his ax, puts himself
at the head of his family, and wanders away in search of
new lands—again to fell trees—again to clear cornfields—
again to build a shingle palace, and again to sell off and
wander.

Such were the people of Connecticut, who bordered upon
the eastern frontier of Nieuw Nederlandts; and my readers
may easily imagine what obnoxious neighbors this light-
hearted but restless tribe must have been to our tranquil
progenitors. If they cannot, I would ask them if they have
ever known one of our regular, well-organized Dutch families whom it hath pleased Heaven to afflict with the neighborhood of a French boarding-house? The honest old burgher

cannot take his afternoon's pipe on the bench before his door, but he is persecuted with the scraping of fiddles, the chattering of women, and the squalling of children—he cannot sleep at night for the horrible melodies of some amateur, who chooses to serenade the moon, and display his terrible proficiency in *execution*, on the clarionet, the hautboy, or some other soft-toned instrument—nor can he leave the street door open, but his house is defiled by the unsavory visits of a troop of pug dogs, who even sometimes carry their loathsome ravages into the sanctum sanctorum, the parlor!

If my readers have ever witnessed the sufferings of such a family, so situated, they may form some idea how our worthy ancestors were distressed by their mercurial neighbors of Connecticut.

Gangs of these marauders, we are told, penetrated into the New Netherland settlements, and threw whole villages into consternation by their unparalleled volubility and their intolerable inquisitiveness—two evil habits hitherto unknown in those parts, or only known to be abhorred; for our ancestors were noted as being men of truly Spartan taciturnity, and who neither knew nor cared aught about anybody's concerns but their own. Many enormities were committed on the highways, where several unoffending burghers were brought to a stand, and tortured with questions and guesses, which outrages occasioned as much vexation and heartburning as does the modern right of search on the high seas.

Great jealousy did they likewise stir up by their intermeddling and successes among the divine sex; for being a race of brisk, likely, pleasant-tongued varlets, they soon seduced the light affections of the simple damsels from their ponderous Dutch gallants. Among other hideous customs, they attempted to introduce among them that of *bundling*, which the Dutch lasses of the Nederlandts, with that eager passion for novelty and foreign fashions natural to their sex, seemed very well inclined to follow, but that their mothers, being more experienced in the world and better acquainted with men and things, strenuously discountenanced all such outlandish innovations.

But what chiefly operated to embroil our ancestors with these strange folk was an unwarrantable liberty which they occasionally took of entering in hordes into the territories of the New Netherlands, and settling themselves down, without leave or license, to *improve* the land, in the manner I have before noticed. This unceremonious mode of taking possession of *new land* was technically termed *squatting*, and hence is derived the appellation of *squatters;* a name odious in the ears of all great landholders, and which is given to those enterprising worthies who seize upon land first, and take their chance to make good their title to it afterward.

All these grievances, and many others which were constantly accumulating, tended to form that dark and portentous cloud which, as I observed in a former chapter, was slowly gathering over the tranquil province of New Netherlands. The pacific cabinet of Van Twiller, however, as will be perceived in the sequel, bore them all with a magnanimity that redounds to their immortal credit—becoming by passive endurance inured to this increasing mass of wrongs; like that mighty man of old, who, by dint of carrying about a calf from the time it was born, continued to carry it without difficulty when it had grown to be an ox.

CHAPTER EIGHT

HOW THE FORT GOED HOOP WAS FEARFULLY BELEAGUERED —HOW THE RENOWNED WOUTER FELL INTO A PROFOUND DOUBT, AND HOW HE FINALLY EVAPORATED

By this time my readers must fully perceive what an arduous task I have undertaken—collecting and collating, with painful minuteness, the chronicles of past times, whose events almost defy the powers of research—exploring a little

kind of Herculaneum of history, which had lain nearly for
ages buried under the rubbish of years, and almost totally
forgotten—raking up the limbs and fragments of disjointed
facts, and endeavoring to put them scrupulously together, so
as to restore them to their original form and connection—
now lugging forth the character of an almost forgotten hero,
like a mutilated statue—now deciphering a half-defaced inscription, and now lighting upon a mouldering manuscript,
which, after painful study, scarce repays the trouble of perusal.

In such case, how much has the reader to depend upon
the honor and probity of his author, lest, like a cunning antiquarian, he either impose upon him some spurious fabrication of his own, for a precious relic from antiquity; or else
dress up the dismembered fragment with such false trappings
that it is scarcely possible to distinguish the truth from the
fiction with which it is enveloped! This is a grievance which
I have more than once had to lament in the course of my
wearisome researches among the works of my fellow-his-
torians, who have strangely disguised and distorted the facts
respecting this country; and particularly respecting the great
province of New Netherlands; as will be perceived by any
who will take the trouble to compare their romantic effu-
sions, tricked out in the meretricious gauds of fable, with
this authentic history.

I have had more vexations of this kind to encounter in
those parts of my history which treat of the transactions on
the eastern border than in any other, in consequence of the
troops of historians who have infested those quarters, and
have shown the honest people of Nieuw Nederlandts no
mercy in their works. Among the rest, Mr. Benjamin
Trumbull arrogantly declares that "The Dutch were always
mere intruders." Now to this I shall make no other reply
than to proceed in the steady narration of my history, which
will contain not only proofs that the Dutch had clear title
and possession in the fair valleys of the Connecticut, and
that they were wrongfully dispossessed thereof—but like-

* * * G

wise that they have been scandalously maltreated ever since by the misrepresentations of the crafty historians of New England.   And in this I shall be guided by a spirit of truth and impartiality, and a regard to immortal fame—for I would not wittingly dishonor my work by a single falsehood, misrepresentation, or prejudice, though it should gain our forefathers the whole country of New England.

It was at an early period of the province, and previous to the arrival of the renowned Wouter, that the cabinet of Nieuw Nederlandts purchased the lands about the Connecticut, and established, for their superintendence and protection, a fortified post on the banks of the river, which was called Fort Goed Hoop, and was situated hard by the present fair city of Hartford.   The command of this important post, together with the rank, title, and appointment of commissary, were given in charge to the gallant Jacobus Van Curlet, or, as some historians will have it, Van Curlis—a most doughty soldier, of that stomachful class of which we have such numbers on parade days—who are famous for eating all they kill.   He was of a very soldier-like appearance, and would have been an exceeding tall man had his legs been in proportion to his body; but the latter being long, and the former uncommonly short, it gave him the uncouth appearance of a tall man's body mounted upon a little man's legs. He made up for this turnspit construction of body by throwing his legs to such an extent when he marched that you would have sworn he had on the identical seven-league boots of the far-famed Jack the Giant-Killer; and so astonishingly high did he tread, on any great military occasion, that his soldiers were ofttimes alarmed lest he should trample himself underfoot.

But notwithstanding the erection of this fort, and the appointment of this ugly little man of war as a commander, the intrepid Yankees continued those daring interlopings which I have hinted at in my last chapter; and, taking advantage of the character which the cabinet of Wouter Van Twiller soon acquired for profound and phlegmatic tranquil-

lity, did audaciously invade the territories of the Nieuw
Nederlandts, and *squat* themselves down within the very
jurisdiction of Fort Goed Hoop.

On beholding this outrage, the long-bodied Van Curlet
proceeded as became a prompt and valiant officer. He immediately protested against these unwarrantable encroachments, in Low Dutch, by way of inspiring more terror, and
forthwith dispatched a copy of the protest to the governor at
New Amsterdam, together with a long and bitter account of
the aggressions of the enemy. This done, he ordered men,
one and all, to be of good cheer—shut the gate of the fort,
smoked three pipes, went to bed, and awaited the result with
a resolute and intrepid tranquillity that greatly animated his
adherents, and no doubt struck sore dismay and affright into
the hearts of the enemy.

Now it came to pass that about this time the renowned
Wouter Van Twiller, full of years and honors and council
dinners, had reached that period of life and faculty which,
according to the great Gulliver, entitles a man to admission
into the ancient order of Struldbruggs. He employed his
time in smoking his Turkish pipe, amid an assembly of sages
equally enlightened and nearly as venerable as himself, and
who, for their silence, their gravity, their wisdom, and their
cautious averseness to coming to any conclusion in business,
are only to be equaled by certain profound corporations which
I have known in my time. Upon reading the protest of the
gallant Jacobus Van Curlet, therefore, his excellency fell
straightway into one of the deepest doubts that ever he was
known to encounter; his capacious head gradually drooped
on his chest, he closed his eyes, and inclined his ear to one
side, as if listening with great attention to the discussion that
was going on in his belly; which all who knew him declared
to be the huge court-house or council chamber of his thoughts;
forming to his head what the House of Representatives do
to the Senate. An inarticulate sound, very much resembling
a snore, occasionally escaped him—but the nature of this internal cogitation was never known, as he never opened his

lips on the subject to man, woman, or child. In the meantime, the protest of Van Curlet laid quietly on the table, where it served to light the pipes of the venerable sages assembled in council; and in the great smoke which they raised the gallant Jacobus, his protest, and his mighty Fort Goed Hoop, were soon as completely beclouded and forgotten as is a question of emergency swallowed up in the speeches and resolution of a modern session of Congress.

There are certain emergencies when your profound legislators and sage deliberative councils are mightily in the way of a nation; and when an ounce of hare-brained decision is worth a pound of sage doubt and cautious discussion. Such, at least, was the case at present; for while the renowned Wouter Van Twiller was daily battling with his doubts, and his resolution growing weaker and weaker in the contest, the enemy pushed further and further into his territories, and assumed a most formidable appearance in the neighborhood of Fort Goed Hoop. Here they founded the mighty town of *Piquag*, or, as it has since been called, *Weathersfield*, a place which, if we may credit the assertion of that worthy historian, John Josselyn, Gent., "Hath been infamous by reason of the witches therein."—And so daring did these men of Piquag become that they extended those plantations of onions, for which their town is illustrious, under the very noses of the garrison of Fort Goed Hoop; insomuch that the honest Dutchmen could not look toward that quarter without tears in their eyes.

This crying injustice was regarded with proper indignation by the gallant Jacobus Van Curlet. He absolutely trembled with the amazing violence of his choler and the exacerbations of his valor; which seemed to be the more turbulent in their workings from the length of the body in which they were agitated. He forthwith proceeded to strengthen his redoubts, heighten his breastworks, deepen his fosse, and fortify his position with a double row of abattis; after which valiant precautions he dispatched a fresh courier with tremendous accounts of his perilous situation.

The courier chosen to bear these alarming dispatches was a fat, oily little man, as being least liable to be worn out, or to lose leather on the journey; and, to insure his speed, he was mounted on the fleetest wagon-horse in the garrison, remarkable for his length of limb, largeness of bone, and hardness of trot; and so tall that the little messenger was obliged to climb on his back by means of his tail and crupper. Such extraordinary speed did he make that he arrived at Fort Amsterdam in little less than a month, though the distance was full two hundred pipes, or about a hundred and twenty miles.

The extraordinary appearance of this portentous stranger would have thrown the whole town of New Amsterdam into a quandary had the good people troubled themselves about anything more than their domestic affairs. With an appearance of great hurry and business, and smoking a short traveling pipe, he proceeded on a long swing trot through the muddy lanes of the metropolis, demolishing whole batches of dirt pies which the little Dutch children were making in the road, and for which kind of pastry the children of this city have ever been famous. On arriving at the governor's house he climbed down from his steed in great trepidation; roused the gray-headed doorkeeper, old Skaats, who, like his lineal descendant and faithful representative, the venerable crier of our court, was nodding at his post; rattled at the door of the council chamber, and startled the members as they were dozing over a plan for establishing a public market.

At that very moment a gentle grunt, or rather a deep-drawn snore, was heard from the chair of the governor; a whiff of smoke was at the same instant observed to escape from his lips, and a light cloud to ascend from the bowl of his pipe. The council of course supposed him engaged in deep sleep for the good of the community, and, according to custom in all such cases established, every man bawled out silence, in order to maintain tranquillity; when, of a sudden, the door flew open, and the little courier straddled into the apartment, cased to the middle in a pair of Hessian boots, which he had got into for the sake of expedition. In his

right hand he held forth the ominous dispatches, and with
his left he grasped firmly the waistband of his galligaskins,
which had unfortunately given way, in the exertion of descending from his horse.   He stumped resolutely up to the
governor, and with more hurry than perspicuity delivered his
message.   But fortunately his ill tidings came too late to ruffle
the tranquillity of this most tranquil of rulers.   His venerable excellency had just breathed and smoked his last—his
lungs and his pipe having been exhausted together, and his
peaceful soul having escaped in the last whiff that curled
from his tobacco-pipe.   In a word, the renowned Walter the
Doubter, who had so often slumbered with his contemporaries, now slept with his fathers, and Wilhelmus Kieft
governed in his stead.

BOOK FOUR

*CONTAINING THE CHRONICLES OF THE REIGN OF WILLIAM
THE TESTY*

CHAPTER ONE

SHOWING THE NATURE OF HISTORY IN GENERAL; CONTAIN-
ING FURTHERMORE THE UNIVERSAL ACQUIREMENTS OF
WILLIAM THE TESTY, AND HOW A MAN MAY LEARN SO
MUCH AS TO RENDER HIMSELF GOOD FOR NOTHING

WHEN the lofty Thucydides is about to enter upon his
description of the plague that desolated Athens, one of his
modern commentators assures the reader that the history is
now going to be exceeding solemn, serious, and pathetic;
and hints, with that air of chuckling gratulation with which
a good dame draws forth a choice morsel from a cupboard
to regale a favorite, that this plague will give his history a
most agreeable variety.

In like manner did my heart leap within me when I came
to the dolorous dilemma of Fort Good Hope, which I at once
perceived to be the forerunner of a series of great events and
entertaining disasters. Such are the true subjects for the
historic pen. For what is history, in fact, but a kind of
Newgate calendar, a register of the crimes and miseries that
man has inflicted on his fellowman? It is a huge libel on
human nature, to which we industriously add page after
page, volume after volume, as if we were building up a
monument to the honor rather than the infamy of our
species. If we turn over the pages of these chronicles that
man has written of himself, what are the characters dignified by the appellation of great and held up to the admiration of posterity? Tyrants, robbers, conquerors, renowned
only for the magnitude of their misdeeds and the stupendous
wrongs and miseries they have inflicted on mankind—warriors who have hired themselves to the trade of blood, not
from motives of virtuous patriotism, or to protect the injured
and defenseless, but merely to gain the vaunted glory of being adroit and successful in massacring their fellow-beings!
What are the great events that constitute a glorious era?—
The fall of empires—the desolation of happy countries—splendid cities smoking in their ruins—the proudest works of art
tumbled in the dust—the shrieks and groans of whole nations
ascending unto heaven!

It is thus that historians may be said to thrive on the miseries of mankind, like birds of prey that hover over the field
of battle to fatten on the mighty dead. It was observed by
a great projector of inland lock-navigation that rivers, lakes
and oceans were only formed to feed canals. In like manner
I am tempted to believe that plots, conspiracies, wars, victories and massacres are ordained by Providence only as
food for the historian.

It is a source of great delight to the philosopher, in studying the wonderful economy of nature, to trace the mutual dependencies of things; how they are created reciprocally for
each other, and how the most noxious and apparently unnec-

essary animal has its uses. Thus those swarms of flies which are so often execrated as useless vermin are created for the sustenance of spiders—and spiders, on the other hand, are evidently made to devour flies. So those heroes who have been such scourges to the world were bounteously provided as themes for the poet and the historian, while the poet and the historian were destined to record the achievements of heroes!

These and many similar reflections naturally arose in my mind as I took up my pen to commence the reign of William Kieft. For now the stream of our history, which hitherto has rolled in a tranquil current, is about to depart forever from its peaceful haunts, and brawl through many a turbulent and rugged scene. Like some sleek ox which, having fed and fattened in a rich clover-field, lies sunk in luxurious repose, and will bear repeated taunts and blows before it heaves its unwieldy limbs and clumsily arouses from its slumbers; so the province of the Nieuw Nederlandts, having long thrived and grown corpulent, under the prosperous reign of the Doubter, was reluctantly awakened to a melancholy conviction that, by patient sufferance, its grievances had become so numerous and aggravating that it was preferable to repel than endure them. The reader will now witness the manner in which a peaceful community advances toward a state of war; which it is too apt to approach, as a horse does a drum, with much prancing and parade, but with little progress—and too often with the wrong end foremost.

WILHELMUS KIEFT, who, in 1634, ascended the *gubernatorial* chair (to borrow a favorite though clumsy appellation of modern phraseologists), was in form, feature and character the very reverse of Wouter Van Twiller, his renowned predecessor. He was of very respectable descent, his father being Inspector of Windmills in the ancient town of Saardam; and our hero, we are told, made very curious investigations into the nature and operations of those machines when a boy, which is one reason why he afterward came to be so ingenious a governor. His name, according to the most ingenious etymologists, was a corruption of *Kyver*, that is to say, *wrangler* or *scolder*, and expressed the heredi-tary disposition of his family; which for nearly two centuries had kept the windy town of Saardam in hot water, and pro-duced more tartars and brimstones than any ten families in the place—and so truly did Wilhelmus Kieft inherit this fam-ily endowment that he had scarcely been a year in the dis-charge of his government before he was universally known by the appellation of William the Testy.

He was a brisk, waspish, little old gentleman, who had dried and withered away, partly through the natural process of years, and partly from being parched and burned up by his fiery soul; which blazed like a vehement rushlight in his bosom, constantly inciting him to most valorous broils, alter-cations, and misadventures. I have heard it observed by a profound and philosophical judge of human nature that if a woman waxes fat as she grows old, the tenure of her life is very precarious, but if haply she withers, she lives forever —such likewise was the case with William the Testy, who grew tougher in proportion as he dried. He was some such a little Dutchman as we may now and then see stumping briskly about the streets of our city, in a broad-skirted coat, with huge buttons, an old-fashioned cocked-hat stuck on the back of his head, and a cane as high as his chin. His visage was broad and his features sharp, his nose turned up with the most petulant curl; his cheeks were scorched into a dusky red—doubtless in consequence of the neighborhood of two fierce little gray eyes, through which his torrid soul beamed with tropical fervor. The corners of his mouth were curi-ously modeled into a kind of fretwork, not a little resembling the wrinkled proboscis of an irritable pug dog—in a word, he was one of the most positive, restless, ugly little men that ever put himself in a passion about nothing.

Such were the personal endowments of William the Testy; but it was the sterling riches of his mind that raised him to dignity and power. In his youth he had passed with great credit through a celebrated academy at the Hague, noted for producing finished scholars with a dispatch unequaled, except by certain of our American colleges. Here he skirmished very smartly on the frontiers of several of the sciences, and made so gallant an inroad in the dead languages as to bring off captive a host of Greek nouns and Latin verbs, together with divers pithy saws and apothegms, all which he constantly paraded in conversation and writing, with as much vainglory as would a triumphant general of yore display the spoils of the countries he had ravaged. He had, moreover, puzzled himself considerably with logic, in which he had advanced so far as to attain a very familiar acquaintance, by name at least, with the whole family of syllogisms and dilemmas; but what he chiefly valued himself on was his knowledge of metaphysics, in which, having once upon a time ventured too deeply, he came wellnigh being smothered in a slough of unintelligible learning—a fearful peril, from the effects of which he never perfectly recovered. This, I must confess, was in some measure a misfortune; for he never engaged in argument, of which he was exceeding fond, but what, between logical deductions and metaphysical jargon, he soon involved himself and his subject in a fog of contradictions and perplexities, and then would get into a mighty passion with his adversary for not being convinced gratis.

It is in knowledge as in swimming: he who ostentatiously sports and flounders on the surface makes more noise and splashing, and attracts more attention, than the industrious pearl-diver who plunges in search of treasures to the bottom. The "universal acquirements" of William Kieft were the subject of great marvel and admiration among his countrymen—he figured about at the Hague with as much vainglory as does a profound Bonze at Pekin, who has mastered half the letters of the Chinese alphabet; and, in a word, was unanimously pronounced a *universal genius!*—I have known many universal geniuses in my time, though, to speak my mind freely, I never knew one who, for the ordinary purposes of life, was worth his weight in straw—but, for the purposes of government, a little sound judgment, and plain common sense, is worth all the sparkling genius that ever wrote poetry or invented theories.

Strange as it may sound, therefore, the *universal acquirements* of the illustrious Wilhelmus were very much in his way; and had he been a less learned man it is possible he would have been a much greater governor. He was exceedingly fond of trying philosophical and political experiments; and having stuffed his head full of scraps and remnants of ancient republics, and oligarchies, and aristocracies, and monarchies, and the laws of Solon, and Lycurgus, and Charondas, and the imaginary commonwealth of Plato, and the Pandects of Justinian, and a thousand other fragments of venerable antiquity, he was forever bent upon introducing some one or other of them into use; so that, between one contradictory measure and another, he entangled the government of the little province of Nieuw Nederlandts in more knots, during his administration, than half a dozen successors could have untied.

No sooner had this bustling little man been blown by a whiff of fortune into the seat of government than he called together his council, and delivered a very animated speech on the affairs of the province. As everybody knows what a glorious opportunity a governor, a president, or even an emperor, has, of drubbing his enemies in his speeches, messages, and bulletins, where he has the talk all on his own side, they may be sure the high-mettled William Kieft did not suffer so favorable an occasion to escape him of evincing that gallantry of tongue common to all able legislators. Before he commenced it is recorded that he took out his pocket-handkerchief and gave a very sonorous blast of the nose, according to the usual custom of great orators. This, in general, I believe, is intended as a signal trumpet to call the attention of the auditors, but with William the Testy it boasted a more classic cause, for he had read of the singular expedient of that famous demagogue, Caius Gracchus, who, when he harangued the Roman populace, modulated his tones by an oratorical flute or pitchpipe.

This preparatory symphony being performed, he commenced by expressing a humble sense of his own want of talents—his utter unworthiness of the honor conferred upon him, and his humiliating incapacity to discharge the important duties of his new station—in short, he expressed so contemptible an opinion of himself that many simple country members present, ignorant that these were mere words of course, always used on such occasions, were very uneasy, and even felt wroth that he should accept an office for which he was consciously so inadequate.

He then proceeded in a manner highly classic and profoundly erudite, though nothing at all to the purpose, being nothing more than a pompous account of all the governments of ancient Greece, and the wars of Rome and Carthage, together with the rise and fall of sundry outlandish empires, about which the assembly knew no more than their great-grandchildren yet unborn. Thus having, after the manner of your learned orators, convinced the audience that he was a man of many words and great erudition, he at length came to the less important part of his speech, the situation of the province—and here he soon worked himself into a fearful rage against the Yankees, whom he compared to the Gauls who desolated Rome, and the Goths and Vandals who overran the fairest plains of Europe—nor did he forget to mention, in terms of adequate opprobrium, the insolence with which they had encroached upon the territories of New Netherlands, and the unparalleled audacity with which they had commenced the town of New Plymouth, and planted the onion-patches of Weathersfield under the very walls of Fort Goed Hoop.

Having thus artfully wrought up his tale of terror to a climax, he assumed a self-satisfied look, and declared, with a nod of knowing import, that he had taken measures to put a final stop to these encroachments—that he had been obliged to have recourse to a dreadful engine of warfare, lately invented, awful in its effects, but authorized by direful necessity. In a word, he was resolved to conquer the Yankees—by proclamation!

For this purpose he had prepared a tremendous instrument of the kind, ordering, commanding, and enjoining the intruders aforesaid forthwith to remove, depart, and withdraw from the districts, regions, and territories aforesaid, under pain of suffering all the penalties, forfeitures, and punishments in such case made and provided. This proclamation, he assured them, would at once exterminate the enemy from the face of the country, and he pledged his valor as a governor that, within two months after it was published, not one stone should remain on another in any of the towns which they had built.

The council remained for some time silent after he had finished; whether struck dumb with admiration at the brilliancy of his project, or put to sleep by the length of his harangue, the history of the times does not mention. Suffice it to say, they at length gave a universal grunt of acquiescence—the proclamation was immediately dispatched with due ceremony, having the great seal of the province, which was about the size of a buckwheat pancake, attached to it by a broad red ribbon. Governor Kieft, having thus vented his indignation, felt greatly relieved—adjourned the council—put on his cocked hat and corduroy small-clothes, and mounting a tall, raw-boned charger, trotted out to his country-seat, which was situated in a sweet, sequestered swamp, now called Dutch Street, but more commonly known by the name of Dog's Misery.

Here, like the good Numa, he reposed from the toils of legislation, taking lessons in government, not from the nymph Egeria, but from the honored wife of his bosom; who was one of that peculiar kind of females, sent upon earth a little after the flood, as a punishment for the sins of mankind, and commonly known by the appellation of *knowing women*. In fact, my duty as a historian obliges me to make known a circumstance which was a great secret at the time, and consequently was not a subject of scandal at more than half the tea-tables in New Amsterdam, but which, like many other great secrets, has leaked out in the lapse of years—and this was that the great Wilhelmus the Testy, though one of the most potent little men that ever breathed, yet submitted at home to a species of government neither laid down in Aristotle nor Plato; in short, it partook of the nature of a pure, unmixed tyranny, and is familiarly denominated *petticoat government.*—An absolute sway, which, though exceedingly common in these modern days, was very rare among the ancients, if we may judge from the rout made about the domestic economy of honest Socrates; which is the only ancient case on record.

The great Kieft, however, warded off all the sneers and sarcasms of his particular friends, who are ever ready to joke with a man on sore points of the kind, by alleging that it was a government of his own election, to which he submitted through choice; adding at the same time a profound maxim which he had found in an ancient author, that "He who would aspire to *govern* should first learn to *obey.*"

CHAPTER TWO

IN WHICH ARE RECORDED THE SAGE PROJECTS OF A RULER OF UNIVERSAL GENIUS—THE ART OF FIGHTING BY PROC-LAMATION—AND HOW THAT THE VALIANT JACOBUS VAN CURLET CAME TO BE FOULLY DISHONORED AT FORT GOED HOOP

NEVER was a more comprehensive, a more expeditious, or, what is still better, a more economical measure devised, than this of defeating the Yankees by proclamation—an expedient, likewise, so humane, so gentle and pacific, there were ten chances to one in favor of its succeeding—but then there was one chance to ten that it would not succeed—as the ill-natured fates would have it, that single chance carried the day. The proclamation was perfect in all its parts, well constructed, well written, well sealed, and well published— all that was wanting to insure its effect was that the Yankees should stand in awe of it; but, provoking to relate, they treated it with the most absolute contempt, applied it to an unseemly purpose, and thus did the first warlike proclamation come to a shameful end—a fate which I am credibly informed has befallen but too many of its successors.

It was a long time before Wilhelmus Kieft could be persuaded, by the united efforts of all his counselors, that his war measures had failed in producing any effect. On the contrary, he flew in a passion whenever any one dared to question its efficacy; and swore that, though it was slow in operating, yet, when once it began to work, it would soon purge the land of these rapacious intruders. Time, however, that test of all experiments, both in philosophy and politics, at length convinced the great Kieft that his proclamation was abortive; and that notwithstanding he had waited nearly four years in a state of constant irritation, yet he was still further off than ever from the object of his wishes. His implacable adversaries in the east became more and more troublesome in their encroachments, and founded the thriving colony of Hartford close upon the skirts of Fort Goed Hoop. They, moreover, commenced the fair settlement of New Haven (otherwise called the Red Hills) within the domains of their High Mightinesses—while the onion patches of Piquag were a continual eyesore to the garrison of Van Curlet. Upon beholding, therefore, the inefficacy of his measure, the sage Kieft, like many a worthy practitioner of physic, laid the blame not to the medicine, but to the quantity administered, and resolutely resolved to double the dose.

In the year 1638, therefore, that being the fourth year of his reign, he fulminated against them a second proclamation, of heavier metal than the former; written in thundering long sentences, not one word of which was under five syllables. This, in fact, was a kind of non-intercourse bill, forbidding and prohibiting all commerce and connection between any and every of the said Yankee intruders, and the said fortified post of Fort Goed Hoop, and ordering, commanding, and

advising all his trusty, loyal, and well-beloved subjects to
furnish them with no supplies of gin, gingerbread, or sauerkraut; to buy none of their pacing horses, measly pork, apple-
brandy, Yankee rum, cider-water, apple sweetmeats, Weathersfield onions, tinware, or wooden bowls, but to starve and
exterminate them from the face of the land.

Another pause of a twelvemonth ensued, during which
this proclamation received the same attention and experienced the same fate as the first. In truth, it was rendered
of no avail by the heroic spirit of the Nederlanders themselves. No sooner were they prohibited the use of Yankee
merchandise, than it immediately became indispensable to
their very existence. The men who all their lives had been
content to drink gin and ride Esopus switch-tails now swore
that it was sheer tyranny to deprive them of apple-brandy
and Narraghanset pacers; and as to the women, they declared there was no comfort in life without Weathersfield
onions, tin kettles and wooden bowls. So they all set to
work, with might and main, to carry on a smuggling trade
over the borders; and the province was as full as ever of
Yankee wares—with this difference, that those who used
them had to pay double price for the trouble and risk incurred
in breaking the laws.

A signal benefit arose from these measures of William
the Testy. The efforts to evade them had a marvelous
effect in sharpening the intellects of the people. They were
no longer to be governed without laws, as in the time of
Oloffe the Dreamer; nor would the jack-knife and tobacco-
box of Walter the Doubter have any more served as a judicial
process. The old Nederlandt maxim, that "honesty is the
best policy," was scouted as the bane of all ingenious enterprise. To use a modern phrase, "a great impulse had been
given to the public mind;" and from the time of this first
experience in smuggling we may perceive a vast increase in
the number, intricacy, and severity of laws and statutes—a
sure proof of the increasing keenness of public intellect.

A twelvemonth having elapsed since the issuing of the

proclamation, the gallant Jacobus Van Curlet dispatched his
annual messenger, with his customary budget of complaints
and entreaties. Whether the regular interval of a year, intervening between the arrival of Van Curlet's couriers, was
occasioned by the systematic regularity of his movements,
or by the immense distance at which he was stationed from
the seat of government, is a matter of uncertainty. Some
have ascribed it to the slowness of his messengers, who, as I
have before noticed, were chosen from the shortest and fattest of his garrison, as least likely to be worn out on the road;
and who, being pursy, short-winded little men, generally
traveled fifteen miles a day, and then laid by a whole week
to rest. All these, however, are matters of conjecture, and I
rather think it may be ascribed to the immemorial maxim of
this worthy country—and which has ever influenced all its
public transactions—not to do things in a hurry.

The gallant Jacobus Van Curlet, in his dispatches, respectfully represented that several years had now elapsed
since his first application to his late excellency, Wouter Van
Twiller; during which interval his garrison had been reduced nearly one-eighth, by the death of two of his most
valiant and corpulent soldiers, who had accidentally over-
eaten themselves on some fat salmon, caught in the Varsche
River. He further stated that the enemy persisted in their
inroads, taking no notice of the fort or its inhabitants: but
squatting themselves down and forming settlements all
around it; so that, in a little while, he should find himself
inclosed and blockaded by the enemy and totally at their
mercy.

But among the most atrocious of his grievances I find
the following still on record, which may serve to show the
bloody-minded outrages of these savage intruders. "In the
meantime they of Hartford have not onely usurped and taken
in the lands of Connecticott, although unrighteously and
against the lawes of nations, but have hindered our nation
in sowing theire own purchased broken up lands, but have
also sowed them with corne in the night, which the Nether-

landers had broken up and intended to sowe: and have beaten the servants of the high and mighty the honored companie, which were laboring upon theire master's lands, from theire lands, with sticks and plow staves in hostile manner laming, and among the rest, struck Ever Duckings* a hole in his head, with a stick, so that the blood ran downe very strongly downe upon his body.''

But what is still more atrocious—

"Those of Hartford sold a hogg, that belonged to the honored companie, under pretense that it had eaten of theire grounde grass, when they had not any foot of inheritance. They proffered the hogg for 5s. if the commissioners would have given 5s. for damage; which the commissioners denied, because noe man's own hogg (as men used to say) can trespass upon his owne master's grounde."†

The receipt of this melancholy intelligence incensed the whole community—there was something in it that spoke to the dull comprehension and touched the obtuse feelings, even of the puissant vulgar, who generally require a kick in the rear to awaken their slumbering dignity. I have known my profound fellow-citizens bear, without murmur, a thousand essential infringements of their rights, merely because they were not immediately obvious to their senses—but the moment the unlucky Pearce was shot upon our coasts, the whole body politic was in a ferment—so the enlightened Nederlanders, though they had treated the encroachments of their eastern neighbors with but little regard, and left their quill-valiant governor to bear the whole brunt of war with his single pen—yet now every individual felt his head broken in the broken head of Duckings—and the unhappy fate of their fellow-citizen the hog being impressed, carried and sold into captivity, awakened a grunt of sympathy from every bosom.

---

* This name is no doubt misspelled. In some old Dutch MSS. of the time we find the name of Evert Duyckingh, who is unquestionably the unfortunate hero above alluded to.

† Haz. Col. State Papers.

The governor and council, goaded by the clamors of the multitude, now set themselves earnestly to deliberate upon what was to be done.—Proclamations had at length fallen into temporary disrepute: some were for sending the Yankees a tribute, as we make peace-offering to the petty Barbary powers, or as the Indians sacrifice to the devil; others were for buying them out; but this was opposed, as it would be acknowledging their title to the land they had seized. A variety of measures were, as usual in such cases, produced, discussed, and abandoned; and the council had at last to adopt the means which, being the most common and obvious, had been knowingly overlooked—for your amazing acute politicians are forever looking through telescopes, which only enable them to see such objects as are far off, and unattainable, but which incapacitate them to see such things as are in their reach, and obvious to all simple folks, who are content to look with the naked eyes Heaven has given them. The profound council, as I have said, in the pursuit after Jack-o'-lanterns, accidentally stumbled on the very measure they were in need of: which was to raise a body of troops and dispatch them to the relief and re-enforcement of the garrison. This measure was carried into such prompt operation that in less than twelve months the whole expedition, consisting of a sergeant and twelve men, was ready to march; and was reviewed for that purpose in the public square, now known by the name of the Bowling Green. Just at this juncture the whole community was thrown into consternation by the sudden arrival of the gallant Jacobus Van Curlet, who came straggling into town at the head of his crew of tatterdemalions, and bringing the melancholy tidings of his own defeat, and the capture of the redoubtable post of Fort Goed Hoop by the ferocious Yankees.

The fate of this important fortress is an impressive warning to all military commanders. It was neither carried by storm nor famine; no practicable breach was effected by cannon or mines; no magazines were blown up by red-hot shot, nor were the barracks demolished or the garrison destroyed by the bursting of bombshells. In fact the place was taken by a stratagem no less singular than effectual; and one that can never fail of success, whenever an opportunity occurs of putting it in practice. Happy am I to add, for the credit of our illustrious ancestors, that it was a stratagem which, though it impeached the vigilance, yet left the bravery of the intrepid Van Curlet and his garrison perfectly free from reproach.

It appears that the crafty Yankees, having heard of the regular habits of the garrison, watched a favorable opportunity, and silently introduced themselves into the fort, about the middle of a sultry day; when its vigilant defenders, having gorged themselves with a hearty dinner, and smoked out their pipes, were one and all snoring most obstreperously at their posts, little dreaming of so disastrous an occurrence. The enemy most inhumanly seized Jacobus Van Curlet and his sturdy myrmidons by the nape of the neck, gallanted them to the gate of the fort, and dismissed them severally, with a kick on the crupper, as Charles the Twelfth dismissed the heavy-bottomed Russians, after the battle of Narva— only taking care to give two kicks to Van Curlet, as a signal mark of distinction.

A strong garrison was immediately established in the fort, consisting of twenty long-sided, hard fisted Yankees, with Weathersfield onions stuck in their hats by way of cock- ades and feathers—long rusty fowling-pieces for muskets— hasty-pudding, dumb-fish, pork and molasses for stores; and a huge pumpkin was hoisted on the end of a pole, as a stand- ard—liberty caps not having yet come into fashion.

CHAPTER THREE

CONTAINING THE FEARFUL WRATH OF WILLIAM THE TESTY,
AND THE GREAT DOLOR OF THE NEW AMSTERDAMERS,
BECAUSE OF THE AFFAIR OF FORT GOED HOOP—AND,
MOREOVER, HOW WILLIAM THE TESTY DID STRONGLY
FORTIFY THE CITY—TOGETHER WITH THE EXPLOITS OF
STOFFEL BRINKERHOFF

LANGUAGE cannot express the prodigious fury into which
the testy Wilhelmus Kieft was thrown by this provoking intelligence. For three good hours the rage of the little man
was too great for words, or rather the words were too great
for him; and he was nearly choked by some dozen huge,
misshapen, nine-cornered Dutch oaths that crowded all at
once into his gullet. Having blazed off the first broadside,
he kept up a constant firing for three whole days—anathe-
matizing the Yankees, man, woman and child, body and soul,
for a set of dieven, schob-bejaken, deugenieten, twist-zoe-
keren, loozen-schalken, blaes-kaken, kakken-bedden, and a
thousand other names, of which, unfortunately for posterity,
history does not make mention. Finally, he swore that he
would have nothing more to do with such as quatting, bundling, guessing, questioning, swapping, pumpkin-eating, mo-
lasses-daubing, shingle-splitting, cider-watering, horse-jock-
eying, notion-peddling crew—that they might stay at Fort
Goed Hoop and rot, before he would dirty his hands by
attempting to drive them away; in proof of which, he ordered the new-raised troops to be marched forthwith into
winter quarters, although it was not as yet quite mid-sum-
mer. Governor Kieft faithfully kept his word, and his adversaries as faithfully kept their post; and thus the glorious
river Connecticut, and all the gay valleys through which it
rolls, together with the salmon. shad. and other fish within

its waters, fell into the hands of the victorious Yankees, by whom they are held at this very day.

Great despondency seized upon the city of New Amsterdam, in consequence of these melancholy events. The name of Yankee became as terrible among our good ancestors as was that of Gaul among the ancient Romans; and all the sage old women of the province used it as a bugbear, wherewith to frighten their unruly children into obedience.

The eyes of all the province were now turned upon their governor, to know what he would do for the protection of the common weal, in these days of darkness and peril. Great apprehensions prevailed among the reflecting part of the community, especially the old women, that these terrible warriors of Connecticut, not content with the conquest of Fort Goed Hoop, would incontinently march on to New Amsterdam and take it by storm—and as these old ladies, through means of the governor's spouse, who, as has been already hinted, was "the better horse," had obtained considerable influence in public affairs, keeping the province under a kind of petticoat government, it was determined that measures should be taken for the effective fortification of the city.

Now it happened that at this time there sojourned in New Amsterdam one Anthony Van Corlear,* a jolly fat Dutch trumpeter, of a pleasant burly visage, famous for his long wind and his huge whiskers, and who, as the story goes, could twang so potently upon his instrument as to produce an effect upon all within hearing as though ten thousand bagpipes were singing right lustily i' the nose. Him did the illustrious Kieft pick out as the man of all the world most fitted to be the champion of New Amsterdam, and to garrison its fort; making little doubt but that his instrument would be as effectual and offensive in war as was that of the Paladin

---

* David Pietrez *De Vries*, in his "Reyze naer Nieuw-Nederlant onder het year 1640," makes mention of one *Corlear*, a trumpeter in Fort Amsterdam, who gave name to Corlear's Hook, and who was doubtless this same champion described by Mr. Knickerbocker.—EDITOR.

Astolpho, or the more classic horn of Alecto. It would have
done one's heart good to have seen the governor snapping
his fingers and fidgeting with delight, while his sturdy trumpeter strutted up and down the ramparts, fearlessly twanging
his trumpet in the face of the whole world, like a thrice-
valorous editor daringly insulting all the principalities and
powers—on the other side of the Atlantic.

Nor was he content with thus strongly garrisoning the
fort, but he likewise added exceedingly to its strength, by
furnishing it with a formidable battery of Quaker guns—
rearing a stupendous flagstaff in the center, which over-
topped the whole city—and, moreover, by building a great
windmill on one of the bastions.* This last, to be sure, was
somewhat of a novelty in the art of fortification, but, as I
have already observed, William Kieft was notorious for innovations and experiments; and traditions do affirm that he
was much given to mechanical inventions — constructing
patent smoke-jacks—carts that went before the horses, and
especially erecting windmills, for which machines he had
acquired a singular predilection in his native town of Saardam.

All these scientific vagaries of the little governor were
cried up with ecstasy by his adherents, as proofs of his universal genius—but there were not wanting ill-natured grum-
blers, who railed at him as employing his mind in frivolous
pursuits, and devoting that time to smoke-jacks and windmills which should have been occupied in the more important
concerns of the province. Nay, they even went so far as to
hint, once or twice, that his head was turned by his experiments, and that he really thought to manage his government
as he did his mills—by mere wind!—such are the illiberality
and slander to which enlightened rulers are ever subject.

Notwithstanding all the measures, therefore, of William

---

* De Vries mentions that this windmill stood on the southeast bastion; and it is likewise to be seen, together with the flagstaff, in Justus
Danker's View of New Amsterdam.

the Testy, to place the city in a posture of defense, the inhabitants continued in great alarm and despondency. But
fortune, who seems always careful, in the very nick of time,
to throw a bone for hope to gnaw upon, that the starveling
elf may be kept alive, did about this time crown the arms
of the province with success in another quarter, and thus
cheered the drooping hearts of the forlorn Nederlanders;
otherwise, there is no knowing to what lengths they might
have gone in the excess of their sorrowing—"for grief," says
the profound historian of the seven champions of Christendom, "is companion with despair, and despair a procurer of
infamous death!"

Among the numerous inroads of the mosstroopers of
Connecticut, which for some time past had occasioned such
great tribulation, I should particularly have mentioned a
settlement made on the eastern part of Long Island, at a
place which, from the peculiar excellence of its shell-fish, was
called Oyster Bay. This was attacking the province in the
most sensible part, and occasioned great agitation at New
Amsterdam.

It is an incontrovertible fact, well known to skillful physiologists, that the high road to the affections is through the
throat; and this may be accounted for on the same principles
which I have already quoted in my strictures on fat aldermen. Nor is the fact unknown to the world at large; and
hence do we observe that the surest way to gain the hearts
of the million is to feed them well—and that a man is never
so disposed to flatter, to please and serve another, as when
he is feeding at his expense; which is one reason why your
rich men, who give frequent dinners, have such abundance
of sincere and faithful friends. It is on this principle that
our knowing leaders of parties secure the affections of their
partisans, by rewarding them bountifully with loaves and
fishes; and entrap the suffrages of the greasy mob by treating them with bull feasts and roasted oxen. I have known
many a man, in this same city, acquire considerable importance in society, and usurp a large share of the good-will of

his enlightened fellow-citizens, when the only thing that could be said in his eulogium was that "he gave a good dinner and kept excellent wine."

Since, then, the heart and the stomach are so nearly allied, it follows conclusively that what affects the one must sympathetically affect the other. Now, it is an equally incontrovertible fact that of all offerings to the stomach there is none more grateful than the testaceous marine animal, known commonly by the vulgar name of Oyster. And in such great reverence has it ever been held, by my gormandizing fellow-citizens, that temples have been dedicated to it, time out of mind, in every street, lane, and alley throughout this well-fed city. It is not to be expected, therefore, that the seizing of Oyster Bay, a place abounding with their favorite delicacy, would be tolerated by the inhabitants of New Amsterdam. An attack upon their honor they might have pardoned; even the massacre of a few citizens might have been passed over in silence; but an outrage that affected the larders of the great city of New Amsterdam, and threatened the stomachs of its corpulent burgomasters, was too serious to pass unrevenged.—The whole council was unanimous in opinion that the intruders should be immediately driven by force of arms from Oyster Bay and its vicinity, and a detachment was accordingly dispatched for the purpose, under the command of one Stoffel Brinkerhoff or Brinkerhoofd (i.e. Stoffel, the head-breaker), so-called because he was a man of mighty deeds, famous throughout the whole extent of Nieuw Nederlandts for his skill at quarter-staff; and for size he would have been a match for Colbrand, the Danish champion, slain by Guy of Warwick.

Stoffel Brinkerhoff was a man of few words, but prompt actions—one of your straight-going officers, who march directly forward, and do their orders without making any parade. He used no extraordinary speed in his movements, but trudged steadily on, through Nineveh and Babylon, and Jericho and Patchog, and the mighty town of Quag, and various other renowned cities of yore, which, by some un-

*** H

accountable witchcraft of the Yankees, have been strangely
transplanted to Long Island, until he arrived in the neighborhood of Oyster Bay.

Here was he encountered by a tumultuous host of valiant
warriors, headed by Preserved Fish, and Habbakuk Nutter,
and Return Strong, and Zerubbabel Fisk, and Jonathan
Doolittle, and Determined Cock!—at the sound of whose
names the courageous Stoffel verily believed that the whole
parliament of Praise-God-Barebones had been let loose to
discomfit him.   Finding, however, that this formidable body
was composed merely of the "select men" of the settlement,
armed with no other weapon but their tongues, and that they
had issued forth with no other intent than to meet him on the
field of argument—he succeeded in putting them to the rout
with little difficulty, and completely broke up their settlement.   Without waiting to write an account of his victory
on the spot, and thus letting the enemy slip through his
fingers while he was securing his own laurels, as a more
experienced general would have done, the brave Stoffel
thought of nothing but completing his enterprise and utterly
driving the Yankees from the island.   This hardy enterprise
he performed in much the same manner as he had been
accustomed to drive his oxen; for as the Yankees fled before
him, he pulled up his breeches and trudged steadily after
them, and would infallibly have driven them into the sea,
had they not begged for quarter and agreed to pay tribute.

The news of this achievement was a seasonable restora-
tive to the spirits of the citizens of New Amsterdam.   To
gratify them still more the governor resolved to astonish
them with one of those gorgeous spectacles, known in the
days of classic antiquity, a full account of which had been
flogged into his memory when a school-boy at the Hague.
A grand triumph, therefore, was decreed to Stoffel Brinkerhoff, who made his triumphant entrance into town riding on
a Narraghanset pacer; five pumpkins, which, like Roman
eagles, had served the enemy for standards, were carried
before him—fifty cartloads of oysters, five hundred bushels

of Weathersfield onions, a hundred quintals of codfish, two
hogsheads of molasses, and various other treasures, were
exhibited as the spoils and tribute of the Yankees; while
three notorious counterfeiters of Manhattan notes* were led
captive, to grace the hero's triumph. The procession was
enlivened by martial music from the trumpet of Anthony
Van Corlear, the champion, accompanied by a select band
of boys and negroes performing on the national instruments
of rattle-bones and clam-shells. The citizens devoured the
spoils in sheer gladness of heart—every man did honor to
the conqueror, by getting devoutly drunk on New England
rum—and the learned Wilhelmus Kieft, calling to mind, in
a momentary fit of enthusiasm and generosity, that it was
customary among the ancients to honor their victorious
generals with public statues, passed a gracious decree, by
which every tavern-keeper was permitted to paint the head
of the intrepid Stoffel on his sign!

CHAPTER FOUR

PHILOSOPHICAL REFLECTIONS ON THE FOLLY OF BEING
HAPPY IN TIMES OF PROSPERITY—SUNDRY TROUBLES
ON THE SOUTHERN FRONTIERS — HOW WILLIAM THE
TESTY HAD WELLNIGH RUINED THE PROVINCE THROUGH
A CABALISTIC WORD—AS ALSO THE SECRET EXPEDITION
OF JAN JANSEN ALPENDAM, AND HIS ASTONISHING RE-
WARD

IF we could but get a peep at the tally of Dame Fortune,
where, like a notable landlady, she regularly chalks up the
debtor and creditor accounts of mankind, we should find

---

* This is one of those trivial anachronisms that now and then
occur in the course of this otherwise authentic history. How could
Manhattan notes be counterfeited when as yet Banks were unknown
in this country?—and our simple progenitors had not even dreamed of
those inexhaustible mines of *paper opulence.*—PRINT. DEV.

that, upon the whole, good and evil are pretty near balanced
in this world; and that though we may for a long while
revel in the very lap of prosperity, the time will at length
come when we must ruefully pay off the reckoning. Fortune, in fact, is a pestilent shrew, and withal a most inexorable creditor; for though she may indulge her favorites in
long credits, and overwhelm them with her favors, yet sooner
or later she brings up her arrears with the rigor of an experienced publican, and washes out her scores with their
tears. "Since," says good old Boetius, "no man can retain
her at his pleasure, and since her flight is so deeply lamented,
what are her favors but sure prognostications of approaching
trouble and calamity?"

There is nothing that more moves my contempt at the
stupidity and want of reflection of my fellowmen, than to
behold them rejoicing and indulging in security and self-
confidence in times of prosperity. To a wise man, who is
blessed with the light of reason, those are the very moments
of anxiety and apprehension; well knowing that according
to the system of things, happiness is at best but transient—
and that the higher he is elevated by the capricious breath
of fortune, the lower must be his proportionate depression.
Whereas, he who is overwhelmed by calamity has the less
chance of encountering fresh disasters, as a man at the bottom of a ladder runs very little risk of breaking his neck by
tumbling to the top.

This is the very essence of true wisdom, which consists
in knowing when we ought to be miserable; and was discovered much about the same time with that invaluable secret,
that "everything is vanity and vexation of spirit"; in consequence of which maxim, your wise men have ever been
the unhappiest of the human race; esteeming it as an infallible mark of genius to be distressed without reason—since
any man may be miserable in time of misfortune, but it is
the philosopher alone who can discover cause for grief in
the very hour of prosperity.

According to the principle I have just advanced, we find

that the colony of New Netherlands, which, under the reign
of the renowned Van Twiller, had flourished in such alarming and fatal serenity, is now paying for its former welfare,
and discharging the enormous debt of comfort which it contracted. Foes harass it from different quarters; the city of
New Amsterdam, while yet in its infancy, is kept in constant
alarm; and its valiant commander, William the Testy,
answers the vulgar, but expressive idea, of "a man in a
peck of troubles."

While busily engaged repelling his bitter enemies the
Yankees on one side, we find him suddenly molested in
another quarter, and by other assailants. A vagrant colony
of Swedes, under the conduct of Peter Minnewits, and professing allegiance to that redoubtable virago, Christina,
Queen of Sweden, had settled themselves and erected a fort
on South (or Delaware) River—within the boundaries claimed
by the government of the New Netherlands. History is
mute as to the particulars of their first landing, and their
real pretensions to the soil; and this is the more to be
lamented as this same colony of Swedes will hereafter be
found most materially to affect not only the interests of the
Nederlanders but of the world at large!

In whatever manner, therefore, this vagabond colony of
Swedes first took possession of the country, it is certain that
in 1638 they established a fort, and Minnewits, according to
the off-hand usage of his contemporaries, declared himself
governor of all the adjacent country, under the name of the
province of NEW SWEDEN. No sooner did this reach the
ears of the choleric Wilhelmus than, like a true-spirited
chieftain, he immediately broke into a violent rage, and,
calling together his council, belabored the Swedes most
lustily in the longest speech that had ever been heard in the
colony since the memorable dispute of Ten Breeches and
Tough Breeches. Having thus given vent to the first ebulli-
tions of his indignation, he had resort to his favorite measure
of proclamation, and dispatched one, piping hot, in the first
year of his reign, informing Peter Minnewits that the whole

territory, bordering on the South River, had, time out of mind, been in possession of the Dutch colonists, having been "beset with forts and sealed with their blood."

The latter sanguinary sentence would convey an idea of direful war and bloodshed, were we not relieved by the information that it merely related to a fray, in which some half-a-dozen Dutchmen had been killed by the Indians, in their benevolent attempts to establish a colony and promote civilization. By this it will be seen that William Kieft, though a very small man, delighted in big expressions, and was much given to a praiseworthy figure of rhetoric, generally cultivated by your little great men, called hyperbole—a figure which has been found of infinite service among many of his class, and which has helped to swell the grandeur of many a mighty, self-important, but windy chief magistrate. Nor can I refrain in this place from observing how much my beloved country is indebted to this same figure of hyperbole for supporting certain of her greatest characters—statesmen, orators, civilians, and divines; who, by dint of big words, inflated periods, and windy doctrines, are kept afloat on the surface of society, as ignorant swimmers are buoyed up by blown bladders.

The proclamation against Minnewits concluded by ordering the self-dubbed governor and his gang of Swedish adventurers immediately to leave the country, under penalty of the high displeasure and inevitable vengeance of the puissant government of the Nieuw Nederlandts. This "strong measure," however, does not seem to have had a whit more effect than its predecessors which had been thundered against the Yankees—the Swedes resolutely held on to the territory they had taken possession of—whereupon matters for the present remained in statu quo.

That Wilhelmus Kieft should put up with this insolent obstinacy in the Swedes would appear incompatible with his valorous temperament; but we find that about this time the little man had his hands full, and, what with one annoyance and another, was kept continually on the bounce.

There is a certain description of active legislators, who, by shrewd management, contrive always to have a hundred irons on the anvil, every one of which must be immediately attended to; who consequently are ever full of temporary shifts and expedients, patching up the public welfare, and cobbling the national affairs, so as to make nine holes where they mend one—stopping chinks and flaws with whatever comes first to hand, like the Yankees I have mentioned, stuffing old clothes in broken windows. Of this class of statesmen was William the Testy—and had he only been blessed with powers equal to his zeal, or his zeal been disciplined by a little discretion, there is very little doubt that he would have made the greatest governor of his size on record—the renowned governor of the island of Barataria alone excepted.

The great defect of Wilhelmus Kieft's policy was, that though no man could be more ready to stand forth in an hour of emergency, yet he was so intent upon guarding the national pocket that he suffered the enemy to break its head —in other words, whatever precaution for public safety he adopted, he was so intent upon rendering it cheap that he invariably rendered it ineffectual. All this was a remote consequence of his profound education at the Hague; where, having acquired a smattering of knowledge, he was ever after a great conner of indexes, continually dipping into books, without ever studying to the bottom of any subject; so that he had the scum of all kinds of authors fermenting in his pericranium. In some of these title-page researches he unluckily stumbled over a grand political *cabalistic word*, which, with his customary facility, he immediately incorporated into his great scheme of government, to the irretrievable injury and delusion of the honest province of Nieuw Nederlandts, and the eternal misleading of all experimental rulers.

In vain have I pored over the theurgia of the Chaldeans, the cabala of the Jews, the necromancy of the Arabians, the magic of the Persians, the hocuspocus of the English, the witchcraft of the Yankees, or the powwowing of the Indians, to discover where the little man first laid eyes on this terrible word. Neither the Sephir Jetzirah, that famous cabalistic volume, ascribed to the patriarch Abraham; nor the pages of Zohar, containing the mysteries of the cabala, recorded by the learned rabbi Simon Sochaides, yield any light to my inquiries—nor am I in the least benefited by my painful researches in the Shem-ham-phorah of Benjamin, the wandering Jew, though it enabled Davidus Elm to make a ten days' journey in twenty-four hours. Neither can I perceive the slightest affinity in the Tetragrammaton, or sacred name of four letters, the profoundest word of the Hebrew cabala; a mystery sublime, ineffable, and incommunicable—and the letters of which, Jod-He-Vau-He, having been stolen by the pagans, constituted their great name, Jao or Jove. In short, in all my cabalistic, theurgic, necromantic, magical, and astrological researches, from the Tetractys of Pythagoras to the recondite works of Breslaw and Mother Bunch, I have not discovered the least vestige of an origin of this word, nor have I discovered any word of sufficient potency to counteract it.

Not to keep my reader in any suspense, the word which had so wonderfully arrested the attention of William the Testy, and which in German characters had a particularly black and ominous aspect, on being fairly translated into the English, is no other than ECONOMY—a talismanic term, which, by constant use and frequent mention, has ceased to be formidable in our eyes, but which has as terrible potency as any in the arcana of necromancy.

When pronounced in a national assembly, it has an immediate effect in closing the hearts, beclouding the intellects, drawing the purse-strings and buttoning the breeches-pockets of all philosophic legislators. Nor are its effects on the eyes less wonderful. It produces a contraction of the retina, an obscurity of the crystalline lens, a viscidity of the vitreous, and an inspissation of the aqueous humors, an induration of the tunica sclerotica and a convexity of the cornea; insomuch that the organ of vision loses its strength and perspicuity, and the unfortunate patient becomes *myopes*, or, in plain English, purblind; perceiving only the amount of immediate expense, without being able to look further, and regard it in connection with the ultimate object to be effected —"So that," to quote the words of the eloquent Burke, "a brier at his nose is of greater magnitude than an oak at five hundred yards' distance." Such are its instantaneous operations, and the results are still more astonishing. By its magic influence, seventy-fours shrink into frigates—frigates into sloops, and sloops into gunboats.

This all-potent word, which served as his touchstone in politics, at once explains the whole system of proclamations, protests, empty threats, windmills, trumpeters, and paper war, carried on by Wilhelmus the Testy—and we may trace its operations in an armament which he fitted out in 1642, in a moment of great wrath, consisting of two sloops and thirty men, under the command of Mynheer Jan Jansen Alpendam, as admiral of the fleet and commander-in-chief of the forces. This formidable expedition, which can only be paralleled by some of the daring cruises of our infant navy about the bay and up the Sound, was intended to drive the Marylanders from the Schuylkill, of which they had recently taken possession—and which was claimed as part of the province of New Nederlandts—for it appears that at this time our infant colony was in that enviable state, so much coveted by ambitious nations, that is to say, the government had a vast extent of territory, part of which it enjoyed, and the greater part of which it had continually to quarrel about.

Admiral Jan Jansen Alpendam was a man of great mettle and prowess, and no way dismayed at the character of the enemy, who were represented as a gigantic, gunpowder race of men, who lived on hoe-cakes and bacon, drank mint-juleps and apple-toddy, and were exceedingly expert at boxing, biting, gouging, tar and feathering, and a variety of other athletic accomplishments, which they had borrowed from their cousins-german and prototypes, the Virginians, to whom they have ever borne considerable resemblance.

Notwithstanding all these alarming representations, the admiral entered the Schuylkill most undauntedly with his fleet and arrived without disaster or opposition at the place of destination.

Here he attacked the enemy in a vigorous speech in Low Dutch, which the wary Kieft had previously put in his pocket; wherein he courteously commenced by calling them a pack of lazy, louting, dram-drinking, cock-fighting, horse-racing, slave-driving, tavern-haunting, Sabbath-breaking, mulatto-breeding upstarts—and concluded by ordering them to evacuate the country immediately—to which they most laconically replied in plain English, "They'd see him d—d first."

Now this was a reply for which neither Jan Jansen Alpendam nor Wilhelmus Kieft had made any calculation—and finding himself totally unprepared to answer so terrible a rebuff with suitable hostility, he concluded that his wisest course was to return home and report progress. He accordingly sailed back to New Amsterdam, where he was received with great honors, and considered as a pattern for all commanders; having achieved a most hazardous enterprise at a trifling expense of treasure, and without losing a single man to the State!—He was unanimously called the deliverer of his country (an appellation liberally bestowed on all great men); his two sloops, having done their duty, were laid up (or dry-docked) in a cove now called the Albany basin, where they quietly rotted in the mud; and to immortalize his name they erected, by subscription, a magnificent shingle monument on the top of Flattenbarrack hill, which lasted three whole years; when it fell to pieces and was burned for firewood.

CHAPTER FIVE

HOW WILLIAM THE TESTY ENRICHED THE PROVINCE BY A
MULTITUDE OF LAWS, AND CAME TO BE THE PATRON OF
LAWYERS AND BUM-BAILIFFS—AND HOW THE PEOPLE
BECAME EXCEEDINGLY ENLIGHTENED AND UNHAPPY UN-
DER HIS INSTRUCTIONS

AMONG the many wrecks and fragments of exalted wisdom
which have floated down the stream of time from venerable
antiquity, and have been carefully picked up by those humble but industrious wights who ply along the shores of literature, we find the following sage ordinance of Charondas, the
Locrian legislator. Anxious to preserve the ancient laws of
the state from the additions and improvements of profound
"country members," or officious candidates for popularity,
he ordained that whoever proposed a new law should do it
with a halter about his neck; so that in case his proposition
was rejected they just hung him up—and there the matter
ended.

This salutary institution had such an effect that for more
than two hundred years there was only one trifling alteration in the criminal code—and the whole race of lawyers
starved to death for want of employment. The consequence
of this was that the Locrians, being unprotected by an overwhelming load of excellent laws and undefended by a standing army of pettifoggers and sheriffs officers, lived very
lovingly together, and were such a happy people that they
scarce make any figure throughout the whole Grecian history—for it is well known that none but your unlucky,
quarrelsome, rantipole nations make any noise in the world.

Well would it have been for William the Testy had he
haply, in the course of his "universal acquirements," stumbled upon this precaution of the good Charondas. On the
contrary, he conceived that the true policy of a legislator was

to multiply laws, and thus secure the property, the persons, and the morals of the people, by surrounding them in a manner with men-traps and spring-guns, and besetting even the sweet sequestered walks of private life with quickset hedges, so that a man could scarcely turn without the risk of encountering some of these pestiferous protectors. Thus was he continually coining petty laws for every petty offense that occurred, until in time they became too numerous to be remembered, and remained like those of certain modern legislators, mere dead-letters—revived occasionally for the purpose of individual oppression, or to entrap ignorant offenders.

Petty courts consequently began to appear, where the law was administered with nearly as much wisdom and impartiality as in those august tribunals, the alderman's and justice's courts of the present day. The plaintiff was generally favored, as being a customer and bringing business to the shop; the offenses of the rich were discreetly winked at—for fear of hurting the feelings of their friends—but it could never be laid to the charge of the vigilant burgomasters that they suffered vice to skulk unpunished, under the disgraceful rags of poverty.

About this time may we date the first introduction of capital punishments—a goodly gallows being erected on the waterside, about where Whitehall stairs are at present, a little to the east of the Battery. Hard by also was erected another gibbet of a very strange, uncouth, and unmatchable description, but on which the ingenious William Kieft valued himself not a little, being a punishment entirely of his own invention.

It was for loftiness of altitude not a whit inferior to that of Haman, so renowned in Bible history; but the marvel of the contrivance was that the culprit, instead of being suspended by the neck, according to venerable custom, was hoisted by the waistband, and was kept for an hour together dangling and sprawling between heaven and earth—to the infinite entertainment and doubtless great edification of the multitude of respectable citizens who usually attend upon exhibitions of the kind.

It is incredible how the little governor chuckled at beholding caitiff vagrants and sturdy beggars thus swinging by the
crupper, and cutting antic gambols in the air. He had a
thousand pleasantries and mirthful conceits to utter upon
these occasions. He called them his dandlelions—his wild-
fowl—his high-flyers—his spread-eagles—his goshawks—his
scarecrows, and, finally, his *gallows-birds*, which ingenious
appellation, though originally confined to worthies who had
taken the air in this strange manner, has since grown to be
a cant name given to all candidates for legal elevation. This
punishment, moreover, if we may credit the assertions of
certain grave etymologists, gave the first hint for a kind of
harnessing, or strapping, by which our forefathers braced up
their multifarious breeches, and which has of late years been
revived, and continues to be worn at the present day.

Such were the admirable improvements of William Kieft
in criminal law—nor was his civil code less a matter of won-
derment; and much does it grieve me that the limits of my
work will not suffer me to expatiate on both, with the prolix-
ity they deserve. Let it suffice then to say that in a little
while the blessings of innumerable laws became notoriously
apparent. It was soon found necessary to have a certain
class of men to expound and confound them—divers pettifoggers accordingly made their appearance, under whose
protecting care the community was soon set together by
the ears.

I would not here be thought to insinuate anything derogatory to the profession of the law, or to its dignified members.
Well am I aware that we have in this ancient city innumerable worthy gentlemen who have embraced that honorable
order, not for the sordid love of filthy lucre, nor the selfish
cravings of renown, but through no other motives but a fervent zeal for the correct administration of justice, and a generous and disinterested devotion to the interests of their fellow-citizens!—Sooner would I throw this trusty pen into the
flames, and cork up my ink-bottle forever, than infringe even
for a nail's breadth upon the dignity of this truly benevolent

class of citizens—on the contrary, I allude solely to that crew of caitiff scouts who, in these latter days of evil, have become so numerous—who infest the skirts of the profession as did the recreant Cornish knights the honorable order of chivalry —who, under its auspices, commit their depredations on society—who thrive by quibbles, quirks, and chicanery, and, like vermin, swarm most where there is most corruption.

Nothing so soon awakens the malevolent passions as the facility of gratification. The courts of law would never be so constantly crowded with petty, vexatious, and disgraceful suits, were it not for the herds of pettifogging lawyers that infest them. These tamper with the passions of the lower and more ignorant classes; who, as if poverty were not a sufficient misery in itself, are always ready to heighten it by the bitterness of litigation. They are in law what quacks are in medicine—exciting the malady for the purpose of profiting by the cure, and retarding the cure for the purpose of augmenting the fees. Where one destroys the constitution, the other impoverishes the purse, and it may likewise be observed that a patient who has once been under the hands of a quack is ever after dabbling in drugs, and poisoning himself with infallible remedies; and an ignorant man, who has once meddled with the law under the auspices of one of these empirics, is forever after embroiling himself with his neighbors, and impoverishing himself with successful lawsuits.— My readers will excuse this digression into which I have been unwarily betrayed; but I could not avoid giving a cool, unprejudiced account of an abomination too prevalent in this excellent city, and with the effects of which I am unluckily acquainted to my cost; having been nearly ruined by a lawsuit, which was unjustly decided against me—and my ruin having been completed by another, which was decided in my favor.

It has been remarked by the observant writer of the Stuyvesant manuscript that under the administration of Wilhelmus Kieft the disposition of the inhabitants of New Amsterdam experienced an essential change, so that they

became very meddlesome and factious. The constant exacerbations of temper into which the little governor was
thrown by the maraudings on his frontiers, and his unfortunate propensity to experiment and innovation, occasioned
him to keep his council in a continual worry—and the council being, to the people at large, what yeast or leaven is to a
batch, they threw the whole community into a ferment—and
the people at large being to the city what the mind is to the
body, the unhappy commotions they underwent operated
most disastrously upon New Amsterdam—insomuch that
in certain of their paroxysms of consternation and perplexity they begat several of the most crooked, distorted, and
abominable streets, lanes, and alleys, with which this metropolis is disfigured.

But the worst of the matter was that just about this time
the mob, since called the sovereign people, like Balaam's ass,
began to grow more enlightened than its rider, and exhibited
a strange desire of governing itself. This was another effect
of the "universal acquirements" of William the Testy. In
some of his pestilent researches among the rubbish of antiquity, he was struck with admiration at the institution of
public tables among the Lacedæmonians, where they discussed topics of a general and interesting nature—at the
schools of the philosophers, where they engaged in profound
disputes upon politics and morals—where graybeards were
taught the rudiments of wisdom, and youths learned to become little men before they were boys. "There is nothing,"
said the ingenious Kieft, shutting up the book, "there is
nothing more essential to the well-management of a country
than education among the people: the basis of a good government should be laid in the public mind."—Now this was
true enough, but it was ever the wayward fate of William
the Testy that when he thought right he was sure to go to
work wrong. In the present instance, he could scarcely eat
or sleep until he had set on foot brawling debating societies
among the simple citizens of New Amsterdam. This was
the one thing wanting to complete his confusion. The hon-

est Dutch burghers, though in truth but little given to argument or wordy altercation, yet by dint of meeting often together, fuddling themselves with strong drink, beclouding their brains with tobacco-smoke, and listening to the harangues of some half a dozen oracles, soon became exceedingly wise, and—as is always the case where the mob is politically enlightened—exceedingly discontented. They found out, with wonderful quickness of discernment, the fearful error in which they had indulged, in fancying themselves the happiest people in creation—and were fortunately convinced that, all circumstances to the contrary notwithstanding, they were a very unhappy, deluded, and consequently ruined people.

In a short time the quidnuncs of New Amsterdam formed themselves into sage juntos of political croakers, who daily met together to groan over political affairs and make themselves miserable; thronging to these unhappy assemblages with the same eagerness that zealots have in all ages abandoned the milder and more peaceful paths of religion to crowd to the howling convocations of fanaticism. We are naturally prone to discontent, and avaricious after imaginary causes of lamentation—like lubberly monks, we belabor our own shoulders, and seem to take a vast satisfaction in the music of our own groans. Nor is this said for the sake of paradox; daily experience shows the truth of these observations. It is almost impossible to elevate the spirits of a man groaning under ideal calamities; but nothing is more easy than to render him wretched, though on the pinnacle of felicity; as it is a herculean task to hoist a man to the top of a steeple, though the merest child can topple him off thence.

In the sage assemblages I have noticed the reader will at once perceive the faint germs of those sapient convocations called popular meetings, prevalent at our day. Thither resorted all those idlers and "squires of low degree," who, like rags, hang loose upon the back of society, and are ready to be blown away by every wind of doctrine. Cobblers abandoned their stalls, and hastened thither to give lessons on

political economy—blacksmiths left their handicraft and suffered their own fires to go out, while they blew the bellows
and stirred up the fire of faction; and even tailors, though
but the shreds and patches, the ninth parts of humanity,
neglected their own measures to attend to the measures of
government.—Nothing was wanting but half a dozen newspapers and patriotic editors to have completed this public
illumination, and to have thrown the whole province in an
uproar!

I should not forget to mention that these popular meetings were held at a noted tavern; for houses of that description have always been found the most fostering nurseries of
politics; abounding with those genial streams which give
strength and sustenance to faction. We are told that the
ancient Germans had an admirable mode of treating any
question of importance; they first deliberated upon it when
drunk, and afterward reconsidered it when sober. The
shrewder mobs of America, who dislike having two minds
upon a subject, both determine and act upon it drunk; by
which means a world of cold and tedious speculation is dis-
pensed with—and as it is universally allowed that when a
man is drunk he sees double, it follows most conclusively
that he sees twice as well as his sober neighbors.

CHAPTER SIX

OF THE GREAT PIPE PLOT—AND OF THE DOLOROUS PER-
PLEXITIES INTO WHICH WILLIAM THE TESTY WAS
THROWN BY REASON OF HIS HAVING ENLIGHTENED THE
MULTITUDE

WILHELMUS KIEFT, as has already been made manifest,
was a great legislator upon a small scale. He was of an
active, or rather a busy mind; that is to say, his was one of
those small, but brisk minds, which make up by bustle and
constant motion for the want of great scope and power. He

had, when quite a youngling, been impressed with the advice of Solomon, "Go to the ant, thou sluggard; consider her ways and be wise"; in conformity to which he had ever been of a restless, ant-like turn, worrying hither and thither, busying himself about little matters, with an air of great importance and anxiety—laying up wisdom by the morsel, and often toiling and puffing at a grain of mustard-seed, under the full conviction that he was moving a mountain.

Thus we are told that once upon a time, in one of his fits of mental bustle, which he termed deliberation, he framed an unlucky law, to prohibit the universal practice of smoking. This he proved, by mathematical demonstration, to be, not merely a heavy tax on the public pocket, but an incredible consumer of time, a great encourager of idleness, and, of course, a deadly bane to the prosperity and morals of the people. Ill-fated Kieft! had he lived in this enlightened and libel-loving age, and attempted to subvert the inestimable liberty of the press, he could not have struck more closely on the sensibilities of the million.

The populace were in as violent a turmoil as the constitutional gravity of their deportment would permit—a mob of factious citizens had even the hardihood to assemble before the governor's house, where, setting themselves resolutely down, like a besieging army before a fortress, they one and all fell to smoking with a determined perseverance that seemed as though it were their intention to smoke him into terms. The testy William issued out of his mansion like a wrathful spider, and demanded to know the cause of this seditious assemblage, and this lawless fumigation; to which these sturdy rioters made no other reply than to loll back phlegmatically in their seats and puff away with redoubled fury; whereby they raised such a murky cloud that the governor was fain to take refuge in the interior of his castle.

The governor immediately perceived the object of this unusual tumult, and that it would be impossible to suppress a practice which, by long indulgence, had become a second nature. And here I would observe, partly to explain why I have so often made mention of this practice in my history, that it was inseparably connected with all the affairs, both public and private, of our revered ancestors. The pipe, in fact, was never from the mouth of the true-born Nederlander. It was his companion in solitude, the relaxation of his gayer hours, his counselor, his consoler, his joy, his pride; in a word, he seemed to think and breathe through his pipe.

When William the Testy bethought himself of all these matters, which he certainly did, although a little too late, he came to a compromise with the besieging multitude. The result was, that though he continued to permit the custom of smoking, yet did he abolish the fair long pipes which were used in the days of Wouter Van Twiller, denoting ease, tranquillity, and sobriety of deportment; and, in place thereof, did introduce little, captious, short pipes, two inches in length; which, he observed, could be stuck in one corner of the mouth, or twisted in the hat-band, and would not be in the way of business. By this the multitude seemed somewhat appeased, and dispersed to their habitations. Thus ended this alarming insurrection, which was long known by the name of the *pipe plot*, and which, it has been somewhat quaintly observed, did end, like most other plots, seditions, and conspiracies, in mere smoke.

But mark, oh reader! the deplorable consequences that did afterward result. The smoke of these villainous little pipes, continually ascending in a cloud about the nose, penetrated into, and befogged the cerebellum, dried up all the kindly moisture of the brain, and rendered the people that used them as vaporish and testy as their renowned little governor—nay, what is more, from a goodly, burly race of folk they became, like our worthy Dutch farmers, who smoke short pipes, a lantern-jawed, smoke-dried, leathern-hided race of men.

Nor was this all, for from hence may we date the rise of parties in this province. Certain of the more wealthy and important burghers adhering to the ancient fashion, formed a kind of aristocracy, which went by the appellation of the

Long Pipes—while the lower orders, submitting to the innovation, which they found to be more convenient in their handicraft employments, and to leave them more liberty of action, were branded with the plebeian name of *Short Pipes*. A third party likewise sprang up, differing from both the others, headed by the descendants of the famous Robert Chewit, the companion of the great Hudson. These entirely discarded the use of pipes, and took to chewing tobacco, and hence they were called *Quids*. It is worthy of notice that this last appellation has since come to be invariably applied to those mongrel or third parties that will sometimes spring up between two great contending parties, as a mule is produced between a horse and an ass.

And here I would remark the great benefit of these party distinctions, by which the people at large are saved the vast trouble of thinking. Hesiod divides mankind into three classes : those who think for themselves, those who let others think for them, and those who will neither do one nor the other. The second class, however, comprises the great mass of society; and hence is the origin of *party*, by which is meant a large body of people, some few of whom think, and all the rest talk. The former, who are called the leaders, marshal out and discipline the latter, teaching them what they must approve—what they must hoot at—what they must say—whom they must support—but, above all, whom they must hate—for no man can be a right good partisan unless he be a determined and thoroughgoing hater.

But when the sovereign people are thus properly broken to the harness, yoked, curbed, and reined, it is delectable to see with what docility and harmony they jog onward, through mud and mire, at the will of their drivers, dragging the dirt-carts of faction at their heels. How many a patriotic member of Congress have I seen, who would never have known how to make up his mind on any question, and might have run a great risk of voting right by mere accident, had he not had others to think for him, and a file-leader to vote after!

Thus then the enlightened inhabitants of the Manhattoes,

being divided into parties, were enabled to organize dissension, and to oppose and hate one another more accurately. And now the great business of politics went bravely on—the parties assembling in separate beer-houses, and smoking at each other with implacable animosity, to the great support of the state, and emolument of the tavern-keepers. Some, indeed, who were more zealous than the rest, went further, and began to bespatter one another with numerous very hard names and scandalous little words, to be found in the Dutch language; every partisan believing religiously that he was serving his country when he traduced the character or impoverished the pocket of a political adversary. But, however they might differ between themselves, all parties agreed on one point, to cavil at and condemn every measure of government, whether right or wrong; for as the governor was by his station independent of their power, and was not elected by their choice, and as he had not decided in favor of either faction, neither of them was interested in his success, or in the prosperity of the country, while under his administration.

"Unhappy William Kieft!" exclaims the sage writer of the Stuyvesant manuscript—"doomed to contend with enemies too knowing to be entrapped, and to reign over a people too wise to be governed!" All his expeditions against his enemies were baffled and set at naught, and all his measures for the public safety were caviled at by the people. Did he propose levying an efficient body of troops for internal defense—the mob, that is to say those vagabond members of the community who have nothing to lose, immediately took the alarm, vociferated that their interests were in danger— that a standing army was a legion of moths, preying on the pockets of society; a rod of iron in the hands of government; and that a government with a military force at its command would inevitably swell into a despotism. Did he, as was but too commonly the case, defer preparation until the moment of emergency, and then hastily collect a handful of undisciplined vagrants—the measure was hooted at as feeble and inadequate, as trifling with the public dignity and safety, and as lavishing the public funds on impotent enterprises. Did he resort to the economic measure of proclamation—he was laughed at by the Yankees; did he back it by non-intercourse —it was evaded and counteracted by his own subjects. Whichever way he turned himself, he was beleaguered and distracted by petitions of "numerous and respectable meetings," consisting of some half-a-dozen brawling pothouse politicians—all of which he read, and, what is worse, all of which he attended to. The consequence was, that by incessantly changing his measures he gave none of them a fair trial; and by listening to the clamors of the mob, and endeavoring to do everything, he, in sober truth, did nothing.

I would not have it supposed, however, that he took all these memorials and interferences good-naturedly, for such an idea would do injustice to his valiant spirit; on the contrary, he never received a piece of advice in the whole course of his life without first getting into a passion with the giver. But I have ever observed that your passionate little men, like small boats with large sails, are the easiest upset or blown out of their course; and this is demonstrated by Governor Kieft, who, though in temperament as hot as an old radish, and with a mind the territory of which was subjected to perpetual whirlwinds and tornadoes, yet never failed to be carried away by the last piece of advice that was blown into his ear. Lucky was it for him that his power was not dependent upon the greasy multitude, and that as yet the populace did not possess the important privilege of nominating their chief magistrate! They, however, did their best to help along public affairs; pestering their governor incessantly, by goading him on with harangues and petitions, and then thwarting his fiery spirit with reproaches and memorials, like Sunday jockeys managing an unlucky devil of a hackhorse—so that Wilhelmus Kieft may be said to have been kept either on a worry or a hand-gallop throughout the whole of his administration.

CHAPTER SEVEN

CONTAINING DIVERS FEARFUL ACCOUNTS OF BORDER WARS,
AND THE FLAGRANT OUTRAGES OF THE MOSSTROOPERS
OF CONNECTICUT—WITH THE RISE OF THE GREAT AM-
PHYCTIONIC COUNCIL OF THE EAST AND THE DECLINE
OF WILLIAM THE TESTY

IT was asserted by the wise men of ancient times, who
were intimately acquainted with these matters, that at the
gate of Jupiter's palace lay two huge tuns, the one filled with
blessings, the other with misfortunes—and it verily seems as
if the latter had been completely overturned and left to
deluge the unlucky province of Nieuw Nederlandts.   Among
the many internal and external causes of irritation, the incessant irruptions of the Yankees upon his frontiers were continually adding fuel to the inflammable temper of William
the Testy.   Numerous accounts of these molestations may
still be found among the records of the times; for the commanders on the frontiers were especially careful to evince
their vigilance and zeal by striving who should send home
the most frequent and voluminous budgets of complaints—
as your faithful servant is eternally running with complaints
to the parlor, of the petty squabbles and misdemeanors of the
kitchen.

Far be it from me to insinuate, however, that our worthy
ancestors indulged in groundless alarms; on the contrary,
they were daily suffering a repetition of cruel wrongs,* not

---

* From among a multitude of bitter grievances still on record, I
select a few of the most atrocious, and leave my readers to judge if our
ancestors were not justifiable in getting into a very valiant passion on
the occasion.

"24 June, 1641. Some of Hartford have taken a hogg out of the

one of which but was a sufficient reason, according to the
maxims of national dignity and honor, for throwing the
whole universe into hostility and confusion.

Oh, ye powers! into what indignation did every one of
these outrages throw the philosophic William! letter after
letter, protest after protest, proclamation after proclamation,
bad Latin, worse English, and hideous Low Dutch were exhausted in vain upon the inexorable Yankees; and the four-
and-twenty letters of the alphabet, which, excepting his
champion, the sturdy trumpeter Van Corlear, composed the
only standing army he had at his command, were never off
duty throughout the whole of his administration.   Nor was
Antony the trumpeter a whit behind his patron in fiery zeal;
but like a faithful champion of the public safety, on the
arrival of every fresh article of news, he was sure to sound
his trumpet from the ramparts, with most disastrous notes,
throwing the people into violent alarms, and disturbing their
rest at all times and seasons—which caused him to be held
in very great regard, the public pampering and rewarding
him, as we do brawling editors for similar services.

I am well aware of the perils that environ me in this
part of my history.   While raking with curious hands, but
pious heart, among the mouldering remains of former days,

---

vlact or common, and shut it up out of meer hate or other prejudice,
causing it to starve for hunger in the stye!"

"26 July. The foremencioned English did again drive the Companie's hoggs out of the vlact of Sicojoke into Hartford; contending
daily with reproaches, blows, beating the people with all disgrace that
they could imagine."

"May 20, 1642. The English of Hartford have violently cut loose
a horse of the honoured Companie's, that stood bound upon the common or vlact."

"May 9, 1643. The Companie's horses pastured upon the Companie's ground, were driven away by them of Connecticott or Hartford,
and the herdsmen lustily beaten with hatchets and sticks."

"16. Again they sold a young hogg belonging to the Companie,
which piggs had pastured on the Companie's land."

—*Haz. Col. State Papers.*

anxious to draw therefrom the honey of wisdom, I may fare
somewhat like that valiant worthy, Samson, who, in meddling with the carcass of a dead lion, drew a swarm of bees
about his ears. Thus, while narrating the many misdeeds
of the Yanokie or Yankee tribe, it is ten chances to one but
I offend the morbid sensibilities of certain of their unreason
able descendants, who may fly out and raise such a buzzing
about this unlucky head of mine that I shall need the tough
hide of an Achilles or an Orlando Furioso to protect me from
their stings.

Should such be the case, I should deeply and sincerely
lament—not my misfortune in giving offense, but the wrong-
headed perverseness of an ill-natured generation in taking
offense at anything I say. That their ancestors did use my
ancestors ill is true, and I am very sorry for it. I would,
with all my heart, the fact were otherwise; but as I am recording the sacred events of history, I'd not bate one nail's
breadth of the honest .truth, though I were sure the whole
edition of my work should be bought up and burned by the
common hangman of Connecticut. And in sooth, now that
these testy gentlemen have drawn me out, I will make bold
to go further and observe that this is one of the grand purposes for which we impartial historians are sent into the
world—to redress wrongs and render justice on the heads of
the guilty. So that, though a powerful nation may wrong
its neighbors with temporary impunity, yet sooner or later a
historian springs up who wreaks ample chastisement on it in
return.

Thus these mosstroopers of the east little thought, I'll
warrant it, while they were harassing the inoffensive province
of Nieuw Nederlandts, and driving its unhappy governor to
his wit's end, that a historian should ever arise and give them
their own with interest. Since, then, I am but performing
my bounden duty as a historian, in avenging the wrongs of
our revered ancestors, I shall make no further apology; and,
indeed, when it is considered that I have all these ancient
borderers of the east in my power, and at the mercy of my

* * * I

pen, I trust that it will be admitted I conduct myself with great humanity and moderation.

To resume, then, the course of my history. Appearances to the eastward began now to assume a more formidable aspect than ever—for I would have you note that hitherto the province had been chiefly molested by its immediate neighbors, the people of Connecticut, particularly of Hartford; which, if we may judge from ancient chronicles, was the stronghold of these sturdy mosstroopers, from whence they sallied forth on their daring incursions, carrying terror and devastation into the barns, the hen-roosts and pigsties of our revered ancestors.

Albeit, about the year 1643, the people of the east country, inhabiting the colonies of Massachusetts, Connecticut, New Plymouth and New Haven, gathered together into a mighty conclave, and after buzzing and debating for many days, like a political hive of bees in swarming time, at length settled themselves into a formidable confederation, under the title of the United Colonies of New England. By this union, they pledged themselves to stand by one another in all perils and assaults, and to co-operate in all measures, offensive and defensive, against the surrounding savages, among which were doubtlessly included our honored ancestors of the Manhattoes; and to give more strength and system to this confederation, a general assembly or grand council was to be annually held, composed of representatives from each of the provinces.

On receiving accounts of this combination, Wilhelmus Kieft was struck with consternation, and, for the first time in his whole life, forgot to bounce, at hearing an unwelcome piece of intelligence—which a venerable historian of the time observes was especially noticed among the politicians of New Amsterdam. The truth was, on turning over in his mind all that he had read at the Hague, about leagues and combinations, he found that this was an exact imitation of the Amphyctionic council, by which the states of Greece were enabled to attain to such power and supremacy, and the very

idea made his heart to quake for the safety of his empire at
the Manhattoes.

He strenuously insisted that the whole object of this confederation was to drive the Nederlanders out of their fair
domains; and always flew into a great rage if any one presumed to doubt the probability of his conjecture. Nor was
he wholly unwarranted in such a suspicion; for at the very
first annual meeting of the grand council, held at Boston
(which Governor Kieft denominated the Delphos of this truly
classic league), strong representations were made against the
Nederlanders, forasmuch as that in their dealings with the
Indians they carried on a traffic in "guns, powther, and
shott—a trade damnable and injurious to the colonists."[*]

Not but what certain of the Connecticut traders did likewise dabble a little in this "damnable traffic"—but then they
always sold the Indians such scurvy guns that they burst at
the first discharge—and consequently hurt no one but these
pagan savages.

The rise of this potent confederacy was a deathblow to
the glory of William the Testy; for from that day forward,
it was remarked by many, he never held up his head, but
appeared quite crestfallen. His subsequent reign, therefore,
affords but scanty food for the historic pen—we find the
grand council continually augmenting in power, and threatening to overwhelm the province of Nieuw Nederlandts;
while Wilhelmus Kieft kept constantly fulminating proclamations and protests, like a shrewd sea captain firing off
carronades and swivels in order to break and disperse a
waterspout—but, alas! they had no more effect than if they
had been so many blank cartridges.

The last document on record of this learned, philosophic,
but unfortunate little man, is a long letter to the council of
the Amphyctions, wherein, in the bitterness of his heart, he
rails at the people of New Haven, or Red Hills, for their uncourteous contempt of his protest, leveled at them for squat-

---

[*] Haz. Col. State Papers.

ting within the province of their High Mightinesses. From
this letter, which is a model of epistolary writing, abounding
with pithy apothegms and classic figures, my limits will
barely allow me to extract the following recondite passage:
"Certainly when we heare the Inhabitants of New Hartford
complayninge of us, we seem to heare Esop's wolfe complayninge of the lamb, or the admonition of the younge man
who cryed out to his mother, chideing with her neighboures,
'Oh, Mother, revile her, lest she first take up that practice
against you.' But being taught by precedent passages, we
received such an answer to our protest from the inhabitants
of New Haven as we expected; *the Eagle always despiseth
the Beetle Fly;* yet notwithstanding we do undauntedly
continue on our purpose of pursuing our own right, by just
arms and righteous means, and doe hope without scruple to
execute the express commands of our superiors."* To show
that this last sentence was not a mere empty menace, he
concluded his letter by intrepidly protesting against the whole
council, as a horde of *squatters* and interlopers, inasmuch
as they held their meeting at New Haven, or the Red Hills,
which he claimed as being within the province of the New
Netherlands.

Thus end the authenticated chronicles of the reign of
William the Testy; for henceforth, in the troubles, the perplexities, and the confusion of the times, he seems to have
been totally overlooked, and to have slipped forever through
the fingers of scrupulous history. Indeed, for some cause or
other which I cannot divine, there appears to have been a
combination among historians to sink his very name into
oblivion, in consequence of which they have one and all for-
borne even to speak of his exploits. This shows how important it is for great men to cultivate the favor of the learned,
if they are ambitious of honor and renown. "Insult not the
dervise," said a wise caliph to his son, "lest thou offend thine
historian"; and many a mighty man of the olden time, had

* Vide Haz. Col. State Papers.

he observed so obvious a maxim, might have escaped divers
cruel wipes of the pen which have been drawn across his
character.

It has been a matter of deep concern to me that such
darkness and obscurity should hang over the latter days of
the illustrious Kieft—for he was a mighty and great little
man, worthy of being utterly renowned, seeing that he was
the first potentate that introduced into this land the art of
fighting by proclamation and defending a country by trumpeters and windmills—an economic and humane mode of
warfare, since revived with great applause, and which promises, if it can ever be carried into full effect, to save great
trouble and treasure, and spare infinitely more bloodshed
than either the discovery of gunpowder or the invention of
torpedoes.

It is true that certain of the early provincial poets, of
whom there were great numbers in the Nieuw Nederlandts,
taking advantage of the mysterious exit of William the Testy,
have fabled that, like Romulus, he was translated to the
skies, and forms a very fiery little star, somewhere on the
left claw of the crab; while others, equally fanciful, declare
that he had experienced a fate similar to that of the good
King Arthur; who, we are assured by ancient bards, was
carried away to the delicious abodes of fairyland, where he
still exists in pristine worth and vigor, and will one day or
another return to restore the gallantry, the honor, and the
immaculate probity which prevailed in the glorious days of
the Round Table.*

---

* "The old Welch bards believed that King Arthur was not dead,
but carried awaie by the fairies into some pleasant place, where he
shold remaine for a time, and then returne againe and reigne in as
great authority as ever."—*Hollingshed*.

"The Britons suppose that he shall come yet and conquere all Bri-
taigne, for certes, this is the prophicye of Merlyn—He say'd that his
deth shall be doubteous; and said soth, for men thereof yet have doubte
and shullen for ever more—for men wyt not whether that he lyveth or
is dede."—*De Leew Chron*.

All these, however, are but pleasing fantasies, the cob-web visions of those dreaming varlets, the poets, to which I would not have my judicious reader attach any credibility. Neither am I disposed to yield any credit to the assertion of an ancient and rather apocryphal historian, who alleges that the ingenious Wilhelmus was annihilated by the blowing down of one of his windmills—nor to that of a writer of later times, who affirms that he fell a victim to a philosophical experiment which he had for many years been vainly striv-ing to accomplish; having the misfortune to break his neck from the garret-window of the stadt-house, in an ineffectual attempt to catch swallows, by sprinkling fresh salt upon their tails.

The most probable account, and to which I am inclined to give my implicit faith, is contained in a very obscure tra-dition, which declares that what with the constant troubles on his frontiers—the incessant schemings and projects going on in his own pericranium—the memorials, petitions, remon-strances and sage pieces of advice from divers respectable meetings of the sovereign people—together with the refrac-tory disposition of his council, who were sure to differ from him on every point, and uniformly to be in the wrong—all these, I say, did eternally operate to keep his mind in a kind of furnace heat, until he at length became as completely burned out as a Dutch family pipe which has passed through three generations of hard smokers. In this manner did the choleric but magnanimous William the Testy undergo a kind of animal combustion, consuming away like a farthing rush-light; so that, when grim Death finally snuffed him out, there was scarce left enough of him to bury!

BOOK FIVE

*CONTAINING THE FIRST PART OF THE REIGN OF PETER
STUYVESANT, AND HIS TROUBLES WITH
THE AMPHYCTIONIC COUNCIL*

CHAPTER ONE

IN WHICH THE DEATH OF A GREAT MAN IS SHOWN TO BE
NO VERY INCONSOLABLE MATTER OF SORROW—AND HOW
PETER STUYVESANT ACQUIRED A GREAT NAME FROM THE
UNCOMMON STRENGTH OF HIS HEAD

To a profound philosopher like myself, who am apt to
see clear through a subject where the penetration of ordinary
people extends but half-way, there is no fact more simple
and manifest than that the death of a great man is a matter
of very little importance. Much as we may think of ourselves, and much as we may excite the empty plaudits of the
million, it is certain that the greatest among us do actually
fill but an exceeding small space in the world; and it is
equally certain that even that small space is quickly supplied
when we leave it vacant. "Of what consequence is it,"
said Pliny, "that individuals appear, or make their exit? the
world is a theater whose scenes and actors are continually
changing." Never did philosopher speak more correctly;
and I only wonder that so wise a remark could have existed
so many ages, and mankind not have laid it more to heart.
Sage follows on in the footsteps of sage; one hero just steps
out of his triumphal car to make way for the hero who comes
after him; and of the proudest monarch it is merely said,
that—"he slept with his fathers, and his successor reigned in
his stead."

The world, to tell the private truth, cares but little for their loss, and if left to itself would soon forget to grieve; and though a nation has often been figuratively drowned in tears on the death of a great man, yet it is ten chances to one if an individual tear has been shed on the occasion, excepting from the forlorn pen of some hungry author. It is the historian, the biographer, and the poet, who have the whole burden of grief to sustain; who—kind souls!—like undertakers in England, act the part of chief mourners—who inflate a nation with sighs it never heaved and deluge it with tears it never dreamed of shedding. Thus, while the patriotic author is weeping and howling, in prose, in blank verse, and in rhyme, and collecting the drops of public sorrow into his volume as into a lachrymal vase, it is more than probable his fellow-citizens are eating and drinking, fiddling and dancing, as utterly ignorant of the bitter lamentations made in their name as are those men of straw, John Doe and Richard Roe, of the plaintiffs for whom they are generously pleased on divers occasions to become sureties.

The most glorious and praiseworthy hero that ever desolated nations might have mouldered into oblivion among the rubbish of his own monument, did not some historian take him into favor and benevolently transmit his name to posterity—and much as the valiant William Kieft worried, and bustled, and turmoiled, while he had the destinies of a whole colony in his hand, I question seriously whether he will not be obliged to this authentic history for all his future celebrity.

His exit occasioned no convulsion in the city of New Amsterdam or its vicinity: the earth trembled not, neither did any stars shoot from their spheres—the heavens were not shrouded in black, as poets would fain persuade us they have been on the unfortunate death of a hero—the rocks (hard-hearted varlets!) melted not into tears, nor did the trees hang their heads in silent sorrow; and as to the sun, he laid abed the next night just as long, and showed as jolly a face when he arose, as he ever did on the same day

of the month in any year, either before or since. The good
people of New Amsterdam, one and all, declared that he
had been a very busy, active, bustling little governor; that
he was "the father of his country"—that he was "the noblest
work of God"—that "he was a man, take him for all in all,
they ne'er should look upon his like again"—together with
sundry other civil and affectionate speeches that are regularly
said on the death of all great men; after which they smoked
their pipes, thought no more about him, and Peter Stuyvesant succeeded to his station.

Peter Stuyvesant was the last, and, like the renowned
Wouter Van Twiller, he was also the best of our ancient
Dutch governors: Wouter having surpassed all who preceded him, and Peter, or Piet, as he was sociably called by
the old Dutch burghers, who were ever prone to familiarize
names, having never been equaled by any successor. He
was, in fact, the very man fitted by Nature to retrieve the
desperate fortunes of her beloved province, had not the fates,
those most potent and unrelenting of all ancient spinsters,
destined them to inextricable confusion.

To say merely that he was a hero would be doing him
great injustice—he was in truth a combination of heroes—
for he was of a sturdy, rawbone make, like Ajax Telamon,
with a pair of round shoulders that Hercules would have
given his hide for (meaning his lion's hide), when he undertook to ease old Atlas of his load. He was, moreover, as
Plutarch describes Coriolanus, not only terrible for the force
of his arm, but likewise of his voice, which sounded as
though it came out of a barrel; and, like the self-same warrior, he possessed a sovereign contempt for the sovereign
people, and an iron aspect which was enough of itself to
make the very bowels of his adversaries quake with terror
and dismay. All this martial excellency of appearance was
inexpressibly heightened by an accidental advantage, with
which I am surprised that neither Homer nor Virgil have
graced any of their heroes. This was nothing less than a
wooden leg, which was the only prize he had gained in

bravely fighting the battles of his country, but of which he was so proud that he was often heard to declare he valued it more than all his other limbs put together; indeed, so highly did he esteem it, that he had it gallantly enchased and relieved with silver devices, which caused it to be related in divers histories and legends that he wore a silver leg.*

Like that choleric warrior, Achilles, he was somewhat subject to extempore bursts of passion, which were often-times rather unpleasant to his favorites and attendants, whose perceptions he was apt to quicken, after the manner of his illustrious imitator, Peter the Great, by anointing their shoulders with his walking-staff.

Though I cannot find that he had read Plato, or Aris-totle, or Hobbes, or Bacon, or Algernon Sydney, or Tom Paine, yet did he sometimes manifest a shrewdness and sagacity in his measures that one would hardly expect from a man who did not know Greek, and had never studied the ancients. True it is, and I confess it with sorrow, that he had an unreasonable aversion to experiments, and was fond of governing his province after the simplest manner; but then he contrived to keep it in better order than did the erudite Kieft, though he had all the philosophers ancient and modern to assist and perplex him. I must likewise own that he made but very few laws; but then again he took care that those few were rigidly and impartially enforced—and I do not know but justice on the whole was as well administered as if there had been volumes of sage acts and statutes yearly made and daily neglected and forgotten.

He was, in fact, the very reverse of his predecessors, being neither tranquil and inert, like Walter the Doubter, nor restless and fidgeting, like William the Testy; but a man, or rather a governor, of such uncommon activity and decision of mind that he never sought or accepted the advice of others; depending confidently upon his single head, as did the heroes of yore upon their single arms, to work his way

---

* See the histories of Masters Josselyn and Bloome.

through all difficulties and dangers. To tell the simple
truth, he wanted no other requisite for a perfect statesman
than to think always right, for no one can deny that he
always acted as he thought; and if he wanted in correctness
he made up for it in perseverance. An excellent quality!
since it is surely more dignified for a ruler to be persevering
and consistent in error than wavering and contradictory in
endeavoring to do what is right. This much is certain—and
it is a maxim worthy the attention of all legislators, both
great and small, who stand shaking in the wind, without
knowing which way to steer—a ruler who acts according to
his own will is sure of pleasing himself, while he who seeks
to satisfy the wishes and whims of others runs a great risk
of pleasing nobody. The clock that stands still, and points
steadfastly in one direction, is certain of being right twice in
the four-and-twenty hours—while others may keep going
continually, and continually be going wrong.

Nor did this magnanimous virtue escape the discernment
of the good people of Nieuw Nederlandts; on the contrary,
so high an opinion had they of the independent mind and
vigorous intellect of their new governor that they universally
called him *Hardkoppig Piet*, or Peter the Headstrong—a
great compliment to his understanding!

If from all that I have said thou dost not gather, worthy
reader, that Peter Stuyvesant was a tough, sturdy, valiant,
weather-beaten, mettlesome, obstinate, leathern-sided, lion-
hearted, generous-spirited old governor, either I have written to but little purpose or thou art very dull at drawing
conclusions.

This most excellent governor, whose character I have
thus attempted feebly to delineate, commenced his administration on the 29th of May, 1647; a remarkably stormy day,
distinguished in all the almanacs of the time which have
come down to us by the name of *Windy Friday*. As he
was very jealous of his personal and official dignity, he was
inaugurated into office with great ceremony; the goodly oaken
chair of the renowned Wouter Van Twiller being carefully

preserved for such occasions, in like manner as the chair and
stone were reverentially preserved at Schone, in Scotland,
for the coronation of the Caledonian monarchs.

I must not omit to mention that the tempestuous state of
the elements, together with its being that unlucky day of the
week termed "hanging day," did not fail to excite much
grave speculation and divers very reasonable apprehensions
among the more ancient and enlightened inhabitants; and
several of the sager sex, who were reputed to be not a little
skilled in the mysteries of astrology and fortune-telling, did
declare outright that they were omens of a disastrous administration—an event that came to be lamentably verified, and
which proves, beyond dispute, the wisdom of attending to
those preternatural intimations furnished by dreams and visions, the flying of birds, falling of stones, and cackling of
geese, on which the sages and rulers of ancient times placed
such reliance—or to those shootings of stars, eclipses of the
moon, howlings of dogs, and flarings of candles, carefully
noted and interpreted by the oracular sybils of our day; who,
in my humble opinion, are the legitimate inheritors and pre-
servers of the ancient science of divination. This much is
certain, that Governor Stuyvesant succeeded to the chair of
state at a turbulent period; when foes thronged and threatened from without; when anarchy and stiff-necked opposition reigned rampant within; when the authority of their
High Mightinesses the Lords States-General, though founded
on the broad Dutch bottom of unoffending imbecility, though
supported by economy and defended by speeches, protests,
and proclamations, yet tottered to its very center; and when
the great city of New Amsterdam, though fortified by flagstaffs, trumpeters, and windmills, seemed, like some fair lady
of easy virtue, to lie open to attack and ready to yield to the
first invader.

CHAPTER TWO

SHOWING HOW PETER THE HEADSTRONG BESTIRRED HIM-
SELF AMONG THE RATS AND COBWEBS, ON ENTERING
INTO OFFICE—AND THE PERILOUS MISTAKE HE WAS
GUILTY OF IN HIS DEALINGS WITH THE AMPHYCTIONS

THE very first movements of the great Peter, on taking
the reins of government, displayed the magnanimity of his
mind, though they occasioned not a little marvel and uneasiness among the people of the Manhattoes. Finding himself
constantly interrupted by the opposition, and annoyed by the
advice, of his privy council, the members of which had acquired the unreasonable habit of thinking and speaking for
themselves during the preceding reign, he determined at once
to put a stop to such grievous abominations. Scarcely, therefore, had he entered upon his authority than he turned out of
office all those meddlesome spirits that composed the factious
cabinet of William the Testy; in place of whom he chose unto
himself counselors from those fat, somniferous, respectable
families that had flourished and slumbered under the easy
reign of Walter the Doubter. All these he caused to be furnished with abundance of fair long pipes, and to be regaled
with frequent corporation dinners, admonishing them to
smoke and eat and sleep for the good of the nation, while
he took all the burden of government upon his own shoulders
—an arrangement to which they gave hearty acquiescence.

Nor did he stop here, but made a hideous rout among the
inventions and expedients of his learned predecessor—demolishing his flagstaffs and windmills, which, like mighty giants,
guarded the ramparts of New Amsterdam—pitching to the
duyvel whole batteries of quaker guns—rooting up his patent
gallows, where caitiff vagabonds were suspended by the
waistband—and, in a word, turning topsy-turvy the whole

philosophic, economic, and windmill system of the immortal
sage of Saardam.

The honest folks of New Amsterdam began to quake now
for the fate of their matchless champion, Antony the trumpeter, who had acquired prodigious favor in the eyes of the
women, by means of his whiskers and his trumpet. Him
did Peter the Headstrong cause to be brought into his presence, and eying him for a moment from head to foot, with a
countenance that would have appalled anything else than
a sounder of brass: "Prithee, who and what art thou?"
said he.—"Sire," replied the other, in no wise dismayed;
"for my name, it is Antony Van Corlear—for my parentage,
I am the son of my mother—for my profession, I am champion and garrison of this great city of New Amsterdam."—
"I doubt me much," said Peter Stuyvesant, "that thou art
some scurvy costardmonger knave. How didst thou acquire
this paramount honor and dignity?"—"Marry, sir," replied
the other, "like many a great man before me, simply *by
sounding my own trumpet.*"—"Ay, is it so?" quoth the
governor, "why, then, let us have a relish of thy art."
Whereupon he put his instrument to his lips, and sounded
a charge with such a tremendous outset, such a delectable
quaver, and such a triumphant cadence, that it was enough
to make your heart leap out of your mouth only to be within
a mile of it. Like as a war-worn charger, while sporting in
peaceful plains, if by chance he hear the strains of martial
music, pricks up his ears, and snorts and paws and kindles
at the noise, so did the heroic soul of the mighty Peter joy
to hear the clangor of the trumpet; for of him might truly
be said what was recorded of the renowned St. George of
England, "There was nothing in all the world that more rejoiced his heart than to hear the pleasant sound of war, and
see the soldiers brandish forth their steeled weapons." Casting his eyes more kindly, therefore, upon the sturdy Van
Corlear, and finding him to be a jolly, fat little man, shrewd
in his discourse, yet of great discretion and immeasurable
wind, he straightway conceived a vast kindness for him,

and discharging him from the troublesome duty of garrisoning, defending, and alarming the city, ever after retained him about his person, as his chief favorite, confidential envoy, and trusty squire. Instead of disturbing the city with disastrous notes he was instructed to play so as to delight the governor while at his repasts, as did the minstrels of yore in the days of glorious chivalry—and on all public occasions to rejoice the ears of the people with warlike melody—thereby keeping alive a noble and martial spirit.

Many other alterations and reformations, both for the better and for the worse, did the governor make, of which my time will not serve me to record the particulars; suffice it to say, he soon contrived to make the province feel that he was its master, and treated the sovereign people with such tyrannical rigor that they were all fain to hold their tongues, stay at home, and attend to their business; insomuch that party feuds and distinctions were almost forgotten, and many thriving keepers of taverns and dram-shops were utterly ruined for want of business.

Indeed, the critical state of public affairs at this time demanded the utmost vigilance and promptitude. The formidable council of the Amphyctions, which had caused so much tribulation to the unfortunate Kieft, still continued augmenting its forces, and threatened to link within its union all the mighty principalities and powers of the east. In the very year following the inauguration of Governor Stuyvesant, a grand deputation departed from the city of Providence (famous for its dusty streets and beauteous women) in behalf of the puissant plantation of Rhode Island, praying to be admitted into the league.

The following mention is made of this application, in certain records of that assemblage of worthies, which are still extant.*

"Mr. Will Cottington and Captain Partridg of Rhoode-Iland presented this insewing request to the commissioners in wrighting—

---

* Haz. Col. State Papers.

"Our request and motion is in behalfe of Rhoode-Iland, that wee the Ilanders of Rhoode-Iland may be rescauied into combination with all the united colonyes of New England in a firme and perpetuall league of friendship and amity of ofence and defence, mutuall advice and succor upon all just occasions for our mutuall safety and wellfaire, etc.

Will Cottington,
Alicxsander Partridg."

There is certainly something in the very physiognomy of this document that might well inspire apprehension. The name of Alexander, however misspelled, has been warlike in every age; and though its fierceness is in some measure softened by being coupled with the gentle cognomen of Partridge, still, like the color of scarlet, it bears an exceeding great resemblance to the sound of a trumpet. From the style of the letter, moreover, and the soldier-like ignorance of orthography displayed by the noble captain Alicxsander Partridg in spelling his own name, we may picture to ourselves this mighty man of Rhodes, strong in arms, potent in the field, and as great a scholar as though he had been educated among that learned people of Thrace, who, Aristotle assures us, could not count beyond the number four.

But, whatever might be the threatening aspect of this famous confederation, Peter Stuyvesant was not a man to be kept in a state of incertitude and vague apprehension; he liked nothing so much as to meet danger face to face and take it by the beard. Determined, therefore, to put an end to all these petty maraudings on the borders, he wrote two or three categorical letters to the grand council; which, though neither couched in bad Latin, nor yet graced by rhetorical tropes about wolves, and lambs, and beetle-flies, yet had more effect than all the elaborate epistles, protests, and proclamations of his learned predecessor put together. In consequence of his urgent propositions, the great confederacy of the east agreed to enter into a final adjustment of grievances and settlement of boundaries, to the end that a perpetual and happy peace might take place between the two powers. For this purpose, Governor Stuyvesant deputed two embassadors to negotiate with commissioners from the grand council of the league; and a treaty was solemnly concluded at Hartford. On receiving intelligence of this event the whole community was in an uproar of exultation. The trumpet of the sturdy Van Corlear sounded all day with joyful clangor from the ramparts of Fort Amsterdam, and at night the city was magnificently illuminated with two hundred and fifty tallow candles; besides a barrel of tar, which was burned before the governor's house, on the cheering aspect of public affairs.

And now my worthy reader is, doubtless, like the great and good Peter, congratulating himself with the idea that his feelings will no longer be molested by afflicting details of stolen horses, broken heads, impounded hogs, and all the other catalogue of heartrending cruelties that disgraced these border wars. But if he should indulge in such expectations, it is a proof that he is but little versed in the paradoxical ways of cabinets; to convince him of which, I solicit his serious attention to my next chapter, wherein I will show that Peter Stuyvesant has already committed a great error in politics; and, by effecting a peace, has materially hazarded the tranquillity of the province.

CHAPTER THREE

CONTAINING DIVERS SPECULATIONS ON WAR AND NEGOTIATIONS—SHOWING THAT A TREATY OF PEACE IS A GREAT NATIONAL EVIL

IT was the opinion of that poetical philosopher, Lucretius, that war was the original state of man, whom he described as being primitively a savage beast of prey, engaged in a constant state of hostility with his own species; and that this ferocious spirit was tamed and meliorated by society. The same opinion has been advocated by Hobbes;* nor have there been wanting many other philosophers to admit and defend it.

For my part, though prodigiously fond of these valuable speculations, so complimentary to human nature, yet, in this instance, I am inclined to take the proposition by halves, believing, with Horace,† that though war may have been originally the favorite amusement and industrious employment of our progenitors, yet, like many other excellent habits, so far from being meliorated, it has been cultivated and confirmed by refinement and civilization, and increases in exact proportion as we approach toward that state of perfection which is the *ne plus ultra* of modern philosophy.

The first conflict between man and man was the mere exertion of physical force unaided by auxiliary weapons—his arm was his buckler, his fist was his mace, and a broken head the catastrophe of his encounters. The battle of unassisted strength was succeeded by the more rugged one of stones and clubs, and war assumed a sanguinary aspect. As man advanced in refinement, as his faculties expanded and his sensibilities became more exquisite, he grew rapidly more ingenious and experienced in the art of murdering his fellow-beings. He invented a thousand devices to defend and to assault—the helmet, the cuirass, and the buckler, the sword, the dart, and the javelin, prepared him to elude the wound as well as to lanch the blow. Still urging on, in the brilliant and philanthropic career of invention, he enlarges and heightens his powers of defense and injury—the Aries, the Scorpio, the Balista, and the Catapulta, give a horror and sublimity to war and magnify its glory by increasing its desolation. Still insatiable, though armed with machinery that seemed to reach the limits of destructive invention, and

---

* Hobbes' Leviathan. Part i., chap. 13.
† Quum prorepserunt primis animalia terris,
  Mutuum ac turpe pecus, glandem atque cubilia propter,
  Unguibus et pugnis, dein fustibus, atque ita porro
  Pugnabant armis, quæ post fabricaverat usus.
                                        —*Hor. Sat.* l. i. s. 8.

to yield a power of injury commensurate even with the desires of revenge—still deeper researches must be made in the diabolical arcana. With furious zeal he dives into the bowels of the earth; he toils midst poisonous minerals and deadly salts—the sublime discovery of gunpowder blazes upon the world—and, finally, the dreadful art of fighting by proclamation seems to endow the demon of war with ubiquity and omnipotence!

This, indeed, is grand! This, indeed, marks the powers of mind, and bespeaks that divine endowment of reason which distinguishes us from the animals, our inferiors. The unenlightened brutes content themselves with the native force which Providence has assigned them. The angry bull butts with his horns, as did his progenitors before him—the lion, the leopard, and the tiger seek only with their talons and their fangs to gratify their sanguinary fury; and even the subtle serpent darts the same venom and uses the same wiles as did his sire before the flood. Man alone, blessed with the inventive mind, goes on from discovery to discovery—enlarges and multiplies his powers of destruction; arrogates the tremendous weapons of Deity itself, and tasks creation to assist him in murdering his brother worm!

In proportion as the art of war has increased in improvement has the art of preserving peace advanced in equal ratio; and as we have discovered, in this age of wonders and inventions, that a proclamation is the most formidable engine in war, so have we discovered the no less ingenious mode of maintaining peace by perpetual negotiations.

A treaty, or, to speak more correctly, a negotiation, therefore, according to the acceptation of experienced statesmen learned in these matters, is no longer an attempt to accommodate differences, to ascertain rights, and to establish an equitable exchange of kind offices; but a contest of skill between two powers, which shall overreach and take in the other. It is a cunning endeavor to obtain, by peaceable maneuver and the chicanery of cabinets, those advantages which a nation would otherwise have wrested by force of arms: in the same manner that a conscientious highwayman reforms and becomes an excellent and praiseworthy citizen, contenting himself with cheating his neighbor out of that property he would formerly have seized with open violence.

In fact, the only time when two nations can be said to be in a state of perfect amity is when a negotiation is open and a treaty pending. Then, as there are no stipulations entered into, no bonds to restrain the will, no specific limits to awaken the captious jealousy of right implanted in our nature, as each party has some advantage to hope and expect from the other, then it is that the two nations are so gracious and friendly to each other; their ministers professing the highest mutual regard, exchanging billets-doux, making fine speeches, and indulging in all those diplomatic flirtations, coquetries and fondlings that do so marvelously tickle the good-humor of the respective nations. Thus it may paradoxically be said that there is never so good an understanding between two nations as when there is a little misunderstanding—and that, so long as there are no terms, they are on the best terms in the world!

I do not by any means pretend to claim the merit of having made the above political discovery. It has, in fact, long been secretly acted upon by certain enlightened cabinets, and is, together with divers other notable theories, privately copied out of the commonplace book of an illustrious gentleman who has been member of Congress and enjoyed the unlimited confidence of heads of departments. To this principle may be ascribed the wonderful ingenuity that has been shown of late years in protracting and interrupting negotiations. Hence the cunning measure of appointing as embassador some political pettifogger skilled in delays, sophisms, and misapprehensions, and dexterous in the art of baffling argument—or some blundering statesman, whose errors and misconstructions may be a plea for refusing to ratify his engagements. And hence, too, that most notable expedient, so popular with our government, of sending out a brace of embassadors; who, having each an individual will to consult, character to estab-

lish, and interest to promote, you may as well look for una-
nimity and concord between two lovers with one mistress,
two dogs with one bone, or two naked rogues with one pair
of breeches. This disagreement, therefore, is continually
breeding delays and impediments, in consequence of which
the negotiation goes on swimmingly—insomuch as there is
no prospect of its ever coming to a close. Nothing is lost by
these delays and obstacles but time, and in a negotiation, according to the theory I have exposed, all time lost is in reality so much time gained. With what delightful paradoxes
does modern political economy abound!

Now all that I have here advanced is so notoriously true
that I almost blush to take up the time of my readers with
treating of matters which must many a time have stared
them in the face. But the proposition to which I would most
earnestly call their attention is this—that though a negotiation be the most harmonizing of all national transactions, yet
a treaty of peace is a great political evil, and one of the most
fruitful sources of war.

I have rarely seen an instance of any special contract between individuals that did not produce jealousies, bickerings,
and often downright ruptures between them; nor did I ever
know of a treaty between two nations that did not occasion
continual misunderstandings. How many worthy country
neighbors have I known who, after living in peace and good-
fellowship for years, have been thrown into a state of distrust, caviling, and animosity, by some ill-starred agreement about fences, runs of water, and stray cattle. And
how many well-meaning nations, who would otherwise have
remained in the most amicable disposition toward each other,
have been brought to swords' points about the infringement
or misconstruction of some treaty which in an evil hour they
had concluded by way of making their amity more sure!

Treaties, at best, are but complied with so long as interest requires their fulfillment; consequently, they are virtually
binding on the weaker party only, or, in plain truth, they
are not binding at all. No nation will wantonly go to war

with another if it has nothing to gain thereby, and, therefore, needs no treaty to restrain it from violence, and if it
have anything to gain, I much question, from what I have
witnessed of the righteous conduct of nations, whether any
treaty could be made so strong that it could not thrust the
sword through—nay, I would hold, ten to one, the treaty
itself would be the very source to which resort would be had
to find a pretext for hostilities.

Thus, therefore, I conclude—that though it is the best of
all policies for a nation to keep up a constant negotiation with
its neighbors, yet it is the summit of folly for it ever to be
beguiled into a treaty; for then comes on the non-fulfillment
and infraction, then remonstrance, then altercation, then retaliation, then recrimination, and finally open war. In a
word, negotiation is like courtship, a time of sweet words,
gallant speeches, soft looks, and endearing caresses; but the
marriage ceremony is the signal for hostilities.

CHAPTER FOUR

HOW PETER STUYVESANT WAS GREATLY BELIED BY HIS ADVERSARIES, THE MOSSTROOPERS—AND HIS CONDUCT THEREUPON

IF my painstaking reader be not somewhat perplexed, in
the course of the ratiociation of my last chapter, he will
doubtless at one glance perceive that the great Peter, in concluding a treaty with his eastern neighbors, was guilty of
a lamentable error and heterodoxy in politics. To this unlucky agreement may justly be ascribed a world of little infringements, altercations, negotiations and bickerings which
afterward took place between the irreproachable Stuyvesant
and the evil-disposed council of Amphyctions. All these did
not a little disturb the constitutional serenity of the good
burghers of Manna-hata; but in sooth they were so very pitiful in their nature and effects that a grave historian, who

grudges the time spent in anything less than recording the
fall of empires, and the revolution of worlds, would think
them unworthy to be inscribed on his sacred page.

The reader is, therefore, to take it for granted, though I
scorn to waste in the detail that time which my furrowed
brow and trembling hand inform me is invaluable, that, all
the while the great Peter was occupied in those tremendous
and bloody contests that I shall shortly rehearse, there was a
continued series of little, dirty, sniveling skirmishes, scourings, broils, and maraudings, made on the eastern frontiers,
by the mosstroopers of Connecticut. But, like that mirror
of chivalry, the sage and valorous Don Quixote, I leave these
petty contests for some future Sancho Panza of a historian,
while I reserve my prowess and my pen for achievements of
higher dignity.

Now did the great Peter conclude that his labors had
come to a close in the east, and that he had nothing to do
but apply himself to the internal prosperity of his beloved
Manhattoes. Though a man of great modesty, he could not
help boasting that he had at length shut the temple of Janus,
and that, were all rulers like a certain person who should be
nameless, it would never be opened again. But the exultation of the worthy governor was put to a speedy check; for
scarce was the treaty concluded, and hardly was the ink
dried on the paper, before the crafty and discourteous council of the league sought a new pretense for reilluming the
flames of discord.

It seems to be the nature of confederacies, republics, and
such like powers, that want the true masculine character, to
indulge exceedingly in certain feminine panics and suspicions.
Like some good lady of delicate and sickly virtue, who is in
constant dread of having her vestal purity contaminated or
seduced, and who if a man do but take her by the hand, or
look her in the face, is ready to cry out, rape! and ruin!—so
these squeamish governments are perpetually on the alarm
for the virtue of the country; every manly measure is a violation of the constitution—every monarchy or other mascu-

line government around them is laying snares for their seduc-
tion; and they are forever detecting infernal plots, by which
they were to be betrayed, dishonored, and "brought upon the
town."

If any proof were wanting of the truth of these opinions,
I would instance the conduct of a certain republic of our day;
who, good dame, has already withstood so many plots and
conspiracies against her virtue, and has so often come near
being made "no better than she should be." I would notice
her constant jealousies of poor old England, who, by her own
account, has been incessantly trying to sap her honor; though,
from my soul, I never could believe the honest old gentleman
meant her any rudeness. Whereas, on the contrary, I think
I have several times caught her squeezing hands and indulging in certain amorous oglings with that sad fellow Bonaparte—who all the world knows to be a great despoiler of
national virtue, to have ruined all the empires in his neighborhood, and to have debauched every republic that came in
his way—but so it is, these rakes seem always to gain singular favor with the ladies.

But I crave pardon of my reader for thus wandering, and
will endeavor in some measure to apply the foregoing remarks; for in the year 1651, we are told, the great confederacy of the east accused the immaculate Peter—the soul of
honor and heart of steel—that by divers gifts and promises
he had been secretly endeavoring to instigate the Narrohi-
gansett (or Narraganset), Mohaque, and Pequot Indians, to
surprise and massacre the Yankee settlements. "For," as
the council slanderously observed, "the Indians round about
for divers hundred miles cercute, seeme to have drunke deep
of an intoxicating cupp, att or from the Manhatoes against
the English, whoe have sought their good, both in bodily and
spirituall respects."

History does not make mention how the great council of
the Amphyctions came by this precious plot; whether it was
honestly bought at a fair market price, or discovered by sheer
good fortune—it is certain, however, that they examined di-

vers Indians, who all swore to the fact as sturdily as though they had been so many Christian troopers; and to be more sure of their veracity, the sage council previously made every mother's son of them devoutly drunk, remembering an old and trite proverb, which it is not necessary for me to repeat.

Though descended from a family which suffered much injury from the losel Yankees of those times—my great-grandfather having had a yoke of oxen and his best pacer stolen, and having received a pair of black eyes and a bloody nose in one of these border wars; and my grandfather, when a very little boy tending pigs, having been kidnaped and severely flogged by a long-sided Connecticut schoolmaster—yet I should have passed over all these wrongs with forgiveness and oblivion—I could even have suffered them to have broken Evert Ducking's head, to have kicked the doughty Jacobus Van Curlet and his ragged regiment out of doors, carried every hog into captivity, and depopulated every henroost on the face of the earth, with perfect impunity.—But this wanton attack upon one of the most gallant and irreproachable heroes of modern times is too much even for me to digest, and has overset, with a single puff, the patience of the historian, and the forbearance of the Dutchman.

Oh, reader, it was false!—I swear to thee, it was false! if thou hast any respect to my word—if the undeviating character for veracity which I have endeavored to maintain throughout this work, has its due weight with thee, thou wilt not give thy faith to this tale of slander; for I pledge my honor and my immortal fame to thee, that the gallant Peter Stuyvesant was not only innocent of this foul conspiracy, but would have suffered his right arm, or even his wooden leg, to consume with slow and everlasting flames, rather than attempt to destroy his enemies in any other way than open, generous warfare—beshrew those caitiff scouts that conspired to sully his honest name by such an imputation!

Peter Stuyvesant, though he perhaps had never heard of a knight-errant, yet had he as true a heart of chivalry as

*** J

ever beat at the round table of King Arthur. There was a spirit of native gallantry, a noble and generous hardihood diffused through his rugged manners, which altogether gave unquestionable tokens of a heroic mind. He was, in truth, a hero of chivalry, struck off by the hand of Nature at a single heat, and though she had taken no further care to polish and refine her workmanship, he stood forth a miracle of her skill.

But, not to be figurative (a fault in historic writing which I particularly eschew), the great Peter possessed, in an eminent degree, the seven renowned and noble virtues of knighthood, which, as he had never consulted authors in the disciplining and cultivating of his mind, I verily believe must have been implanted in the corner of his heart by Dame Nature herself—where they flourished among his hardy qualities like so many sweet wild flowers, shooting forth and thriving with redundant luxuriance among stubborn rocks. Such was the mind of Peter the Headstrong, and if my admiration for it has, on this occasion, transported my style beyond the sober gravity which becomes the laborious scribe of historic events, I can plead as an apology, that though a little gray-headed Dutchman, arrived almost at the bottom of the down-hill of life, I still retain some portion of that celestial fire which sparkles in the eye of youth when contemplating the virtues and achievements of ancient worthies. Blessed, thrice and nine times blessed be the good St. Nicholas—that I have escaped the influence of that chilling apathy which too often freezes the sympathies of age; which, like a churlish spirit, sits at the portals of the heart, repulsing every genial sentiment and paralyzing every spontaneous glow of enthusiasm!

No sooner, then, did this scoundrel imputation on his honor reach the ear of Peter Stuyvesant than he proceeded in a manner which would have redounded to his credit, even though he had studied for years in the library of Don Quixote himself. He immediately dispatched his valiant trumpeter and squire, Antony Van Corlear, with orders to ride night and day, as herald, to the Amphyctionic council, reproaching them, in terms of noble indignation, for giving ear to the slanders of heathen Infidels, against the character of a Christian, a gentleman, and a soldier—and declaring, that as to the treacherous and bloody plot alleged against him, whoever affirmed it to be true lied in his teeth!—to prove which, he defied the president of the council and all his compeers, or, if they pleased, their puissant champion, Captain Alicxsander Partridg, that mighty man of Rhodes, to meet him in single combat, where he would trust the vindication of his innocence to the prowess of his arm.

This challenge being delivered with due ceremony, Antony Van Corlear sounded a trumpet of defiance before the whole council, ending with a most horrific and nasal twang, full in the face of Captain Partridge, who almost jumped out of his skin in an ecstasy of astonishment at the noise. This done, he mounted a tall Flanders mare, which he always rode, and trotted merrily toward the Manhattoes—passing through Hartford, and Piquag, and Middletown, and all the other border towns—twanging his trumpet like a very devil, so that the sweet valleys and banks of the Connecticut resounded with the warlike melody—and stopping occasionally to eat pumpkin pies, dance at country frolics, and bundle with the beauteous lasses of those parts—whom he rejoiced exceedingly with his soul-stirring instrument.

But the grand council, being composed of considerate men, had no idea of running a tilting with such a fiery hero as the hardy Peter—on the contrary, they sent him an answer couched in the meekest, the most mild and provoking terms, in which they assured him that his guilt was proved to their perfect satisfaction, by the testimony of divers sober and respectable Indians, and concluding with this truly amiable paragragh—

"For youre confidant denialls of the Barbarous plott charged will waigh little in balance against such evidence, soe that we must still require and seeke due satisfaction and cecurite, so we rest, Sir,

"Youres in wayes of Righteousness," etc.

I am aware that the above transaction has been differently recorded by certain historians of the east and elsewhere; who seem to have inherited the bitter enmity of their ancestors to the brave Peter—and much good may their inheritance do them. These declare that Peter Stuyvesant requested to have the charges against him inquired into, by commissioners to be appointed for the purpose; and yet, that when such commissioners were appointed he refused to submit to their examination. In this artful account there is but the semblance of truth—he did, indeed, most gallantly offer, when that he found a deaf ear was turned to his challenge, to submit his conduct to the rigorous inspection of a court of honor—but then he expected to find it an august tribunal, composed of courteous gentlemen, the governors and nobility of the confederate plantations, and of the province of New Netherlands; where he might be tried by his peers, in a manner worthy of his rank and dignity—whereas, let me perish if they did not send to the Manhattoes two lean-sided hungry pettifoggers, mounted on Narraghanset pacers, with saddle-bags under their bottoms, and green satchels under their arms, as though they were about to beat the hoof from one county court to another in search of a lawsuit.

The chivalric Peter, as might be expected, took no notice of these cunning varlets; who, with professional industry, fell to prying and sifting about, in quest of *ex parte* evidence; perplexing divers simple Indians and old women with their cross-questioning, until they contradicted and forswore themselves most horribly. Thus having fulfilled their errand to their own satisfaction, they returned to the grand council with their satchels and saddle-bags stuffed full of villainous rumors, apocryphal stories, and outrageous calumnies—for all which the great Peter did not care a tobacco-stopper; but, I warrant me, had they attempted to play off the same trick upon William the Testy, he would have treated them both to an aerial gambol on his patent gallows.

The grand council of the east held a very solemn meeting, on the return of their envoys; and, after they had pondered

a long time on the situation of affairs, were upon the point
of adjourning without being able to agree upon anything.
At this critical moment, one of those meddlesome, indefatigable spirits, who endeavor to establish a character for patriotism by blowing the bellows of party until the whole furnace
of politics is red-hot with sparks and cinders—and who have
just cunning enough to know that there is no time so favorable
for getting on the people's backs as when they are in a state
of turmoil, and attending to everybody's business but their
own—this inspiring imp of faction, who was called a great
politician, because he had secured a seat in council by ca-
lumniating all his opponents—he, I say, conceived this a fit
opportunity to strike a blow that should secure his popularity
among his constituents who lived on the borders of Nieuw
Nederlandts, and were the greatest poachers in Christendom,
excepting the Scotch border nobles.   Like a second Peter the
Hermit, therefore, he stood forth and preached up a crusade
against Peter Stuyvesant and his devoted city.

He made a speech which lasted six hours, according to
the ancient custom in these parts, in which he represented
the Dutch as a race of impious heretics, who neither believed
in witchcraft nor the sovereign virtues of horseshoes—who
left their country for the lucre of gain, not like themselves
for the enjoyment of *liberty of conscience*—who, in short,
were a race of mere cannibals and anthropophagi, inasmuch
as they never eat codfish on Saturday, devoured swine's flesh
without molasses, and held pumpkins in utter contempt.

This speech had the desired effect, for the council, being
awakened by the sergeant-at-arms, rubbed their eyes and
declared that it was just and politic to declare instant war
against these unchristian anti-pumpkinites.   But it was
necessary that the people at large should first be prepared
for this measure; and for this purpose the arguments of the
orator were preached from the pulpit for several Sundays
subsequent, and earnestly recommended to the consideration
of every good Christian, who professed as well as practiced
the doctrines of meekness, charity, and the forgiveness of

injuries.   This is the first time we hear of the "drum eccle-
siastic" beating up for political recruits in our country; and
it proved of such signal efficacy that it has since been called
into frequent service throughout our Union.   A cunning
politician is often found skulking under the clerical robe,
with an outside all religion and an inside all political rancor.
Things spiritual and things temporal are strangely jumbled
together, like poisons and antidotes on an apothecary's shelf;
and instead of a devout sermon, the simple church-going
folk have often a political pamphlet thrust down their throats,
labeled with a pious text from Scripture.

CHAPTER FIVE

HOW THE NEW AMSTERDAMERS BECAME GREAT IN ARMS,
    AND OF THE DIREFUL CATASTROPHE OF A MIGHTY
    ARMY — TOGETHER WITH PETER STUYVESANT'S MEAS-
    URES TO FORTIFY THE CITY—AND HOW HE WAS THE
    ORIGINAL FOUNDER OF THE BATTERY

BUT, notwithstanding that the grand council, as I have
already shown, were amazingly discreet in their proceedings
respecting the New Netherlands, and conducted the whole
with almost as much silence and mystery as does the sage
British cabinet one of its ill-starred *secret expeditions*—yet
did the ever-watchful Peter receive as full and accurate information of every movement as does the court of France of
all the notable enterprises I have mentioned.   He accordingly
set himself to work to render the machinations of his bitter
adversaries abortive.

I know that many will censure the precipitation of this
stout-hearted old governor, in that he hurried into the expenses of fortification without ascertaining whether they
were necessary, by prudently waiting until the enemy was

at the door. But they should recollect that Peter Stuyvesant had not the benefit of an insight into the modern arcana of politics, and was strangely bigoted to certain obsolete maxims of the old school; among which he firmly believed, that to render a country respected abroad it was necessary to make it formidable at home—and that a nation should place its reliance for peace and security more upon its own strength than on the justice or good-will of its neighbors. He proceeded, therefore, with all diligence, to put the province and metropolis in a strong posture of defense.

Among the few remnants of ingenious inventions which remained from the days of William the Testy were those impregnable bulwarks of public safety, militia laws; by which the inhabitants were obliged to turn out twice a year with such military equipments as it pleased God; and were put under the command of very valiant tailors and man-milliners, who though on ordinary occasions the meekest, pippin-hearted little men in the world, were very devils at parades and courts-martial, when they had cocked hats on their heads and swords by their sides. Under the instructions of these periodical warriors, the gallant train-bands made marvelous proficiency in the mystery of gunpowder. They were taught to face to the right, to wheel to the left, to snap off empty firelocks without winking, to turn a corner without any great uproar or irregularity, and to march through sun and rain from one end of the town to the other without flinching—until in the end they became so valorous, that they fired off blank cartridges without so much as turning away their heads—could hear the largest field-piece discharged without stopping their ears or falling into much confusion—and would even go through all the fatigues and perils of a summer day's parade without having their ranks much thinned by desertion!

True it is, the genius of this truly pacific people was so little given to war that, during the intervals which occurred between field days, they generally contrived to forget all the military tuition they had received; so that when they reap-

peared on parade they scarcely knew the butt-end of the
musket from the muzzle, and invariably mistook the right
shoulder for the left—a mistake which, however, was soon
obviated by chalking their left arms. But whatever might
be their blunders and awkwardness, the sagacious Kieft declared them to be of but little importance—since, as he judiciously observed, one campaign would be of more instruction
to them than a hundred parades; for though two-thirds of
them might be food for powder, yet such of the other third
as did not run away would become most experienced veterans.

The great Stuyvesant had no particular veneration for
the ingenious experiments and institutions of his shrewd predecessor, and among other things held the militia system in
very considerable contempt, which he was often heard to
call in joke—for he was sometimes fond of a joke—Governor
Kieft's broken reed. As, however, the present emergency
was pressing, he was obliged to avail himself of such means
of defense as were next at hand, and accordingly appointed
a general inspection and parade of the train-bands. But oh!
Mars and Bellona, and all ye other powers of war, both great
and small, what a turning out was here!—Here came men
without officers, and officers without men—long fowling-
pieces, and short blunderbusses—muskets of all sorts and
sizes, some without bayonets, others without locks, others
without stocks, and many without either lock, stock, or
barrel—cartridge-boxes, shot-belts, powder horns, swords,
hatchets, snicker-snees, crowbars and broomsticks, all mingled higgledy-piggledy—like one of our continental armies
at the breaking out of the revolution.

This sudden transformation of a pacific community into
a band of warriors is doubtless what is meant, in modern
days, by "putting a nation in armor," and "fixing it in an
attitude"—in which armor and attitude it makes as martial
a figure, and as likely to acquit itself with as much prowess,
as the renowned Sancho Panza, when suddenly equipped to
defend his island of Barataria.

The sturdy Peter eyed this ragged regiment with some such rueful aspect as a man would eye the devil; but knowing, like a wise man, that all he had to do was to make the best out of a bad bargain, he determined to give his heroes a seasoning. Having, therefore, drilled them through the manual exercise over and over again, he ordered the fifes to strike up a quick march, and trudged his sturdy troops backward and forward about the streets of New Amsterdam, and the fields adjacent, until their short legs ached and their fat sides sweated again. But this was not all; the martial spirit of the old governor caught fire from the sprightly music of the fife, and he resolved to try the mettle of his troops, and give them a taste of the hardships of iron war. To this end he encamped them, as the shades of evening fell, upon a hill formerly called Bunker's Hill, at some distance from the town, with a full intention of initiating them into the discipline of camps, and of renewing, the next day, the toils and perils of the field. But so it came to pass that in the night there fell a great and heavy rain, which descended in torrents upon the camp, and the mighty army strangely melted away before it; so that when Gaffer Phœbus came to shed his morning beams upon the place, saving Peter Stuyvesant and his trumpeter, Van Corlear, scarce one was to be found of all the multitude that had encamped there the night before.

This awful dissolution of his army would have appalled a commander of less nerve than Peter Stuyvesant; but he considered it as a matter of but small importance, though he thenceforward regarded the militia system with ten times greater contempt than ever, and took care to provide himself with a good garrison of chosen men, whom he kept in pay, of whom he boasted that they at least possessed the quality, indispensable in soldiers, of being water-proof.

The next care of the vigilant Stuyvesant was to strengthen and fortify New Amsterdam. For this purpose he caused to be built a strong picket fence, that reached across the island, from river to river, being intended to protect the city not merely from the sudden invasions of foreign enemies, but likewise from the incursions of the neighboring savages.*

Some traditions, it is true, have ascribed the building of this wall to a later period, but they are wholly incorrect; for a memorandum in the Stuyvesant manuscript, dated toward the middle of the governor's reign, mentions this wall particularly as a very strong and curious piece of workmanship, and the admiration of all the savages in the neighborhood. And it mentions, moreover, the alarming circumstance of a drove of stray cows breaking through the grand wall of a dark night; by which the whole community of New Amsterdam was thrown into a terrible panic.

In addition to this great wall, he cast up several outworks to Fort Amsterdam, to protect the seaboard, at the point of the island. These consisted of formidable mud batteries, solidly faced, after the manner of the Dutch ovens, common in those days, with clam-shells.

These frowning bulwarks, in process of time, came to be pleasantly overrun by a verdant carpet of grass and clover, and their high embankments overshadowed by widespreading sycamores, among whose foliage the little birds sported about, rejoicing the ear with their melodious notes. The old burghers would repair of an afternoon to smoke their pipes under the shade of their branches, contemplating the golden sun as he gradually sunk into the west, an emblem of that tranquil end toward which themselves were hastening—while the young men and the damsels of the town would take many a moonlight stroll among these favorite haunts, watch-

---

* In an antique view of New Amsterdam, taken some years after the above period, is a representation of this wall, which stretched along the course of Wall street, so called in commemoration of this great bulwark. One gate, called the Land-Poort, opened upon Broadway, hard by where at present stands the Trinity Church; and another, called the Water-Poort, stood about where the Tontine Coffee House is at present—opening upon Smits Vleye, or, as it is commonly called, Smith Fly, then a marshy valley, with a creek or inlet extending up what we call Maiden Lane.

ing the silver beams of chaste Cynthia tremble along the calm
bosom of the bay, or light up the white sail of some gliding
bark, and interchanging the honest vows of constant affection. Such was the origin of that renowned walk, THE
BATTERY, which, though ostensibly devoted to the purpose
of war, has ever been consecrated to the sweet delights of
peace. The favorite walk of declining age—the healthful
resort of the feeble invalid—the Sunday refreshment of the
dusty tradesman—the scene of many a boyish gambol—the
rendezvous of many a tender assignation—the comfort of
the citizen—the ornament of New York and the pride of the
lovely island of Manna-hata.

CHAPTER SIX

HOW THE PEOPLE OF THE EAST COUNTRY WERE SUD-
DENLY AFFLICTED WITH A DIABOLICAL EVIL — AND
THEIR JUDICIOUS MEASURES FOR THE EXTIRPATION
THEREOF

HAVING thus provided for the temporary security of New
Amsterdam, and guarded it against any sudden surprise, the
gallant Peter took a hearty pinch of snuff, and, snapping his
fingers, set the great council of Amphyctions, and their
champion, the doughty Alicxsander Partridg, at defiance.
It is impossible to say, notwithstanding, what might have
been the issue of this affair, had not the council been all at
once involved in sad perplexity, and as much dissension sown
among its members, as of yore was stirred up in the camp
of the brawling warriors of Greece.

The council of the league, as I have shown in my last
chapter, had already announced its hostile determinations,
and already was the mighty colony of New Haven, and the
puissant town of Piquag, otherwise called Weathersfield—
famous for its onions and its witches—and the great trading
house of Hartford, and all the other redoubtable border

towns, in a prodigious turmoil, furbishing up their rusty
fowling-pieces, and shouting aloud for war; by which they
anticipated easy conquests, and gorgeous spoils, from the
little fat Dutch villages. But this joyous brawling was soon
silenced by the conduct of the colony of Massachusetts.
Struck with the gallant spirit of the brave old Peter, and
convinced by the chivalric frankness and heroic warmth of
his vindication, they refused to believe him guilty of the infamous plot most wrongfully laid at his door. With a generosity for which I would yield them immortal honor, they
declared that no determination of the grand council of the
league should bind the general court of Massachusetts to join
in an offensive war which should appear to such general
court to be unjust.[*]

This refusal immediately involved the colony of Massachusetts and the other combined colonies in very serious
difficulties and disputes, and would no doubt have produced
a dissolution of the confederacy, but that the council of
Amphyctions, finding that they could not stand alone, if
mutilated by the loss of so important a member as Massachusetts, were fain to abandon for the present their hostile
machinations against the Manhattoes. Such is the marvelous energy and the puissance of those confederacies, composed of a number of sturdy, self-willed, discordant parts,
loosely banded together by a puny general government. As
it was, however, the warlike towns of Connecticut had no
cause to deplore this disappointment of their martial ardor;
for, by my faith—though the combined powers of the league
might have been too potent, in the end, for the robustious
warriors of the Manhattoes—yet in the interim would the
lion-hearted Peter and his myrmidons have choked the stomachful heroes of Piquag with their own onions, and have
given the other little border towns such a scouring, that I
warrant they would have had no stomach to squat on the
land, or invade the hen-roost of a New Nederlander, for a
century to come.

---

[*] Haz. Col. State Papers.

Indeed, there was more than one cause to divert the attention of the good people of the east from their hostile purposes; for just about this time were they horribly beleaguered and harassed by the inroads of the prince of darkness, divers of whose liege subjects they detected lurking within their camp, all of whom they incontinently roasted as so many spies and dangerous enemies. Not to speak in parables, we are informed, that at this juncture the New England provinces were exceedingly troubled by multitudes of losel witches, who wrought strange devices to beguile and distress the multitude; and notwithstanding numerous judicious and bloody laws had been enacted against all "solemn conversing or compacting with the divil, by way of conjuracon or the like,"* yet did the dark crime of witchcraft continue to increase to an alarming degree, that would almost transcend belief, were not the fact too well authenticated to be even doubted for an instant.

What is particularly worthy of admiration is, that this terrible art, which so long has baffled the painful researches and abstruse studies of philosophers, astrologers, alchemists, theurgists, and other sages, was chiefly confined to the most ignorant, decrepit, and ugly old women in the community, who had scarcely more brains than the broomsticks they rode upon.

When once an alarm is sounded, the public, who love dearly to be in a panic, are not long in want of proofs to support it—raise but the cry of yellow fever, and immediately every headache and indigestion, and overflowing of the bile, is pronounced the terrible epidemic. In like manner, in the present instance, whoever was troubled with colic or lumbago was sure to be bewitched; and woe to any unlucky old woman that lived in his neighborhood. Such a howling abomination could not be suffered to remain long unnoticed, and it accordingly soon attracted the fiery indignation of the sober and reflective part of the community—

* New Plymouth Record.

more especially of those who, whilom, had evinced so much active benevolence in the conversion of Quakers and Anabaptists. The grand council of the Amphyctions publicly set their faces against so deadly and dangerous a sin; and a severe scrutiny took place after those nefarious witches, who were easily detected by devil's pinches, black cats, broomsticks, and the circumstance of their only being able to weep three tears, and those out of the left eye.

It is incredible the number of offenses that were detected, "for every one of which," says the profound and reverend Cotton Mather, in that excellent work, the "History of New England"—"we have such a sufficient evidence, that no reasonable man in this whole country ever did question them; *and it will be unreasonable to do it in any other.*" *

Indeed, that authentic and judicious historian, John Josselyn, Gent., furnishes us with unquestionable facts on this subject. "There are none," observes he, "that beg in this country, but there be witches too many—bottle-bellied witches and others, that produce many strange apparitions, if you will believe report, of a shallop at sea manned with women—and of a ship, and great red horse standing by the mainmast; the ship being in a small cove to the eastward, vanished of a sudden," etc.

The number of delinquents, however, and their magical devices, were not more remarkable than their diabolical obstinacy. Though exhorted in the most solemn, persuasive, and affectionate manner, to confess themselves guilty, and be burned for the good of religion and the entertainment of the public; yet did they most pertinaciously persist in asserting their innocence. Such incredible obstinacy was in itself deserving of immediate punishment, and was sufficient proof, if proof were necessary, that they were in league with the devil, who is perverseness itself. But their judges were just and merciful, and were determined to punish none that were not convicted on the best of testimony; not that they needed

---

* Mather's Hist. New Eng., b. 6, ch. 7.

any evidence to satisfy their own minds, for, like true and
experienced judges, their minds were perfectly made up,
and they were thoroughly satisfied of the guilt of the prisoners before they proceeded to try them; but still something
was necessary to convince the community at large—to quiet
those prying quidnuncs who should come after them—in
short, the world must be satisfied. Oh, the world—the
world!—all the world knows the world of trouble the world
is eternally occasioning!—The worthy judges, therefore, were
driven to the necessity of sifting, detecting, and making evident as noon-day, matters which were at the commencement
all clearly understood and firmly decided upon in their own
pericraniums—so that it may truly be said that the witches
were burned to gratify the populace of the day—but were
tried for the satisfaction of the whole world that should come
after them.

Finding, therefore, that neither exhortation, sound reason,
nor friendly entreaty had any avail on these hardened
offenders, they resorted to the more urgent arguments of the
torture, and having thus absolutely wrung the truth from
their stubborn lips, they condemned them to undergo the
roasting due unto the heinous crimes they had confessed.
Some even carried their perverseness so far as to expire
under the torture, protesting their innocence to the last; but
these were looked upon as thoroughly and absolutely possessed by the devil, and the pious bystanders only lamented
that they had not lived a little longer, to have perished in
the flames.

In the city of Ephesus we are told that the plague was
expelled by stoning a ragged old beggar to death, whom
Appolonius pointed out as being the evil spirit that caused
it, and who actually showed himself to be a demon, by
changing into a shagged dog. In like manner, and by
measures equally sagacious, a salutary check was given to
this growing evil. The witches were all burned, banished,
or panic struck, and in a little while there was not an ugly
old woman to be found throughout New England—which is

doubtless one reason why all the young women there are so handsome. Those honest folk who had suffered from their incantations gradually recovered, excepting such as had been afflicted with twitches and aches, which, however, assumed the less alarming aspect of rheumatism, sciatics, and lumbagos—and the good people of New England, abandoning the study of the occult sciences, turned their attention to the more profitable hocus-pocus of trade, and soon became expert in the legerdemain art of turning a penny. Still, however, a tinge of the old leaven is discernible, even unto this day, in their characters—witches occasionally start up among them in different disguises, as physicians, civilians and divines. The people at large show a keenness, a cleverness, and a profundity of wisdom that savors strongly of witchcraft—and it has been remarked that whenever any stones fall from the moon the greater part of them are sure to tumble into New England!

CHAPTER SEVEN

WHICH RECORDS THE RISE AND RENOWN OF A VALIANT COMMANDER, SHOWING THAT A MAN, LIKE A BLADDER, MAY BE PUFFED UP TO GREATNESS AND IMPORTANCE BY MERE WIND

WHEN treating of these tempestuous times, the unknown writer of the Stuyvesant manuscript breaks out into a vehement apostrophe in praise of the good St. Nicholas; to whose protecting care he entirely ascribes the strange dissensions that broke out in the council of the Amphyctions, and the direful witchcraft that prevailed in the east country— whereby the hostile machinations against the Nederlanders were for a time frustrated, and his favorite city of New Amsterdam preserved from imminent peril and deadly warfare. Darkness and lowering superstition hung over the fair valleys of the east; the pleasant banks of the Connecticut no

longer echoed with the sounds of rustic gayety; direful
phantoms and portentous apparitions were seen in the air—
gliding spectrums haunted every wild brook and dreary glen
—strange voices, made by viewless forms, were heard in
desert solitudes—and the border towns were so occupied in
detecting and punishing the knowing old women who had
produced these alarming appearances, that for a while the
province of Nieuw Nederlandts and its inhabitants were
totally forgotten.

The great Peter, therefore, finding that nothing was to
be immediately apprehended from his eastern neighbors,
turned himself about, with a praiseworthy vigilance that
ever distinguished him, to put a stop to the insults of the
Swedes. These freebooters, my attentive reader will recollect, had begun to be very troublesome toward the latter
part of the reign of William the Testy, having set the proclamations of that doughty little governor at naught, and
put the intrepid Jan Jansen Alpendam to a perfect nonplus!

Peter Stuyvesant, however, as has already been shown,
was a governor of different habits and turn of mind—without
more ado he immediately issued orders for raising a corps
of troops to be stationed on the southern frontier, under the
command of Brigadier-General Jacobus Van Poffenburgh.
This illustrious warrior had risen to great importance during
the reign of Wilhelmus Kieft, and, if histories speak true,
was second in command to the hapless Van Curlet, when he
and his ragged regiment were inhumanly kicked out of Fort
Good Hope by the Yankees. In consequence of having been
in such a "memorable affair," and of having received more
wounds on a certain honorable part that shall be nameless
than any of his comrades, he was ever after considered as a
hero, who had "seen some service." Certain it is, he enjoyed the unlimited confidence and friendship of William the
Testy; who would sit for hours and listen with wonder to
his gunpowder narratives of surprising victories—he had
never gained, and dreadful battles—from which he had run
away.

It was tropically observed by honest old Socrates that heaven had infused into some men at their birth a portion of intellectual gold; into others of intellectual silver; while others were bounteously furnished out with abundance of brass and iron—now of this last class was undoubtedly the great General Van Poffenburgh; and from the display he continually made thereof, I am inclined to think that Dame Nature, who will sometimes be partial, had blessed him with enough of those valuable materials to have fitted up a dozen ordinary braziers. But what is most to be admired is, that he contrived to pass off all his brass and copper upon Wilhelmus Kieft, who was no great judge of base coin, as pure and genuine gold. The consequence was, that upon the resignation of Jacobus Van Curlet, who, after the loss of Fort Good Hope, retired, like a veteran general, to live under the shade of his laurels, the mighty "copper captain" was promoted to his station. This he filled with great importance, always styling himself "commander-in-chief of the armies of New Netherlands"; though, to tell the truth, the armies, or rather army, consisted of a handful of hen-stealing, bottle-bruising ragamuffins.

Such was the character of the warrior appointed by Peter Stuyvesant to defend his southern frontier; nor may it be uninteresting to my reader to have a glimpse of his person. He was not very tall, but, notwithstanding, a huge, full-bodied man, whose bulk did not so much arise from his being fat as windy; being so completely inflated with his own importance that he resembled one of those bags of wind which Æolus, in an incredible fit of generosity, gave to that wandering warrior Ulysses.

His dress comported with his character, for he had almost as much brass and copper without as nature had stored away within—his coat was crossed and slashed and carbonadoed with stripes of copper lace, and swathed round the body with a crimson sash of the size and texture of a fishing-net, doubtless to keep his valiant heart from bursting through his ribs. His head and whiskers were profusely powdered, from the midst of which his full-blooded face glowed like a fiery furnace; and his magnanimous soul seemed ready to bounce out at a pair of large, glassy, blinking eyes, which projected like those of a lobster.

I swear to thee, worthy reader, if report belie not this warrior, I would give all the money in my pocket to have seen him accoutered cap-a-pie in martial array—booted to the middle—sashed to the chin—collared to the ears—whiskered to the teeth—crowned with an overshadowing cocked hat, and girded with a leathern belt ten inches broad, from which trailed a falchion of a length that I dare not mention. Thus equipped he strutted about as bitter-looking a man of war as the far-famed More of More Hall, when he sallied forth, armed at all points, to slay the Dragon of Wantley.*

Notwithstanding all these great endowments and transcendent qualities of this renowned general, I must confess he was not exactly the kind of man that the gallant Peter would have chosen to command his troops—but the truth is that in those days the province did not abound, as at present, in great military characters; who, like so many Cincinnatuses, people every little village—marshaling out cabbages instead of soldiers, and signalizing themselves in the cornfield instead of the field of battle;—who have surrendered the toils of war for the more useful but inglorious arts of peace; and so blended the laurel with the olive that you may have a general for a landlord, a colonel for a stage-driver, and your horse shod by a valiant "captain of volunteers." The redoubtable General Van Poffenburgh, therefore, was appointed to the command of the new-levied troops,

---

* "Had you but seen him in his dress,
   How fierce he look'd and how big;
  You would have thought him for to be
   Some Egyptian Porcupig.

 "He frighted all, cats, dogs, and all,
   Each cow, each horse, and each hog;
  For fear they did flee, for they took him to be
   Some strange outlandish hedge-hog."
                              —*Ballad of Drag. of Want.*

chiefly because there were no competitors for the station, and
partly because it would have been a breach of military etiquette to have appointed a younger officer over his head—an
injustice which the great Peter would have rather died than
have committed.

No sooner did this thrice-valiant copper captain receive
marching orders than he conducted his army undauntedly
to the southern frontier; through wild lands and savage
deserts; over insurmountable mountains, across impassable
floods, and through impenetrable forests; subduing a vast
tract of uninhabited country, and encountering more perils,
according to his own account, than did ever the great Xeno-
phon in his far-famed retreat with his ten thousand Grecians.
All this accomplished, he established on the South (or Delaware) River, a redoubtable redoubt, named FORT CASIMIR,
in honor of a favorite pair of brimstone-colored trunk breeches
of the governor. As this fort will be found to give rise to
very important and interesting events, it may be worth while
to notice that it was afterward called Nieuw Amstel, and
was the original germ of the present flourishing town of NEW
CASTLE, an appellation erroneoously substituted for *No
Castle*, there neither being, nor ever having been, a castle
or anything of the kind upon the premises.

The Swedes did not suffer tamely this menacing movement of the Nederlanders; on the contrary, Jan Printz, at
that time governor of New Sweden, issued a protest against
what he termed an encroachment upon his jurisdiction. But
Van Poffenburgh had become too well versed in the nature
of proclamations and protests, while he served under William
the Testy, to be in any wise daunted by such paper warfare.
His fortress being finished, it would have done any man's
heart good to behold into what a magnitude he immediately
swelled. He would stride in and out a dozen times a day,
surveying it in front and in rear; on this side and on that.
Then would he dress himself in full regimentals, and strut
backward and forward, for hours together, on the top of his
little rampart—like a vainglorious cock-pigeon vaporing on

the top of his coop. In a word, unless my readers have noticed, with curious eye, the petty commander of one of our
little, sniveling military posts, swelling with all the vanity
of new regimentals, and the pomposity derived from com
manding a handful of tatterdemalions, I despair of giving
them any adequate idea of the prodigious dignity of General
Van Poffenburgh.

It is recorded, in the delectable romance of Pierce Forest,
that a young knight, being dubbed by King Alexander, did
incontinently gallop into an adjoining forest, and belabored
the trees with such might and main that the whole court
was convinced that he was the most potent and courageous
gentleman on the face of the earth. In like manner the
great Van Poffenburgh would ease off that valorous spleen,
which like wind is so apt to grow unruly in the stomachs of
new-made soldiers, impelling them to box-lobby brawls and
broken-headed quarrels. For at such times, when he found
his martial spirit waxing hot within him, he would prudently
sally forth into the fields, and lugging out his trusty saber,
would lay about him most lustily, decapitating cabbages by
platoons; hewing down whole phalanxes of sunflowers, which
he termed gigantic Swedes; and if, peradventure, he espied
a colony of honest, big-bellied pumpkins quietly basking
themselves in the sun, "Ah, caitiff Yankees," would he
roar, "have I caught ye at last?"—so saying, with one
sweep of his sword he would cleave the unhappy vegetables
from their chins to their waistbands; by which warlike havoc
his choler being in some sort allayed, he would return to his
garrison with a full conviction that he was a very miracle of
military prowess.

The next ambition of General Van Poffenburgh was to
be thought a strict disciplinarian. Well knowing that discipline is the soul of all military enterprise, he enforced it
with the most rigorous precision; obliging every man to turn
out his toes and hold up his head on parade, and prescribing
the breadth of their ruffles to all such as had any shirts to
their backs.

Having one day, in the course of his devout researches
in the Bible (for the pious Eneas himself could not exceed
him in outward religion), encountered the history of Absalom
and his melancholy end, the general, in an evil hour, issued
orders for cropping the hair of both officers and men throughout the garrison. Now it came to pass that among his officers
was one Kildermeester, a sturdy veteran, who had cherished,
through the course of a long life, a rugged mop of hair, not
a little resembling the shag of a Newfoundland dog, terminating with an immoderate queue like the handle of a frying-pan; and queued so tightly to his head that his eyes and
mouth generally stood ajar, and his eyebrows were drawn
up to the top of his forehead. It may naturally be supposed
that the possessor of so goodly an appendage would resist
with abhorrence an order condemning it to the shears. On
hearing the general orders, he discharged a tempest of veteran, soldier-like oaths, and dunder and blixums—swore he
would break any man's head who attempted to meddle with
his tail—queued it stiffer than ever, and whisked it about the
garrison as fiercely as the tail of a crocodile.

The eel-skin queue of old Kildermeester became instantly
an affair of the utmost importance. The commander-in-chief
was too enlightened an officer not to perceive that the discipline of the garrison, the subordination and good order of the
armies of the Nieuw Nederlandts, the consequent safety of
the whole province, and ultimately the dignity and prosperity
of their High Mightinesses, the Lords States-General, but
above all, the dignity of the great General Van Poffenburgh,
all imperiously demanded the docking of that stubborn queue.
He therefore determined that old Kildermeester should be
publicly shorn of his glories in the presence of the whole garrison—the old man as resolutely stood on the defensive—
whereupon the general, as became a great man, was highly
exasperated, and the offender was arrested and tried by a
court-martial for mutiny, desertion, and all the other list of
offenses noticed in the articles of war, ending with a "vide-
licet, in wearing an eel-skin queue, three feet long, contrary

to orders."—Then came on arraignments, and trials, and pleadings; and the whole country was in a ferment about this unfortunate queue. As it is well known that the commander of a distant frontier post has the power of acting pretty much after his own will, there is little doubt that the veteran would have been hanged or shot at least, had he not luckily fallen ill of a fever, through mere chagrin and mortification—and most flagitiously deserted from all earthly command, with his beloved locks unviolated. His obstinacy remained unshaken to the very last moment, when he directed that he should be carried to his grave with his eel-skin queue sticking out of a hole in his coffin.

This magnanimous affair obtained the general great credit as an excellent disciplinarian, but it is hinted that he was ever after subject to bad dreams and fearful visitations in the night—when the grizzly spectrum of old Kildermeester would stand sentinel by his bedside, erect as a pump, his enormous queue strutting out like the handle.

BOOK SIX

CONTAINING THE SECOND PART OF THE REIGN OF PETER THE HEADSTRONG, AND HIS GALLANT ACHIEVEMENTS ON THE DELAWARE

CHAPTER ONE

IN WHICH IS EXHIBITED A WARLIKE PORTRAIT OF THE GREAT PETER—AND HOW GENERAL VAN POFFENBURGH DISTINGUISHED HIMSELF AT FORT CASIMIR

HITHERTO, most venerable and courteous reader, have I shown thee the administration of the valorous Stuyvesant under the mild moonshine of peace, or rather the grim tran-

quillity of awful expectation; but now the war-drum rumbles
from afar, the brazen trumpet brays its thrilling note, and
the rude clash of hostile arms speaks fearful prophecies of
coming troubles.   The gallant warrior starts from soft repose, from golden visions, and voluptuous ease; where, in
the dulcet, "piping time of peace," he sought sweet solace
after all his toils. No more in beauty's siren lap reclined,
he weaves fair garlands for his lady's brows; no more en-
twines with flowers his shining sword, nor through the livelong lazy summer's day chants forth his lovesick soul in
madrigals.   To manhood roused, he spurns the amorous
flute; doffs from his brawny back the robe of peace, and
clothes his pampered limbs in panoply of steel. O'er his
dark brow, where late the myrtle waved, where wanton
roses breathed enervate love, he rears the beaming casque
and nodding plume; grasps the bright shield and shakes the
ponderous lance; or mounts with eager pride his fiery steed,
and burns for deeds of glorious chivalry!

But soft, worthy reader! I would not have you imagine
that any *preux chevalier*, thus hideously begirt with iron,
existed in the city of New Amsterdam.   This is but a lofty
and gigantic mode in which heroic writers always talk of
war, thereby to give it a noble and imposing aspect; equip-
ping our warriors with bucklers, helms, and lances, and such
like outlandish and obsolete weapons, the like of which perchance they had never seen or heard of; in the same manner
that a cunning statuary arrays a modern general or an admiral in the accouterments of a Cæsar or an Alexander.
The simple truth, then, of all this oratorical flourish is this
—that the valiant Peter Stuyvesant all of a sudden found it
necessary to scour his trusty blade, which too long had rusted
in its scabbard, and prepare himself to undergo those hardy
toils of war in which his mighty soul so much delighted.

Methinks I at this moment behold him in my imagination
—or rather, I behold his goodly portrait, which still hangs
up in the family mansion of the Stuyvesants—arrayed in all
the terrors of a true Dutch general. His regimental coat of

German blue, gorgeously decorated with a goodly show of
large brass buttons reaching from his waistband to his chin.
The voluminous skirts turned up at the corners, and separating gallantly behind, so as to display the seat of a sumptuous
pair of brimstone-colored trunk breeches—a graceful style
still prevalent among the warriors of our day, and which is
in conformity to the custom of ancient heroes, who scorned
to defend themselves in the rear.—His face rendered exceedingly terrible and warlike by a pair of black mustachios; his
hair strutting out on each side in stiffly pomatumed ear-locks,
and descending in a rat-tail queue below his waist; a shining
stock of black leather supporting his chin, and a little but
fierce cocked hat stuck with a gallant and fiery air over his
left eye.   Such was the chivalric port of Peter the Headstrong; and when he made a sudden halt, planted himself
firmly on his solid supporter, with his wooden leg inlaid with
silver, a little in advance, in order to strengthen his position,
his right hand grasping a gold-headed cane, his left resting
upon the pommel of his sword; his head dressing spiritedly
to the right, with a most appalling and hard-favored frown
upon his brow—he presented altogether one of the most commanding, bitter-looking, and soldier-like figures that ever
strutted upon canvas.   Proceed we now to inquire the cause
of this warlike preparation.

The encroaching disposition of the Swedes, on the South,
or Delaware River, has been duly recorded in the chronicles
of the reign of William the Testy.   These encroachments
having been endured with that heroic magnanimity which
is the corner-stone of true courage, had been repeatedly and
wickedly aggravated.

The Swedes, who were of that class of cunning pretend-
ers to Christianity, who read the Bible upside-down, whenever it interferes with their interests, inverted the golden
maxim, and when their neighbor suffered them to smite him
on the one cheek they generally smote him on the other also,
whether turned to them or not.   Their repeated aggressions
had been among the numerous sources of vexation that con-

spired to keep the irritable sensibilities of Wilhelmus Kieft in a constant fever, and it was only owing to the unfortunate circumstance that he had always a hundred things to do at once that he did not take such unrelenting vengeance as their offenses merited. But they had now a chieftain of a different character to deal with; and they were soon guilty of a piece of treachery that threw his honest blood into a ferment, and precluded all further sufferance.

Printz, the governor of the province of New Sweden, being either deceased or removed, for of this fact some uncertainty exists, was succeeded by Jan Risingh, a gigantic Swede, and who, had he not been rather knock-kneed and splay-footed, might have served for the model of a Samson or a Hercules. He was no less rapacious than mighty, and withal as crafty as he was rapacious; so that, in fact, there is very little doubt, had he lived some four or five centuries before, he would have been one of those wicked giants who took such a cruel pleasure in pocketing distressed damsels, when gadding about the world, and locking them up in enchanted castles, without a toilet, a change of linen, or any other convenience—in consequence of which enormities they fell under the high displeasure of chivalry, and all true, loyal, and gallant knights were instructed to attack and slay outright any miscreant they might happen to find above six feet high; which is doubtless one reason that the race of large men is nearly extinct, and the generations of latter ages so exceeding small.

No sooner did Governor Risingh enter upon his office than he immediately cast his eyes upon the important post of Fort Casimir, and formed the righteous resolution of taking it into his possession. The only thing that remained to consider was the mode of carrying his resolution into effect; and here I must do him the justice to say that he exhibited a humanity rarely to be met with among leaders, and which I have never seen equaled in modern times, excepting among the English, in their glorious affair at Copenhagen. Willing to spare the effusion of blood, and the miseries of open warfare,

he benevolently shunned everything like avowed hostility or
regular siege, and resorted to the less glorious, but more
merciful expedient of treachery.

Under pretense, therefore, of paying a neighborly visit to
General Van Poffenburgh, at his new post of Fort Casimir,
he made requisite preparation, sailed in great state up the
Delaware, displayed his flag with the most ceremonious punctilio, and honored the fortress with a royal salute, previous
to dropping anchor. The unusual noise awakened a veteran
Dutch sentinel, who was napping faithfully at his post, and
who, having suffered his match to go out, contrived to return
the compliment, by discharging his rusty musket with the
spark of a pipe, which he borrowed from one of his comrades.
The salute indeed would have been answered by the guns of
the fort had they not unfortunately been out of order, and
the magazine deficient in ammunition—accidents to which
forts have in all ages been liable, and which were the more
excusable in the present instance, as Fort Casimir had only
been erected about two years, and General Van Poffenburgh,
its mighty commander, had been fully occupied with matters
of much greater importance.

Risingh, highly satisfied with this courteous reply to his
salute, treated the fort to a second, for he well knew its commander was marvelously delighted with these little cere-
monials, which he considered as so many acts of homage
paid unto his greatness. He then landed in great state, attended by a suite of thirty men—a prodigious and vainglorious retinue for a petty governor of a petty settlement in
those days of primitive simplicity; and to the full as great
an army as generally swells the pomp and marches in the
rear of our frontier commanders at the present day.

The number, in fact, might have awakened suspicion had
not the mind of the great Van Poffenburgh been so completely engrossed with an all-pervading idea of himself that
he had not room to admit a thought besides. In fact, he
considered the concourse of Risingh's followers as a compliment to himself—so apt are great men to stand between

themselves and the sun, and completely eclipse the truth by
their own shadow.

It may readily be imagined how much General Van Poffenburgh was flattered by a visit from so august a personage; his only embarrassment was, how he should receive
him in such a manner as to appear to the greatest advantage
and make the most advantageous impression. The main
guard was ordered immediately to turn out, and the arms
and regimentals (of which the garrison possessed full half
a dozen suits) were equally distributed among the soldiers.
One tall lank fellow appeared in a coat intended for a small
man, the skirts of which reached a little below his waist, the
buttons were between his shoulders, and the sleeves half-
way to his wrists, so that his hands looked like a couple of
huge spades—and the coat, not being large enough to meet
in front, was linked together by loops made of a pair of red
worsted garters. Another had an old cocked hat stuck on
the back of his head, and decorated with a bunch of cocks'
tails—a third had a pair of rusty gaiters hanging about his
heels—while a fourth, who was short and duck-legged, was
equipped in a huge pair of the general's cast-off breeches,
which he held up with one hand while he grasped his firelock with the other. The rest were accoutered in similar
style, excepting three graceless ragamuffins, who had no
shirts, and but a pair and a half of breeches between them,
wherefore they were sent to the black hole to keep them out
of view. There is nothing in which the talents of a prudent
commander are more completely testified than in thus setting
matters off to the greatest advantage; and it is for this reason that our frontier posts at the present day (that of Ni-
agara, for example) display their best suit of regimentals on
the back of the sentinel who stands in sight of travelers.

His men being thus gallantly arrayed—those who lacked
muskets shouldering spades and pickaxes, and every man
being ordered to tuck in his shirt-tail and pull up his brogues
—General Van Poffenburgh first took a sturdy draught of
foaming ale, which, like the magnanimous More of More-

hall,* was his invariable practice on all great occasions—
which done, he put himself at their head, ordered the pine
planks, which served as a drawbridge, to be laid down, and
issued forth from his castle like a mighty giant just refreshed
with wine. But when the two heroes met, then began a
scene of warlike parade and chivalric courtesy that beggars
all description—Risingh, who, as I before hinted, was a
shrewd, cunning politician, and had grown gray much before his time, in consequence of his craftiness, saw at one
glance the ruling passion of the great Van Poffenburgh, and
humored him in all his valorous fantasies.

Their detachments were accordingly drawn up in front of
each other; they carried arms and they presented arms; they
gave the standing salute and the passing salute—they rolled
their drums and flourished their fifes, and they waved their
colors—they faced to the left, and they faced to the right,
and they faced to the right about—they wheeled forward,
and they wheeled backward, and they wheeled into *echelon*
—they marched and they countermarched, by grand divisions, by single divisions, and by sub-divisions—by platoons,
by sections, and by files—in quick time, in slow time, and
in no time at all: for, having gone through all the evolutions
of two great armies, including the eighteen maneuvers of
Dundas, having exhausted all that they could recollect or
imagine of military tactics, including sundry strange and
irregular evolutions, the like of which was never seen before
nor since, excepting among certain of our newly-raised militia, the two great commanders and their respective troops
came at length to a dead halt, completely exhausted by the
toils of war. Never did two valiant train-band captains, or
two buskined theatric heroes, in the renowned tragedies of
Pizarro, Tom Thumb, or any other heroical and fighting

---

* "———as soon as he rose,
    To make him strong and mighty,
    He drank by the tale, six pots of ale,
    And a quart of aqua-vitæ."

tragedy, marshal their gallows-looking, duck-legged, heavy-heeled myrmidons with more glory and self admiration.

These military compliments being finished, General Van Poffenburgh escorted his illustrious visitor, with great cere-mony, into the fort; attended him throughout the fortifica-tions; showed him the horn-works, crown-works, half-moons, and various other outworks; or rather the places where they ought to be erected, and where they might be erected if he pleased; plainly demonstrating that it was a place of "great capability," and though at present but a little redoubt, yet that it evidently was a formidable fortress in embryo. This survey over, he next had the whole garrison put under arms, exercised and reviewed, and concluded by ordering the three Bridewell birds to be hauled out of the black hole, brought up to the halberds and soundly flogged for the amusement of his visitor, and to convince him that he was a great disciplinarian.

The cunning Risingh, while he pretended to be struck dumb outright with the puissance of the great Van Poffen-burgh, took silent note of the incompetency of his garrison, of which he gave a hint to his trusty followers, who tipped each other the wink, and laughed most obstreperously—in their sleeves.

The inspection, review, and flogging being concluded, the party adjourned to the table; for among his other great quali-ties, the general was remarkably addicted to huge entertain-ments, or rather carousals, and in one afternoon's campaign would leave more dead men on the field than he ever did in the whole course of his military career. Many bulletins of these bloodless victories do still remain on record; and the whole province was once thrown in a maze by the return of one of his campaigns; wherein it was stated that though, like Captain Bobadil, he had only twenty men to back him, yet in the short space of six months he had conquered and utterly annihilated sixty oxen, ninety hogs, one hundred sheep, ten thousand cabbages, one thousand bushels of po-tatoes, one hundred and fifty kilderkins of small-beer, two thousand seven hundred and thirty-five pipes, seventy-eight pounds of sugar-plums, and forty bars of iron, besides sundry small meats, game, poultry, and garden stuff. An achievement unparalleled since the days of Pantagruel and his all-devouring army, and which showed that it was only necessary to let bellipotent Van Poffenburgh and his garrison loose in an enemy's country, and in a little while they would breed a famine and starve all the inhabitants.

No sooner, therefore, had the general received the first intimation of the visit of Governor Risingh than he ordered a great dinner to be prepared; and privately sent out a detachment of his most experienced veterans to rob all the henroosts in the neighborhood and lay the pigsties under contribution; a service to which they had been long inured, and which they discharged with such incredible zeal and promptitude that the garrison table groaned under the weight of their spoils.

I wish, with all my heart, my readers could see the valiant Van Poffenburgh, as he presided at the head of the banquet; it was a sight worth beholding. There he sat, in his greatest glory, surrounded by his soldiers, like that famous winebibber, Alexander, whose thirsty virtues he did most ably imitate—telling astounding stories of his hair-breadth adventures and heroic exploits, at which, though all his auditors knew them to be most incontinent and outrageous gasconadoes, yet did they cast up their eyes in admiration and utter many interjections of astonishment. Nor could the general pronounce anything that bore the remotest semblance to a joke, but the stout Risingh would strike his brawny fist upon the table till every glass rattled again, throwing himself back in the chair and uttering gigantic peals of laughter, swearing most horribly it was the best joke he ever heard in his life.—Thus all was rout and revelry and hideous carousal within Fort Casimir, and so lustily did Van Poffenburgh ply the bottle that in less than four short hours he made himself and his whole garrison, who all sedulously emulated the deeds of their chieftain, dead drunk, and singing songs, quaffing bumpers, and drinking patriotic toasts, none of

which but was as long as a Welsh pedigree or a plea in
chancery.

No sooner did things come to this pass than the crafty
Risingh and his Swedes, who had cunningly kept themselves
sober, rose on their entertainers, tied them neck and heels;
and took formal possession of the fort, and all its dependencies, in the name of Queen Christina of Sweden: administer-
ing at the same time an oath of allegiance to all the Dutch
soldiers who could be made sober enough to swallow it.
Risingh then put the fortification in order, appointed his discreet and vigilant friend, Suen Scutz, a tall, wind-dried,
water-drinking Swede, to the command, and departed, bearing with him this truly amiable garrison, and their puissant
commander; who, when brought to himself by a sound drubbing, bore no little resemblance to a "deboshed fish," or
bloated sea-monster, caught upon dry land.

The transportation of the garrison was done to prevent
the transmission of intelligence to New Amsterdam; for,
much as the cunning Risingh exulted in his stratagem, he
dreaded the vengeance of the sturdy Peter Stuyvesant; whose
name spread as much terror in the neighborhood as did
whilom that of the unconquerable Scanderberg among his
scurvy enemies, the Turks.

CHAPTER TWO

SHOWING HOW PROFOUND SECRETS ARE OFTEN BROUGHT
TO LIGHT; WITH THE PROCEEDINGS OF PETER THE
HEADSTRONG, WHEN HE HEARD OF THE MISFORTUNES
OF GENERAL VAN POFFENBURGH

WHOEVER first described common fame, or rumor, as
belonging to the sager sex was a very owl for shrewdness.
She has, in truth, certain feminine qualities to an astonishing degree; particularly that benevolent anxiety to take care
of the affairs of others which keeps her continually hunting

after secrets and gadding about proclaiming them.   Whatever is done openly and in the face of the world she takes
but transient notice of; but whenever a transaction is done in
a corner, and attempted to be shrouded in mystery, then her
goddess-ship is at her wit's end to find it out, and takes a
most mischievous and lady-like pleasure in publishing it to
the world.

It is this truly feminine propensity that induces her continually to be prying into cabinets of princes, listening at the
keyholes of senate chambers, and peering through chinks
and crannies, when our worthy Congress are sitting with
closed doors, deliberating between a dozen excellent modes
of ruining the nation.   It is this which makes her so obnoxious to all wary statesmen and intriguing commanders—such
a stumbling-block to private negotiations and secret expeditions; which she often betrays by means and instruments
which never would have been thought of by any but a female
head.

Thus it was in the case of the affair of Fort Casimir.   No
doubt the cunning Risingh imagined that by securing the
garrison he should for a long time prevent the history of its
fate from reaching the ears of the gallant Stuyvesant; but
his exploit was blown to the world when he least expected it,
and by one of the last beings he would ever have suspected
of enlisting as trumpeter to the wide-mouthed deity.

This was one Dirk Schuiler (or Skulker), a kind of hanger-
on to the garrison; who seemed to belong to nobody, and in
a manner to be self-outlawed.   He was one of those vagabond cosmopolites who shark about the world as if they had
no right or business in it, and who infest the skirts of society
like poachers and interlopers.   Every garrison and country
village has one or more scapegoats of this kind, whose life is
a kind of enigma, whose existence is without motive, who
comes from the Lord knows where, who lives the Lord knows
how, and seems to be made for no other earthly purpose but
to keep up the ancient and honorable order of idleness.   This
vagrant philosopher was supposed to have some Indian blood

in his veins, which was manifested by a certain Indian complexion and cast of countenance; but more especially by his propensities and habits. He was a tall, lank fellow, swift of foot and long-winded. He was generally equipped in a half Indian dress, with belt, leggings, and moccasins. His hair hung in straight gallows locks about his ears, and added not a little to his sharking demeanor. It is an old remark that persons of Indian mixture are half civilized, half savage, and half devil, a third half being expressly provided for their particular convenience. It is for similar reasons, and probably with equal truth, that the backwoodsmen of Kentucky are styled half man, half horse, and half alligator, by the settlers on the Mississippi, and held accordingly in great respect and abhorrence.

The above character may have presented itself to the garrison as applicable to Dirk Schuiler, whom they familiarly dubbed Gallows Dirk. Certain it is, he acknowledged allegiance to no one—was an utter enemy to work, holding it in no manner of estimation—but lounged about the fort, depending upon chance for a subsistence, getting drunk whenever he could get liquor, and stealing whatever he could lay his hands on. Every day or two he was sure to get a sound rib-roasting for some of his misdemeanors, which, however, as it broke no bones, he made very light of, and scrupled not to repeat the offense whenever another opportunity presented. Sometimes, in consequence of some flagrant villainy, he would abscond from the garrison, and be absent for a month at a time; skulking about the woods and swamps, with a long fowling-piece on his shoulder, laying in ambush for game— or squatting himself down on the edge of a pond catching fish for hours together, and bearing no little resemblance to that notable bird ycleped the mudpoke. When he thought his crimes had been forgotten or forgiven, he would sneak back to the fort with a bundle of skins or a bunch of poultry, which perchance he had stolen, and would exchange them for liquor, with which, having well soaked his carcass, he would lay in the sun and enjoy all the luxurious indolence

of that swinish philosopher, Diogenes. He was the terror of
all the farmyards in the country, into which he made fearful inroads; and sometimes he would make his sudden appearance at the garrison at daybreak, with the whole neighborhood at his heels, like a scoundrel thief of a fox, detected
in his maraudings and hunted to his hole. Such was this
Dirk Schuiler; and from the total indifference he showed to
the world or its concerns, and from his truly Indian stoicism
and taciturnity, no one would ever have dreamed that he
would have been the publisher of the treachery of Risingh.

When the carousal was going on which proved so fatal
to the brave Van Poffenburgh and his watchful garrison,
Dirk skulked about from room to room, being a kind of privileged vagrant, or useless hound, whom nobody noticed. But
though a fellow of few words, yet, like your taciturn people,
his eyes and ears were always open, and in the course of his
prowlings he overheard the whole plot of the Swedes. Dirk
immediately settled in his own mind how he should turn the
matter to his own advantage. He played the perfect jack-
of-both-sides—that is to say, he made a prize of everything
that came in his reach, robbed both parties, stuck the copper-
bound cocked-hat of the puissant Van Poffenburgh on his
head, whipped a huge pair of Risingh's jack-boots under his
arms, and took to his heels, just before the catastrophe and
confusion at the garrison.

Finding himself completely dislodged from his haunt in
this quarter, he directed his flight toward his native place,
New Amsterdam, from whence he had formerly been obliged
to abscond precipitately, in consequence of misfortune in business—that is to say, having been detected in the act of sheep-
stealing. After wandering many days in the woods, toiling
through swamps, fording brooks, swimming various rivers,
and encountering a world of hardships that would have killed
any other being but an Indian, a backwoodsman, or the devil,
he at length arrived, half famished, and lank as a starved
weasel, at Communipaw, where he stole a canoe and paddled
over to New Amsterdam. Immediately on landing, he re-

paired to Governor Stuyvesant, and in more words than he
had ever spoken before in the whole course of his life, gave
an account of the disastrous affair.

On receiving these direful tidings the valiant Peter started
from his seat—dashed the pipe he was smoking against the
back of the chimney—thrust a prodigious quid of tobacco into
his left cheek—pulled up his galligaskins, and strode up and
down the room, humming, as was customary with him when
in a passion, a hideous northwest ditty. But, as I have before shown, he was not a man to vent his spleen in idle vaporing. His first measure after the paroxysm of wrath had subsided was to stump upstairs to a huge wooden chest, which
served as his armory, from whence he drew forth that identical suit of regimentals described in the preceding chapter.
In these portentous habiliments he arrayed himself, like
Achilles in the armor of Vulcan, maintaining all the while
a most appalling silence, knitting his brows, and drawing
his breath through his clinched teeth. Being hastily equipped,
he strode down into the parlor, jerked down his trusty sword
from over the fireplace, where it was usually suspended; but
before he girded it on his thigh he drew it from its scabbard,
and as his eye coursed along the rusty blade a grim smile
stole over his iron visage—it was the first smile that had
visited his countenance for five long weeks; but every one
who beheld it prophesied that there would soon be warm
work in the province!

Thus armed at all points, with grisly war depicted in
each feature, his very cocked hat assuming an air of uncommon defiance, he instantly put himself upon the alert, and
dispatched Antony Van Corlear hither and thither, this way
and that way, through all the muddy streets and crooked
lanes of the city, summoning by sound of trumpet his trusty
peers to assemble in instant council. This done, by way of
expediting matters, according to the custom of people in a
hurry, he kept in continual bustle, shifting from chair to
chair, popping his head out of every window, and stumping
up and down stairs with his wooden leg in such brisk and

incessant motion that, as we are informed by an authentic historian of the times, the continual clatter bore no small resemblance to the music of a cooper hooping a flour-barrel.

A summons so peremptory, and from a man of the governor's mettle, was not to be trifled with; the sages forthwith repaired to the council chamber, seated themselves with the utmost tranquillity, and lighting their long pipes, gazed with unruffled composure on his excellency and his regimentals; being, as all counselors should be, not easily flustered or taken by surprise. The governor, looking around for a moment with a lofty and soldier-like air, and resting one hand on the pommel of his sword, and flinging the other forth in a free and spirited manner, addressed them in a short, but soul-stirring harangue.

I am extremely sorry that I have not the advantages of Livy, Thucydides, Plutarch, and others of my predecessors, who were furnished, as I am told, with the speeches of all their great emperors, generals, and orators, taken down in shorthand, by the most accurate stenographers of the time; whereby they were enabled wonderfully to enrich their histories, and delight their readers with sublime strains of eloquence. Not having such important auxiliaries, I cannot possibly pronounce what was the tenor of Governor Stuyvesant's speech. I am bold, however, to say, from the tenor of his character, that he did not wrap his rugged subject in silks and ermines, and other sickly trickeries of phrase; but spoke forth, like a man of nerve and vigor, who scorned to shrink, in words, from those dangers which he stood ready to encounter in very deed. This much is certain, that he concluded by announcing his determination of leading on his troops in person, and routing these costardmonger Swedes from their usurped quarters at Fort Casimir. To this hardy resolution such of his council as were awake gave their usual signal of concurrence, and as to the rest who had fallen asleep about the middle of the harangue (their "usual custom in the afternoon")—they made not the least objection.

And now was seen in the fair city of New Amsterdam a

prodigious bustle and preparation for iron war. Recruiting parties marched hither and thither, calling lustily upon all the scrubs, the runagates, and tatterdemalions of the Manhattoes and its vicinity, who had any ambition of sixpence a day, and immortal fame into the bargain, to enlist in the cause of glory. For I would have you note that your warlike heroes who trudge in the rear of conquerors are generally of that illustrious class of gentlemen who are equal candidates for the army or the Bridewell—the halberds or the whipping post—for whom Dame Fortune has cast an even die, whether they shall make their exit by the sword or the halter—and whose deaths shall, at all events, be a lofty example to their countrymen.

But notwithstanding all this martial rout and invitation, the ranks of honor were but scantily supplied; so averse were the peaceful burghers of New Amsterdam from enlisting in foreign broils, or stirring beyond that home which rounded all their earthly ideas. Upon beholding this, the great Peter, whose noble heart was all on fire with war and sweet revenge, determined to wait no longer for the tardy assistance of these oily citizens, but to muster up his merry men of the Hudson; who, brought up among woods and wilds and savage beasts, like our yeomen of Kentucky, delighted in nothing so much as desperate adventures and perilous expeditions through the wilderness. Thus resolving, he ordered his trusty squire, Antony Van Corlear, to have his state galley prepared and duly victualed; which being performed, he attended public service at the great church of St. Nicholas, like a true and pious governor, and then leaving peremptory orders with his council to have the chivalry of the Manhattoes marshaled out and appointed against his return, departed upon his recruiting voyage up the waters of the Hudson.

CHAPTER THREE

CONTAINING PETER STUYVESANT'S VOYAGE UP THE HUDSON
AND THE WONDERS AND DELIGHTS OF THAT
RENOWNED RIVER

Now did the soft breezes of the south steal sweetly over
the beauteous face of nature, tempering the panting heats of
summer into genial and prolific warmth—when that miracle
of hardihood and chivalric virtue, the dauntless Peter Stuyvesant, spread his canvas to the wind and departed from the
fair island of Manna-hata. The galley in which he embarked
was sumptuously adorned with pendents and streamers of
gorgeous dyes, which fluttered gayly in the wind or drooped
their ends in the bosom of the stream. The bow and poop
of this majestic vessel were gallantly bedight, after the
rarest Dutch fashion, with figures of little pursy Cupids with
periwigs on their heads, and bearing in their hands garlands
of flowers, the like of which are not to be found in any book
of botany; being the matchless flowers which flourished in
the golden age, and exist no longer, unless it be in the imaginations of ingenious carvers of wood and discolorers of
canvas.

Thus rarely decorated, in style befitting the state of the
puissant potentate of the Manhattoes, did the galley of Peter
Stuyvesant launch forth upon the bosom of the lordly Hudson; which, as it rolled its broad waves to the ocean, seemed
to pause for a while, and swell with pride, as if conscious of
the illustrious burden it sustained.

But trust me, gentlefolk, far other was the scene presented to the contemplation of the crew from that which
may be witnessed at this degenerate day. Wildness and
savage majesty reigned on the borders of this mighty river
—the hand of cultivation had not as yet laid down the dark

forests, and tamed the features of the landscape—·nor had
the frequent sail of commerce yet broken in upon the profound and awful solitude of ages.   Here and there might be
seen a rude wigwam perched among the cliffs of the mountains, with its curling column of smoke mounting in the
transparent atmosphere — but so loftily situated that the
whoopings of the savage children, gamboling on the margin of the dizzy heights, fell almost as faintly on the ear
as do the notes of the lark when lost in the azure vault of
heaven.   Now and then, from the beetling brow of some
rocky precipice, the wild deer would look timidly down upon
the splendid pageant as it passed below; and then, tossing
his branching antlers in the air, would bound away into the
thickets of the forest.

Through such scenes did the stately vessel of Peter Stuyvesant pass.   Now did they skirt the bases of the rocky heights
of Jersey, which spring up like everlasting walls, reaching
from the waves unto the heavens; and were fashioned, if
traditions may be believed, in times long past, by the mighty
spirit Manetho, to protect his favorite abodes from the un-
hallowed eyes of mortals.   Now did they career it gayly
across the vast expanse of Tappan Bay, whose wide extended
shores present a vast variety of delectable scenery—here the
bold promontory, crowned with embowering trees, advancing into the bay—there the long woodland slope sweeping
up from the shore in rich luxuriance, and terminating in the
upland precipice—while at a distance a long waving line of
rocky heights threw their gigantic shades across the water.
Now would they pass where some modest little interval,
opening among these stupendous scenes, yet retreating, as
it were, for protection into the embraces of the neighboring
mountains, displayed a rural paradise, fraught with sweet
and pastoral beauties; the velvet-tufted lawn—the bushy
copse—the tinkling rivulet, stealing through the fresh and
vivid verdure—on whose banks was situated some little
Indian village, or, peradventure, the rude cabin of some
solitary hunter.

The different periods of the revolving day seemed each, with cunning magic, to diffuse a different charm over the scene. Now would the jovial sun break gloriously from the east, blazing from the summits of the hills, and sparkling the landscape with a thousand dewy gems; while along the borders of the river were seen heavy masses of mist, which, like midnight caitiffs, disturbed at his approach, made a sluggish retreat, rolling in sullen reluctance up the mountains. At such times all was brightness and life and gayety —the atmosphere seemed of an indescribable pureness and transparency—the birds broke forth in wanton madrigals, and the freshening breezes wafted the vessel merrily on her course. But when the sun sunk amid a flood of glory in the west, mantling the heavens and the earth with a thousand gorgeous dyes—then all was calm, and silent, and magnificent. The late swelling sail hung lifelessly against the mast —the seamen with folded arms leaned against the shrouds, lost in that involuntary musing which the sober grandeur of nature commands in the rudest of her children. The vast bosom of the Hudson was like an unruffled mirror, reflecting the golden splendor of the heavens, excepting that now and then a bark canoe would steal across its surface, filled with painted savages, whose gay feathers glared brightly, as perchance a lingering ray of the setting sun gleamed upon them from the western mountains.

But when the hour of twilight spread its magic mists around, then did the face of nature assume a thousand fugitive charms, which, to the worthy heart that seeks enjoyment in the glorious works of its Maker, are inexpressibly captivating. The mellow dubious light that prevailed just served to tinge with illusive colors the softened features of the scenery. The deceived but delighted eye sought vainly to discern, in the broad masses of shade, the separating line between the land and water; or to distinguish the fading objects that seemed sinking into chaos. Now did the busy fancy supply the feebleness of vision, producing with industrious craft a fairy creation of her own. Under her plastic wand the barren rocks frowned upon the watery waste in the semblance of lofty towers and high embattled castles—trees assumed the direful forms of mighty giants, and the inaccessible summits of the mountains seemed peopled with a thousand shadowy beings.

Now broke forth from the shores the notes of an innumerable variety of insects, which filled the air with a strange but not inharmonious concert—while ever and anon was heard the melancholy plaint of the whip-poor-will, who, perched on some lone tree, wearied the ear of night with his incessant moanings. The mind, soothed into a hallowed melancholy, listened with pensive stillness to catch and distinguish each sound that vaguely echoed from the shore—now and then startled perchance by the whoop of some straggling savage, or the dreary howl of a wolf, stealing forth upon his nightly prowlings.

Thus happily did they pursue their course until they entered upon those awful defiles denominated THE HIGHLANDS, where it would seem that the gigantic Titans had erst waged their impious war with heaven, piling up cliffs on cilffs, and hurling vast masses of rock in wild confusion. But in sooth, very different is the history of these cloud-capped mountains. These in ancient days, before the Hudson poured his waters from the lakes, formed one vast prison, within whose rocky bosom the omnipotent Manetho confined the rebellious spirits who repined at his control. Here, bound in adamantine chains, or jammed in rifted pines, or crushed by ponderous rocks, they groaned for many an age. At length the conquering Hudson, in his irresistible career toward the ocean, burst open their prison-house, rolling his tide triumphantly through its stupendous ruins.

Still, however, do many of them lurk about their old abodes; and these it is, according to venerable legends, that cause the echoes which resound throughout these awful solitudes; which are nothing but their angry clamors when any noise disturbs the profoundness of their repose. For when the elements are agitated by tempest, when the winds are up

and the thunder rolls, then horrible is the yelling and howling of these troubled spirits, making the mountains to rebel-
low with their hideous uproar; for at such times, it is said,
they think ;the great Manetho is returning once more to
plunge them in gloomy caverns and renew their intolerable
captivity.

But all these fair and glorious scenes were lost upon the
gallant Stuyvesant; naught occupied his mind but thoughts
of iron war and proud anticipations of hardy deeds of arms.
Neither did his honest crew trouble their vacant heads with
any romantic speculations of the kind. The pilot at the helm
quietly smoked his pipe, thinking of nothing either past,
present, or to come—those of his comrades who were not
industriously snoring under the hatches were listening with
open mouths to Antony Van Corlear; who, seated on the
windlass, was relating to them the marvelous history of those
myriads of fire-flies that sparkled like gems and spangles
upon the dusky robe of night. These, according to tradition,
were originally a race of pestilent sempiternous beldames
who peopled these parts long before the memory of man;
being of that abominated race emphatically called *brimstones;* and who, for their innumerable sins against the
children of men, and to furnish an awful warning to the
beauteous sex, were doomed to infest the earth in the shape
of these threatening and terrible little bugs; enduring the
internal torments of that fire which they formerly carried in
their hearts and breathed forth in their words; but now are
sentenced to bear about forever—in their tails!

And now am I going to tell a fact which I doubt much
my readers will hesitate to believe; but if they do, they are
welcome not to believe a word in this whole history, for
nothing which it contains is more true. It must be known
then that the nose of Antony the trumpeter was of a very
lusty size, strutting boldly from his countenance, like a
mountain of Golconda; being sumptuously bedecked with
rubies and other precious stones—the true regalia of a king
of good fellows, which jolly Bacchus grants to all who bouse

it heartily at the flagon. Now thus it happened that bright
and early in the morning the good Antony, having washed
his burly visage, was leaning over the quarter-railing of the
galley, contemplating it in the glassy wave below—just at
this moment the illustrious sun, breaking in all his splendor
from behind one of the high bluffs of the Highlands, did dart
one of his most potent beams full upon the refulgent nose of
the sounder of brass—the reflection of which shot straightway
down, hissing hot, into the water, and killed a mighty sturgeon that was sporting beside the vessel! This huge monster, being with infinite labor hoisted on board, furnished a
luxurious repast to all the crew, being accounted of excellent
flavor, excepting about the wound, where it smacked a little
of brimstone—and this, on my veracity, was the first time
that ever sturgeon was eaten in these parts by Christian
people.*

When this astonishing miracle came to be made known
to Peter Stuyvesant, and that he tasted of the unknown fish,
he, as may well be supposed, marveled exceedingly; and as
a monument thereof, he gave the name of *Antony's Nose* to
a stout promontory in the neighborhood—and it has continued to be called Antony's Nose ever since that time.

But hold—Whither am I wandering?—By the mass, if I
attempt to accompany the good Peter Stuyvesant on this
voyage, I shall never make an end, for never was there a
voyage so fraught with marvelous incidents, nor a river so
abounding with transcendent beauties worthy of being severally recorded. Even now I have it on the point of my pen
to relate how his crew were most horribly frightened, on
going on shore above the Highlands, by a gang of merry,
roistering devils, frisking and curveting on a huge flat rock
which projected into the river—and which is called the
Duyvel's Dans-Kamer to this very day.—But no! Diedrich

* The learned Hans Megapolensis, treating of the country about
Albany, in a letter which was written some time after the settlement
thereof, says: "There is in the river great plenty of Sturgeon, which we
Christians do not make use of; but the Indians eat them greedilie."

Knickerbocker—it becomes thee not to idle thus in thy historic wayfaring.

Recollect that while dwelling with the fond garrulity of age over these fairy scenes, endeared to thee by the recollections of thy youth and the charms of a thousand legendary tales which beguiled the simple ear of thy childhood; recollect that thou art trifling with those fleeting moments which should be devoted to loftier themes.—Is not Time—relentless Time!—shaking, with palsied hand, his almost exhausted hour-glass before thee? Hasten then to pursue thy weary task, lest the last sands be run ere thou hast finished thy history of the Manhattoes.

Let us then commit the dauntless Peter, his brave galley, and his loyal crew, to the protection of the blessed St. Nicholas; who, I have no doubt, will prosper him in his voyage, while we await his return at the great city of New Amsterdam.

CHAPTER FOUR

DESCRIBING THE POWERFUL ARMY THAT ASSEMBLED AT THE CITY OF NEW AMSTERDAM—TOGETHER WITH THE INTERVIEW BETWEEN PETER THE HEADSTRONG AND GENERAL VAN POFFENBURGH, AND PETER'S SENTIMENTS TOUCHING UNFORTUNATE GREAT MEN

WHILE thus the enterprising Peter was coasting, with flowing sail, up the shores of the lordly Hudson, and arousing all the phlegmatic little Dutch settlements upon its borders, a great and puissant concourse of warriors was assembling at the city of New Amsterdam. And here that invaluable fragment of antiquity, the Stuyvesant manuscript, is more than commonly particular; by which means I am enabled to record the illustrious host that encamped itself in the public square in front of the fort at present denominated the Bowling Green.

In the center, then, was pitched the tent of the men of

battle of the Manhattoes, who, being the inmates of the metropolis, composed the life-guards of the governor. These were commanded by the valiant Stoffel Brinkerhoff, who whilom had acquired such immortal fame at Oyster Bay— they displayed as a standard a beaver *rampant* on a field of orange; being the arms of the province, and denoting the persevering industry and the amphibious origin of the Nederlanders.*

On their right hand might be seen the vassals of that renowned Mynheer, Michael Paw,† who lorded it over the fair regions of ancient Pavonia, and the lands away south, even unto the Navesink Mountains,‡ and was moreover patroon of Gibbet Island. His standard was borne by his trusty squire, Cornelius Van Vorst; consisting of a huge oyster *recumbent* upon a sea-green field; being the armorial bearings of his favorite metropolis, Communipaw. He brought to the camp a stout force of warriors, heavily armed, being each clad in ten pair of linsey-woolsey breeches, and overshadowed by broad-brimmed beavers, with short pipes twisted in their hat-bands. These were the men who vegetated in the mud along the shores of Pavonia; being of the race of genuine copperheads, and were fabled to have sprung from oysters.

At a little distance were encamped the tribe of warriors who came from the neighborhood of Hell-gate. These were

---

* This was likewise the great seal of the New Netherlands, as may still be seen in ancient records.

† Besides what is related in the Stuyvesant MS., I have found mention made of this illustrious Patroon in another manuscript, which says: "De Heer (or the squire) Michael Paw, a Dutch subject, about 10th Aug., 1630, by deed purchased Staten Island. N. B. The same Michael Paw had what the Dutch call a colonie at Pavonia, on the Jersey shore, opposite New York, and his overseer, in 1636, was named Corns. Van Vorst—a person of the same name in 1769 owned Powles Hook, and a large farm at Pavonia, and is a lineal descendant from Van Vorst."

‡ So called from the Navesink tribe of Indians that inhabited these parts—at present they are erroneously denominated the Neversink or Neversunk mountains.

commanded by the Suy Dams, and the Van Dams, incontinent hard swearers, as their names betoken—they were terrible-looking fellows, clad in broad-skirted gaberdines, of that curious-colored cloth called thunder and lightning—and bore as a standard three Devil's-darning-needles, *volant*, in a flame-colored field.

Hard by was the tent of the men of battle from the marshy borders of the Waale-Boght* and the country thereabout—these were of a sour aspect, by reason that they lived on crabs which abound in these parts. They were the first institutors of that honorable order of knighthood called *Fly market shirks*, and, if tradition speak true, did likewise introduce the far-famed step in dancing called "double trouble." They were commanded by the fearless Jacobus Varra Vanger, and had moreover a jolly band of Breuckelen† ferry-men, who performed a brave concerto on conch-shells.

But I refrain from pursuing this minute description, which goes on to describe the warriors of Bloemendael, and Wee-hawk, and Hoboken, and sundry other places, well known in history and song—for now does the sound of martial music alarm the people of New Amsterdam, sounding afar from beyond the walls of the city. But this alarm was in a little while relieved; for lo, from the midst of a vast cloud of dust they recognized the brimstone-colored breeches, and splendid silver leg, of Peter Stuyvesant, glaring in the sunbeams; and beheld him approaching at the head of a formidable army which he had mustered along the banks of the Hudson. And here the excellent but anonymous writer of the Stuyvesant manuscript breaks out into a brave and glorious description of the forces, as they defiled through the principal gate of the city, that stood by the head of Wall Street.

First of all came the Van Bummels, who inhabit the

---

* Since corrupted into the *Wallabout;* the bay where the Navy Yard is situated.

† Now spelled Brooklyn.

pleasant borders of the Bronx—these were short fat men, wearing exceeding large trunk breeches, and are renowned for feats of the trencher—they were the first inventors of suppawn or mush-and-milk.—Close in their rear marched the Van Vlotens, of Kaatskill, most horrible quaffers of new cider, and arrant braggarts in their liquor.—After them came the Van Pelts, of Groodt Esopus, dexterous horsemen, mounted upon goodly switch-tailed steeds of the Esopus breed—these were mighty hunters of minks and muskrats, whence came the word *Peltry.*—Then the Van Nests, of Kinderhook, valiant robbers of birds' nests, as their name denotes; to these, if report may be believed, are we indebted for the invention of slap-jacks, or buckwheat cakes.—Then the Van Higginbottoms, of Wapping's Creek; these came armed with ferules and birchen rods, being a race of school-masters, who first discovered the marvelous sympathy between the seat of honor and the seat of intellect, and that the shortest way to get knowledge into the head was to hammer it into the bottom.—Then the Van Grolls, of Antony's Nose, who carried their liquor in fair round little pot-tles, by reason they could not bouse it out of their canteens, having such rare long noses.—Then the Gardeniers, of Hudson and thereabout, distinguished by many triumphant feats, such as robbing watermelon patches, smoking rabbits out of their holes, and the like; and by being great lovers of roasted pigs' tails; these were the ancestors of the renowned congressman of that name.—Then the Van Hoesens, of Sing Sing, great choristers and players upon the jews-harp; these marched two and two, singing the great song of St. Nich-olas.—Then the Couenhovens, of Sleepy Hollow; these gave birth to a jolly race of publicans who first discovered the magic artifice of conjuring a quart of wine into a pint bottle. —Then the Van Kortlandts, who lived on the wild banks of the Croton, and were great killers of wild ducks, being much spoken of for their skill in shooting with the long bow.— Then the Van Bunschotens, of Nyack and Kakiat, who were the first that did ever kick with the left foot; they were gal-

lant bushwhackers and hunters of raccoons by moonlight.—
Then the Van Winkles, of Haerlem, potent suckers of eggs,
and noted for running of horses and running up of scores at
taverns; they were the first that ever winked with both eyes
at once.—Lastly came the KNICKERBOCKERS, of the great
town of Schaghticoke, where the folk lay stones upon the
houses in windy weather, lest they should be blown away.
These derive their name, as some say, from *Knicker*, to
shake, and *Beker*, a goblet, indicating thereby that they
were sturdy toss-pots of yore; but, in truth, it was derived
from *Knicker*, to nod, and *Boeken*, books; plainly meaning
that they were great nodders or dozers over books—from
them did descend the writer of this history.

Such was the legion of sturdy bush-beaters that poured
in at the grand gate of New Amsterdam; the Stuyvesant
manuscript indeed speaks of many more, whose names I
omit to mention, seeing that it behooves me to hasten to matters of greater moment. Nothing could surpass the joy and
martial pride of the lion-hearted Peter, as he reviewed this
mighty host of warriors, and he determined no longer to
defer the gratification of his much-wished-for revenge upon
the scoundrel Swedes at Fort Casimir.

But before I hasten to record those unmatchable events
which will be found in the sequel of this faithful history, let
me pause to notice the fate of Jacobus Van Poffenburgh, the
discomfited commander-in-chief of the armies of the New
Netherlands. Such is the inherent uncharitableness of
human nature that scarcely did the news become public of
his deplorable discomfiture at Fort Casimir than a thousand
scurvy rumors were set afloat in New Amsterdam, wherein
it was insinuated that he had in reality a treacherous understanding with the Swedish commander; that he had long
been in the practice of privately communicating with the
Swedes; together with divers hints about "secret service
money"—to all which deadly charges I do not give a jot
more credit than I think they deserve.

Certain it is that the general vindicated his character by

* * * L   VOL. IV.

the most vehement oaths and protestations, and put every man out of the ranks of honor who dared to doubt his integrity. Moreover, on returning to New Amsterdam, he paraded up and down the streets with a crew of hard swearers at his heels—sturdy bottle companions, whom he gorged and fattened, and who were ready to bolster him through all the courts of justice—heroes of his own kidney, fierce-whiskered, broad-shouldered, Colbrand-looking swaggerers—not one of whom but looked as though he could eat up an ox and pick his teeth with the horns. These lifeguard men quarreled all his quarrels, were ready to fight all his battles, and scowled at every man that turned up his nose at the general as though they would devour him alive. Their conversation was interspersed with oaths like minute-guns, and every bombastic rodomontade was rounded off by a thundering execration, like a patriotic toast honored with a discharge of artillery.

All these valorous vaporings had a considerable effect in convincing certain profound sages, many of whom began to think the general a hero of unutterable loftiness and magnanimity of soul, particularly as he was continually protesting *on the honor of a soldier*—a marvelously high-sounding asseveration. Nay, one of the members of the council went so far as to propose they should immortalize him by an imperishable statue of plaster of Paris.

But the vigilant Peter the Headstrong was not thus to be deceived.—Sending privately for the commander-in-chief of all the armies, and having heard all his story, garnished with the customary pious oaths, protestations, and ejaculations—"Harkee, comrade," cried he, "though by your own account you are the most brave, upright, and honorable man in the whole province, yet do you lie under the misfortune of being damnably traduced and immeasurably despised. Now, though it is certainly hard to punish a man for his misfortunes, and though it is very possible you are totally innocent of the crimes laid to your charge, yet as Heaven, at present, doubtless for some wise purpose, sees fit to withhold all proofs of your innocence, far be it from me to counteract its sovereign will. Besides I cannot consent to venture my armies with a commander whom they despise, or to trust the welfare of my people to a champion whom they distrust. Retire, therefore, my friend, from the irksome toils and cares of public life, with this comforting reflection —that, if guilty, you are but enjoying your just reward— and, if innocent, you are not the first great and good man who has most wrongfully been slandered and maltreated in this wicked world—doubtless to be better treated in a better world, where there shall be neither error, calumny, nor persecution. In the meantime let me never see your face again, for I have a horrible antipathy to the countenances of unfortunate great men like yourself."

CHAPTER FIVE

IN WHICH THE AUTHOR DISCOURSES VERY INGENUOUSLY
OF HIMSELF—AFTER WHICH IS TO BE FOUND MUCH
INTERESTING HISTORY ABOUT PETER THE HEADSTRONG
AND HIS FOLLOWERS

As my readers and myself are about entering on as many perils as ever a confederacy of meddlesome knights-errant willfully ran their heads into, it is meet that, like those hardy adventurers, we should join hands, bury all differences, and swear to stand by one another, in weal or woe, to the end of the enterprise. My readers must doubtless perceive how completely I have altered my tone and deportment since we first set out together. I warrant they then thought me a crabbed, cynical, impertinent little son of a Dutchman; for I scarcely ever gave them a civil word, nor so much as touched my beaver when I had occasion to address them. But as we jogged along together, in the high-road of my history, I gradually began to relax, to grow more courteous, and occasionally to enter into familiar discourse, until at length I came to conceive a most social, companionable, kind regard for them. This is just my way—I am always a little cold and reserved at first, particularly to people whom I neither know nor care for, and am only to be completely won by long intimacy.

Besides, why should I have been sociable to the crowd of how-d'ye-do acquaintances that flocked around me at my first appearance? Many were merely attracted by a new face; and having stared me full in the title page, walked off without saying a word; while others lingered yawningly through the preface, and having gratified their short-lived curiosity soon dropped off one by one. But more especially to try their mettle, I had recourse to an expedient similar to one which we are told was used by that peerless flower of chivalry, King Arthur; who, before he admitted any knight to his intimacy, first required that he should show himself superior to danger or hardships, by encountering unheard-of mishaps, slaying some dozen giants, vanquishing wicked enchanters, not to say a word of dwarfs, hippogriffs, and fiery dragons. On a similar principle, I cunningly led my readers, at the first sally, into two or three knotty chapters, where they were most wofully belabored and buffeted by a host of pagan philosophers and infidel writers. Though naturally a very grave man, yet could I scarce refrain from smiling outright at seeing the utter confusion and dismay of my valiant cavaliers—some dropped down dead (asleep) on the field; others threw down my book in the middle of the first chapter, took to their heels, and never ceased scampering until they had fairly run it out of sight; when they stopped to take breath, to tell their friends what troubles they had undergone, and to warn all others from venturing on so thankless an expedition. Every page thinned my ranks more and more; and of the vast multitude that first set out but a comparatively few made shift to survive, in exceedingly battered condition, through the five introductory chapters.

What, then! would you have had me take such sunshine,

faint-hearted recreants to my bosom at our first acquaintance? No—no; I reserved my friendship for those who deserved it, for those who undauntedly bore me company, in despite of difficulties, dangers, and fatigues. And now, as to those who adhere to me at present I take them affectionately by the hand.—Worthy and thrice-beloved readers! brave and well-tried comrades! who have faithfully followed my footsteps through all my wanderings—I salute you from my heart—I pledge myself to stand by you to the last; and to conduct you (so Heaven speed this trusty weapon which I now hold between my fingers) triumphantly to the end of this our stupendous undertaking.

But, hark! while we are thus talking, the city of New Amsterdam is in a bustle. The host of warriors encamped in the Bowling Green are striking their tents; the brazen trumpet of Antony Van Corlear makes the welkin to resound with portentous clangor—the drums beat—the standards of the Manhattoes, of Hell-gate, and of Michael Paw, wave proudly in the air. And now behold where the mariners are busily employed hoisting the sails of yon topsail schooner, and those clump-built sloops, which are to waft the army of the Nederlanders to gather immortal honors on the Delaware!

The entire population of the city, man, woman, and child, turned out to behold the chivalry of New Amsterdam, as it paraded the streets previous to embarkation. Many a handkerchief was waved out at the windows; many a fair nose was blown in melodious sorrow on the mournful occasion. The grief of the fair dames and beauteous damsels of Granada could not have been more vociferous on the banishment of the gallant tribe of Abencerrages than was that of the kind-hearted fair ones of New Amsterdam on the departure of their intrepid warriors. Every love-sick maiden fondly crammed the pockets of her hero with gingerbread and doughnuts—many a copper ring was exchanged and crooked sixpence broken, in pledge of eternal constancy—and there remain extant to this day some love-verses written on that occasion, sufficiently crabbed and incomprehensible to confound the whole universe.

But it was a moving sight to seè the buxom lasses, how they hung about the doughty Antony Van Corlear—for he was a jolly, rosy-faced, lusty bachelor, fond of his joke, and withal a desperate rogue among the women. Fain would they have kept him to comfort them while the army was away; for besides what I have said of him, it is no more than justice to add that he was a kind-hearted soul, noted for his benevolent attentions in comforting disconsolate wives during the absence of their husbands—and this made him to be very much regarded by the honest burghers of the city. But nothing could keep the valiant Antony from following the heels of the old governor, whom he loved as he did his very soul—so, embracing all the young vrouws, and giving every one of them that had good teeth and rosy lips a dozen hearty smacks, he departed loaded with their kind wishes.

Nor was the departure of the gallant Peter among the least causes of public distress. Though the old governor was by no means indulgent to the follies and waywardness of his subjects, yet somehow or other he had become strangely popular among the people. There is something so captivating in personal bravery, that, with the common mass of mankind, it takes the lead of most other merits. The simple folk of New Amsterdam looked upon Peter Stuyvesant as a prodigy of valor. His wooden leg, that trophy of his martial encounter, was regarded with reverence and admiration. Every old burgher had a budget of miraculous stories to tell about the exploits of Hardkopping Piet, wherewith he regaled his children of a long winter night; and on which he dwelt with as much delight and exaggeration as do our honest country yeomen on the hardy adventures of old General Putnam (or, as he is familiarly termed, *Old Put.*) during our glorious revolution. Not an individual but verily believed the old governor was a match for Beelzebub himself; and there was even a story told, with great mystery, and under the rose, of his having shot the devil with a silver bullet, one dark, stormy night, as he was sailing in a canoe through Hell-gate.—But this I do not record as being an absolute fact—perish the man who would let fall a drop to discolor the pure stream of history!

Certain it is, not an old woman in New Amsterdam but considered Peter Stuyvesant as a tower of strength, and rested satisfied that the public welfare was secure so long as he was in the city. It is not surprising, then, that they looked upon his departure as a sore affliction. With heavy hearts they dragged at the heels of his troop, as they marched down to the river side to embark. The governor, from the stern of his schooner, gave a short, but truly patriarchal address to his citizens; wherein he recommended them to comport like loyal and peaceable subjects—to go to church regularly on Sundays, and to mind their business all the week besides.—That the women should be dutiful and affectionate to their husbands—looking after nobody's concerns but their own: eschewing all gossipings and morning gaddings—and carrying short tongues and long petticoats.—That the men should abstain from intermeddling in public concerns, intrusting the cares of government to the officers appointed to support them—staying at home like good citizens, making money for themselves, and getting children for the benefit of their country. That the burgomasters should look well to the public interest—not oppressing the poor, nor indulging the rich—not tasking their sagacity to devise new laws, but faithfully enforcing those which were already made—rather bending their attention to prevent evil than to punish it; ever recollecting that civil magistrates should consider themselves more as guardians of public morals than rat-catchers employed to entrap public delinquents. Finally, he exhorted them, one and all, high and low, rich and poor, to conduct themselves *as well as they could;* assuring them that if they faithfully and conscientiously complied with this golden rule, there was no danger but that they would all conduct themselves well enough.—This done, he gave them a paternal benediction; the sturdy Antony sounded a most loving farewell with his trumpet, the jolly crews put up a shout of triumph, and the invincible armada swept off proudly down the bay.

The good people of New Amsterdam crowded down to the Battery—that blessed resort, from whence so many a tender prayer has been wafted, so many a fair hand waved, so many a tearful look been cast by love-sick damsels, after the lessening bark, bearing her adventurous swain to distant climes. Here the populace watched with straining eyes the gallant squadron, as it slowly floated down the bay, and when the intervening land at the Narrows shut it from their sight, gradually dispersed with silent tongues and downcast countenances.

A heavy gloom hung over the late bustling city.—The honest burghers smoked their pipes in profound thoughtfulness, casting many a wistful look to the weathercock on the church of St. Nicholas; and all the old women, having no longer the presence of Peter Stuyvesant to hearten them, gathered their children home and barricadoed the doors and windows every evening at sundown.

In the meanwhile, the armada of the sturdy Peter proceeded prosperously on its voyage, and after encountering about as many storms and waterspouts, and whales, and other horrors and phenomena, as generally befall adventurous landsmen in perilous voyages of the kind; and after undergoing a severe scouring from that deplorable and unpitied malady called sea-sickness, the whole squadron arrived safely in the Delaware.

Without so much as dropping anchor and giving his wearied ships time to breathe after laboring so long in the ocean, the intrepid Peter pursued his course up the Delaware, and made a sudden appearance before Fort Casimir.—Having summoned the astonished garrison by a terrific blast from the trumpet of the long-winded Van Corlear, he demanded in a tone of thunder an instant surrender of the fort. To this demand, Suen Scutz, the wind-dried commandant, replied in a shrill, whiffling voice, which, by reason of his extreme spareness, sounded like the wind whistling through a broken bellows—"that he had no very strong reasons for refusing, except that the demand was particularly disagreeable, as he had been ordered to maintain his post to the last extremity." He requested time, therefore, to consult with Governor Risingh, and proposed a truce for that purpose.

The choleric Peter, indignant at having his rightful fort so treacherously taken from him, and thus pertinaciously withheld, refused the proposed armistice, and swore by the pipe of St. Nicholas, which like the sacred fire was never extinguished, that unless the fort were surrendered in ten minutes he would incontinently storm the works, make all the garrison run the gantlet, and split their scoundrel of a commander like a pickled shad. To give this menace the greater effect, he drew forth his trusty sword and shook it at them with such a fierce and vigorous motion that doubtless, if it had not been exceeding rusty, it would have lightened terror into the eyes and hearts of the enemy. He then ordered his men to bring a broadside to bear upon the fort, consisting of two swivels, three muskets, a long duck fowling-piece, and two brace of horse-pistols.

In the meantime the sturdy Van Corlear marshaled all his forces and commenced his warlike operations. Distending his cheeks like a very Boreas, he kept up a most horrific twanging of his trumpet—the lusty choristers of Sing Sing broke forth into a hideous song of battle—the warriors of Breuckelen and the Wallabout blew a potent and astounding blast on their conch-shells, altogether forming as outrageous a concerto as though five thousand French orchestras were displaying their skill in a modern overture.

Whether the formidable front of war thus suddenly presented smote the garrison with sore dismay; or whether the concluding terms of the summons, which mentioned that he should surrender "at discretion," were mistaken by Suen Scutz—who, though a Swede, was a very considerate, easy-tempered man—as a compliment to his discretion, I will not take upon me to say; certain it is, he found it impossible to resist so courteous a demand. Accordingly, in the very nick of time, just as the cabin-boy had gone after a coal of fire to discharge the swivel, a chamade was beat on the rampart by the only drum in the garrison, to the no small satisfaction of both parties; who, notwithstanding their great stomach for fighting, had full as good an inclination to eat a quiet dinner as to exchange black eyes and bloody noses.

Thus did this impregnable fortress once more return to the domination of their High Mightinesses; Scutz and his garrison of twenty men were allowed to march out with the honors of war, and the victorious Peter, who was as generous as brave, permitted them to keep possession of all their arms and ammunition—the same on inspection being found totally unfit for service, having long rusted in the magazine of the fortress, even before it was wrested by the Swedes from the magnanimous but windy Van Poffenburgh. But I must not omit to mention that the governor was so well pleased with the services of his faithful squire, Van Corlear, in the reduction of this great fortress that he made him on the spot lord of a goodly domain in the vicinity of New Amsterdam—which goes by the name Corlear's Hook unto this very day.

The unexampled liberality of the valiant Stuyvesant toward the Swedes occasioned great surprise in the city of New Amsterdam—nay, certain of these factious individuals, who had been enlightened by the political meetings that prevailed during the days of William the Testy, but who had not dared to indulge their meddlesome habits under the eye of their present ruler, now, emboldened by his absence, dared even to give vent to their censures in the street. Murmurs were heard in the very council chamber of New Amsterdam; and there is no knowing whether they would not have broken out into downright speeches and invectives had not Peter Stuyvesant privately sent home his walking-staff, to be laid as a mace on the table of the council chamber, in the midst of his counselors; who, like wise men, took the hint, and forever after held their peace.

CHAPTER SIX

SHOWING THE GREAT ADVANTAGE THAT THE AUTHOR HAS
OVER HIS READER IN TIME OF BATTLE—TOGETHER WITH
DIVERS PORTENTOUS MOVEMENTS, WHICH BETOKEN THAT
SOMETHING TERRIBLE IS ABOUT TO HAPPEN

LIKE as a mighty alderman, when at a corporation feast
the first spoonful of turtle soup salutes his palate, feels his
impatient appetite but tenfold quickened, and redoubles his
vigorous attacks upon the tureen, while his voracious eyes,
projecting from his head, roll greedily round, devouring
everything at table—so did the mettlesome Peter Stuyvesant feel that intolerable hunger for martial glory, which
raged within his very bowels, inflamed by the capture of
Fort Casimir, and nothing could allay it but the conquest of
all New Sweden. No sooner, therefore, had he secured his
conquest than he stumped resolutely on, flushed with success,
to gather fresh laurels at Fort Christina.*

This was the grand Swedish post, established on a small
river (or, as it is improperly termed, creek) of the same name;
and here that crafty Governor Jan Risingh lay grimly drawn
up, like a gray-bearded spider in the citadel of his web.

But before we hurry into the direful scenes that must attend the meeting of two such potent chieftains it is advisable
that we pause for a moment and hold a kind of warlike council. Battles should not be rushed into precipitately by the
historian and his readers any more than by the general and
his soldiers. The great commanders of antiquity never engaged the enemy without previously preparing the minds of
their followers by animating harangues; spiriting them up to

---

* This is at present a flourishing town, called Christiana, or Chris-
teen, about thirty-seven miles from Philadelphia, on the post-road to
Baltimore.

heroic feelings, assuring them of the protection of the gods, and inspiring them with a confidence in the prowess of their leaders. So the historian should awaken the attention and enlist the passions of his readers, and having set them all on fire with the importance of his subject, he should put himself at their head, flourish his pen, and lead them on to the thickest of the fight.

An illustrious example of this rule may be seen in that mirror of historians, the immortal Thucydides. Having arrived at the breaking out of the Peloponnesian war, one of his commentators observes that "he sounds the charge in all the disposition and spirit of Homer. He catalogues the allies on both sides. He awakens our expectations, and fast engages our attention. All mankind are concerned in the important point now going to be decided. Endeavors are made to disclose futurity. Heaven itself is interested in the dispute. The earth totters, and nature seems to labor with the great event. This is his solemn sublime manner of setting out. Thus he magnifies a war between two, as Rapin styles them, petty states; and thus artfully he supports a little subject by treating it in a great and noble method."

In like manner, having conducted my readers into the very teeth of peril—having followed the adventurous Peter and his band into foreign regions—surrounded by foes and stunned by the horrid din of arms—at this important moment, while darkness and doubt hang o'er each coming chapter, I hold it meet to harangue them, and prepare them for the events that are to follow.

And here I would premise one great advantage which, as the historian, I possess over my reader; and this it is, that though I cannot save the life of my favorite hero, nor absolutely contradict the event of a battle (both which liberties, though often taken by the French writers of the present reign, I hold to be utterly unworthy of a scrupulous historian), yet I can now and then make him to bestow on his enemy a sturdy back stroke sufficient to fell a giant; though, in honest truth, he may never have done anything of the kind—or I can drive his antagonist clear round and round the field, as did Homer make that fine fellow Hector scamper like a poltroon round the walls of Troy; for which, if ever they have encountered one another in the Elysian fields, I'll warrant the prince of poets has had to make the most humble apology.

I am aware that many conscientious readers will be ready to cry out "foul play!" whenever I render a little assistance to my hero—but I consider it one of those privileges exercised by historians of all ages, and one which has never been disputed. In fact, a historian is, as it were, bound in honor to stand by his hero—the fame of the latter is intrusted to his hands, and it is his duty to do the best by it he can. Never was there a general, an admiral, or any other commander, who, in giving an account of any battle he had fought, did not sorely belabor the enemy; and I have no doubt that, had my heroes written the history of their own achievements, they would have dealt much harder blows than any that I shall recount. Standing forth, therefore, as the guardian of their fame, it behooves me to do them the same justice they would have done themselves; and if I happen to be a little hard upon the Swedes, I give free leave to any of their descendants, who may write a history of the State of Delaware, to take fair retaliation, and belabor Peter Stuyvesant as hard as they please.

Therefore stand by for broken heads and bloody noses! —my pen hath long itched for a battle—siege after siege have I carried on without blows or bloodshed; but now I have at length got a chance, and I vow to Heaven and St. Nicholas that, let the chronicles of the time say what they please, neither Sallust, Livy, Tacitus, Polybius, nor any other historian, did ever record a fiercer fight than that in which my valiant chieftains are now about to engage.

And you, oh most excellent readers, whom, for your faithful adherence, I could cherish in the warmest corner of my heart—be not uneasy—trust the fate of our favorite Stuyvesant to me—for by the rood, come what may, I'll stick by

Hardkoppig Piet to the last; I'll make him drive about these losels vile, as did the renowned Launcelot of the lake a herd of recreant Cornish knights—and if he does fall, let me never draw my pen to fight another battle, in behalf of a brave man, if I don't make these lubberly Swedes pay for it.

No sooner had Peter Stuyvesant arrived before Fort Christina than he proceeded without delay to intrench himself, and immediately on running his first parallel dispatched Antony Van Corlear to summon the fortress to surrender. Van Corlear was received with all due formality, hoodwinked at the portal, and conducted through a pestiferous smell of salt fish and onions to the citadel, a substantial hut, built of pine logs. His eyes were here uncovered, and he found himself in the august presence of Governor Risingh. This chieftain, as I have before noted, was a very giantly man; and was clad in a coarse blue coat, strapped round the waist with a leathern belt, which caused the enormous skirts and pockets to set off with a very warlike sweep. His ponderous legs were cased in a pair of foxy-colored jack-boots, and he was straddling in the attitude of the Colossus of Rhodes, before a bit of broken looking-glass, shaving himself with a villainously dull razor. This afflicting operation caused him to make a series of horrible grimaces that heightened exceedingly the grisly terrors of his visage. On Antony Van Corlear's being announced, the grim commander paused for a moment, in the midst of one of his most hard-favored contortions, and after eying him askance over the shoulder, with a kind of snarling grin on his countenance, resumed his labors at the glass.

This iron harvest being reaped, he turned once more to the trumpeter, and demanded the purport of his errand. Antony Van Corlear delivered in a few words, being a kind of shorthand speaker, a long message from his excellency, recounting the whole history of the province, with a recapitulation of grievances and enumeration of claims, and concluding with a peremptory demand of instant surrender; which done, he turned aside, took his nose between his thumb and finger, and blew a tremendous blast, not unlike the flourish of a trumpet of defiance—which it had doubtless learned from a long and intimate neighborhood with that melodious instrument.

Governor Risingh heard him through, trumpet and all, but with infinite impatience; leaning at times, as was his usual custom, on the pommel of his sword, and at times twirling a huge steel watch-chain, or snapping his fingers. Van Corlear having finished, he bluntly replied that Peter Stuyvesant and his summons might go to the d——l, whither he hoped to send him and his crew of ragamuffins before supper-time. Then unsheathing his brass-hilted sword, and throwing away the scabbard—"Fore gad," quod he, "but I will not sheathe thee again, until I make a scabbard of the smoke-dried, leathern hide of this runagate Dutchman." Then, having flung a fierce defiance in the teeth of his adversary, by the lips of his messenger, the latter was reconducted to the portal, with all the ceremonious civility due to the trumpeter, squire, and embassador of so great a commander, and, being again unblinded, was courteously dismissed with a tweak of the nose, to assist him in recollecting his message.

No sooner did the gallant Peter receive this insolent reply than he let fly a tremendous volley of red-hot execrations that would infallibly have battered down the fortifications, and blown up the powder-magazine about the ears of the fiery Swede, had not the ramparts been remarkably strong and the magazine bomb-proof. Perceiving that the works withstood this terrific blast, and that it was utterly impossible (as it really was in those unphilosophic days) to carry on a war with words, he ordered his merry men all to prepare for an immediate assault. But here a strange murmur broke out among his troops, beginning with the tribe of the Van Bummels, those valiant trencher-men of the Bronx, and spreading from man to man, accompanied with certain mutinous looks and discontented murmurs. For once in his life, and only for once, did the great Peter turn pale, for he verily thought his warriors were going to falter in this hour of perilous trial, and thus tarnish forever the fame of the province of New Nederlandts.

But soon did he discover, to his great joy, that in this suspicion he deeply wronged this most undaunted army; for the cause of this agitation and uneasiness simply was that the hour of dinner was at hand, and it would have almost broken the hearts of these regular Dutch warriors to have broken in upon the invariable routine of their habits. Besides, it was an established rule among our valiant ancestors always to fight upon a full stomach, and to this may be doubtless attributed the circumstance that they came to be so renowned in arms.

And now are the hearty men of the Manhattoes, and their no less hearty comrades, all lustily engaged under the trees, buffeting stoutly with the contents of their wallets, and taking such affectionate embraces of their canteens and pottles as though they verily believed they were to be the last. And as I foresee we shall have hot work in a page or two, I advise my readers to do the same, for which purpose I will bring this chapter to a close; giving them my word of honor that no advantage shall be taken of this armistice to surprise, or in any wise molest, the honest Nederlanders while at their vigorous repast.

CHAPTER SEVEN

CONTAINING THE MOST HORRIBLE BATTLE EVER RECORDED IN POETRY OR PROSE—WITH THE ADMIRABLE EXPLOITS OF PETER THE HEADSTRONG

"Now had the Dutchmen snatched a huge repast," and finding themselves wonderfully encouraged and animated thereby, prepared to take the field. Expectation, says the writer of the Stuyvesant manuscript—Expectation now stood on stilts. The world forgot to turn round, or rather stood still, that it might witness the affray; like a fat, round-bellied alderman watching the combat of two chivalric flies upon his jerkin. The eyes of all mankind, as usual in such cases, were turned upon Fort Christina. The sun, like a little man in a crowd at a puppet-show, scampered about the heavens, popping his head here and there, and endeavoring to get a peep between the unmannerly clouds that obtruded themselves in his way. The historians filled their inkhorns —the poets went without their dinners, either that they might buy paper and goose-quills, or because they could not get anything to eat—antiquity scowled sulkily out of its grave to see itself outdone—while even posterity stood mute, gazing in gaping ecstasy of retrospection on the eventful field.

The immortal deities, who whilom had seen service at the "affair" of Troy, now mounted their feather-bed clouds and sailed over the plain or mingled among the combatants in different disguises, all itching to have a finger in the pie. Jupiter sent off his thunderbolt to a noted coppersmith to have it furbished up for the direful occasion. Venus swore by her chastity she'd patronize the Swedes, and in semblance of a blear-eyed trull paraded the battlements of Fort Christina, accompanied by Diana as a sergeant's widow, of cracked reputation.—The noted bully, Mars, stuck two horse-pistols in his belt, shouldered a rusty firelock, and gallantly swaggered at their elbow as a drunken corporal—while Apollo trudged in their rear as a bandy-legged fifer, playing most villainously out of tune.

On the other side, the ox-eyed Juno, who had gained a pair of black eyes overnight, in one of her curtain lectures with old Jupiter, displayed her haughty beauties on a baggage-wagon—Minerva, as a brawny gin sutler, tucked up her skirts, brandished her fists, and swore most heroically in exceeding bad Dutch (having but lately studied the language), by way of keeping up the spirits of the soldiers; while Vulcan halted as a club-footed blacksmith, lately promoted to be a captain of militia. All was silent horror or bustling preparation; war reared his horrid front, gnashed loud his iron fangs, and shook his direful crest of bristling bayonets. And now the mighty chieftains marshaled out their hosts. Here stood stout Risingh, firm as a thousand rocks—incrusted with stockades and intrenched to the chin in mud batteries. His valiant soldiery lined the breastwork in grim array, each having his mustachios fiercely greased, and his hair pomatumed back and queued so stiffly tha the grinned above the ramparts like a grisly death's head.

There came on the intrepid Peter—his brows knit, his teeth set, his fists clinched, almost breathing forth volumes of smoke, so fierce was the fire that raged within his bosom. His faithful squire, Van Corlear, trudged valiantly at his heels, with his trumpet gorgeously bedecked with red and yellow ribbons, the remembrances of his fair mistresses at the Manhattoes.   Then came waddling on the sturdy chivalry of the Hudson.   There were the Van Wycks, and the Van Dycks, and the Ten Eycks—the Van Nesses, the Van Tassels, the Van Grolls, the Van Hœsens, the Van Giesons, and the Van Blarcoms—the Van Warts, the Van Winkles, the Van Dams, the Van Pelts, the Van Rippers, and the Van Brunts.—There were the Van Hornes, the Van Hooks, the Van Bunschotens, the Van Gelders, the Van Arsdales, and the Van Bummels—the Vander Belts, the Vander Hoofs, the Vander Voorts, the Vander Lyns, the Vander Pools, and the Vander Spiegels.—There came the Hoffmans, the Hooghlands, the Hoppers, the Cloppers, the Ryckmans, the Dyckmans, the Hogebooms, the Rosebooms, the Oothouts, the Quackenbosses, the Roerbacks, the Garrebrantzs, the Bensons, the Brouwers, the Waldrons, the Onderdonks, the Varra Vangers, the Schermerhornes, the Stoutenburghs, the Brinkerhoffs, the Bontecous, the Knickerbockers, the Hockstrassers, the Ten Breecheses, and the Tough Breecheses, with a host more of worthies, whose names are too crabbed to be written, or, if they could be written, it would be impossible for man to utter—all fortified with a mighty dinner, and, to use the words of a great Dutch poet,

"Brimful of wrath and cabbage!"

For an instant the mighty Peter paused in the midst of his career, and mounting on a stump, addressed his troops in eloquent Low Dutch, exhorting them to fight like *duyvels*, and assuring them that, if they conquered, they should get plenty of booty—if they fell, they should be allowed the unparalleled satisfaction, while dying, of reflecting that it was in the service of their country—and after they were dead, of seeing their names inscribed in the temple of renown, and handed down, in company with all the other great men of the year, for the admiration of posterity.—Finally, he swore to them, on the word of a governor (and they knew him too well to doubt it for a moment), that if he caught any mother's son of them looking pale, or playing craven, he'd curry his hide till he made him run out of it like a snake in springtime.—Then lugging out his trusty saber, he brandished it three times over his head, ordered Van Corlear to sound a tremendous charge, and shouting the words, "St. Nicholas and the Manhattoes!" courageously dashed forward. His warlike followers, who had employed the interval in lighting their pipes, instantly stuck them in their mouths, gave a furious puff, and charged gallantly under cover of the smoke.

The Swedish garrison, ordered by the cunning Risingh not to fire until they could distinguish the whites of their assailants' eyes, stood in horrid silence on the covert-way until the eager Dutchmen had ascended the glacis. Then did they pour into them such a tremendous volley that the very hills quaked around, and were terrified even unto an incontinence of water, insomuch that certain springs burst forth from their sides, which continue to run unto the present day. Not a Dutchman but would have bitten the dust, beneath that dreadful fire, had not the protecting Minerva kindly taken care that the Swedes should, one and all, observe their usual custom of shutting their eyes and turning away their heads at the moment of discharge.

The Swedes followed up their fire by leaping the counterscarp, and falling tooth and nail upon the foe, with furious outcries. And now might be seen prodigies of valor, of which neither history nor song has ever recorded a parallel. Here was beheld the sturdy Stoffel Brinkerhoff, brandishing his lusty quarter-staff, like the terrible giant Blanderon his oak tree (for he scorned to carry any other weapon), and drumming a horrific tune upon the heads of whole squadrons of Swedes. There were the crafty Van Kortlandts, posted at a distance, like the Locrian archers of yore, and plying it most potently with the long bow, for which they were so justly renowned. At another place were collected on a rising knoll the valiant men of Sing Sing, who assisted marvelously in the fight by chanting forth the great song of St. Nicholas; but as to the Gardeniers of Hudson, they were absent from the battle, having been sent out on a marauding party to lay waste the neighboring watermelon patches. In a different part of the field might be seen the Van Grolls of Antony's Nose; but they were horribly perplexed in a defile between two little hills, by reason of the length of their noses. There were the Van Bunschotens of Nyack and Kakiat, so renowned for kicking with the left foot, but their skill availed them little at present, being short of wind in consequence of the hearty dinner they had eaten, and they would irretrievably have been put to rout had they not been re-enforced by a gallant corps of *Voltigeures*, composed of the Hoppers, who advanced to their assistance nimbly on one foot. Nor must I omit to mention the incomparable achievements of Antony Van Corlear, who, for a good quarter of an hour, waged stubborn fight with a little pursy Swedish drummer, whose hide he drummed most magnificently; and had he not come into the battle with no other weapon but his trumpet, would infallibly have put him to an untimely end.

But now the combat thickened—on came the mighty Jacobus Varra Vanger, and the fighting men of the Wallabout; after them thundered the Van Pelts of Esopus, together with the Van Rippers and the Van Brunts, bearing down all before them—then the Suy Dams and the Van Dams, pressing forward with many a blustering oath, at the head of the warriors of Hell-gate, clad in their thunder and lightning gaoerdines; and lastly, the standard-bearers and body-guards of Peter Stuyvesant, bearing the great beaver of the Manhattoes.

And now commenced the horrid din, the desperate struggle, the maddening ferocity, the frantic desperation, the confusion and self-abandonment of war. Dutchman and Swede commingled, tugged, panted, and blowed. The heavens were darkened with a tempest of missives. Bang! went the guns —whack! struck the broadswords—thump! went the cudgels —crash! went the musket stocks—blows—kicks—cuffs— scratches—black eyes and bloody noses, swelling the horrors of the scene! Thick-thwack, cut and hack, helter-skelter, higgledy-piggledy, hurly-burly, head over heels, rough and tumble!—Dunder and blixum! swore the Dutchmen— splitter and splutter! cried the Swedes.—Storm the works! shouted Hardkoppig Peter.—Fire the mine! roared stout Risingh—Tanta-ra-ra-ra! twanged the trumpet of Antony Van Corlear—until all voice and sound became unintelligible— grunts of pain, yells of fury, and shouts of triumph commingling in one hideous clamor. The earth shook as if struck with a paralytic stroke—trees shrunk aghast, and withered at the sight—rocks burrowed in the ground like rabbits, and even Christina Creek turned from its course and ran up a mountain in breathless terror!

Long hung the contest doubtful; for, though a heavy shower of rain, sent by the "cloud-compelling Jove," in some measure cooled their ardor, as doth a bucket of water thrown on a group of fighting mastiffs, yet did they but pause for a moment to return with tenfold fury to the charge, belaboring each other with black and bloody bruises. Just at this juncture was seen a vast and dense column of smoke, slowly rolling toward the scene of battle, which for a while made even the furious combatants to stay their arms in mute astonishment—but the wind for a moment dispersing the murky cloud, from the midst thereof emerged the flaunting banner of the immortal Michael Paw. This noble chieftain came fearlessly on, leading a solid phalanx of oyster-fed Pavonians, who had remained behind, partly as a *corps de re-serve*, and partly to digest the enormous dinner they had eaten. These sturdy yeomen, nothing daunted, did trudge manfully forward, smoking their pipes with outrageous vigor, so as to raise the awful cloud that has been mentioned; but marching exceedingly slow, being short of leg and of great rotundity in the belt.

And now the protecting deities of the army of New Amsterdam, having unthinkingly left the field and stepped into a neighboring tavern to refresh themselves with a pot of beer, a direful catastrophe had wellnigh chanced to befall the Nederlanders. Scarcely had the myrmidons of the puissant Paw attained the front of battle, before the Swedes, instructed by the cunning Risingh, leveled a shower of blows full at their tobacco-pipes. Astounded at this unexpected assault, and totally discomfited at seeing their pipes broken, the valiant Dutchmen fell in vast confusion—already they begin to fly—like a frightened drove of unwieldy elephants they throw their own army in an uproar, bearing down a whole legion of little Hoppers—the sacred banner, on which is blazoned the gigantic oyster of Communipaw, is trampled in the dirt—the Swedes pluck up new spirits, and pressing on their rear, apply their feet *a parte poste*, with a vigor that prodigiously accelerates their motions—nor doth the renowned Paw himself fail to receive divers grievous and dishonorable visitations of shoe-leather!

But what, oh muse! was the rage of the gallant Peter, when from afar he saw his army yield? With a voice of thunder did he roar after his recreant warriors. The men of the Manhattoes plucked up new courage when they heard their leader—or rather they dreaded his fierce displeasure, of which they stood in more awe than of all the Swedes in Christendom—but the daring Peter, not waiting for their aid, plunged, sword in hand, into the thickest of the foe. Then did he display some such incredible achievements as have never been known since the miraculous days of the giants. Wherever he went, the enemy shrunk before him—

with fierce impetuosity he pushed forward, driving the Swedes, like dogs, into their own ditch—but as he fearlessly advanced, the foe thronged in his rear, and hung upon his flank with fearful peril. One crafty Swede, advancing warily on one side, drove his dastard sword full at the hero's heart; but the protecting power that watches over the safety of all great and good men turned aside the hostile blade, and directed it to a side pocket, where reposed an enormous iron tobacco-box, endowed, like the shield of Achilles, with supernatural powers—no doubt in consequence of its being piously deco-rated with a portrait of the blessed St. Nicholas. Thus was the dreadful blow repelled, but not without occasioning to the great Peter a fearful loss of wind.

Like as a furious bear, when gored by curs, turns fiercely round, gnashes his teeth, and springs upon the foe, so did our hero turn upon the treacherous Swede. The miserable varlet sought in flight for safety—but the active Peter, seiz-ing him by an immeasurable queue that dangled from his head—"Ah, whoreson caterpillar!" roared he, "here is what shall make dog's meat of thee!" So saying, he whirled his trusty sword, and made a blow that would have decapitated him, but that the pitying steel struck short and shaved the queue forever from his crown. At this very moment a cun-ning arquebusier, perched on the summit of a neighboring mound, leveled his deadly instrument, and would have sent the gallant Stuyvesant a wailing ghost to haunt the Stygian shore had not the watchful Minerva, who had just stopped to tie up her garter, seen the great peril of her favorite chief, and dispatched old Boreas with his bellows; who, in the very nick of time, just as the match descended to the pan, gave such a lucky blast as blew all the priming from the touch-hole!

Thus waged the horrid fight—when the stout Risingh, surveying the battle from the top of a little ravelin, perceived his faithful troops banged, beaten, and kicked by the invin-cible Peter. Language cannot describe the choler with which he was seized at the sight—he only stopped for a moment to disburden himself of five thousand anathemas; and then, drawing his immeasurable falchion, straddled down to the field of combat, with some such thundering strides as Jupiter is said by Hesiod to have taken when he strode down the spheres to hurl his thunderbolts at the Titans.

No sooner did these two rival heroes come face to face than they each made a prodigious start, such as is made by your most experienced stage champions. Then did they regard each other for a moment with bitter aspect, like two furious ram-cats on the very point of a clapper-clawing. Then did they throw themselves in one attitude, then in another, striking their swords on the ground, first on the right side, then on the left—at last, at it they went with incredible ferocity. Words cannot tell the prodigies of strength and valor displayed in this direful encounter—an encounter compared to which the far-famed battles of Ajax with Hector, of Eneas with Turnus, Orlando with Rodomont, Guy of Warwick with Colbrand the Dane, or that renowned Welsh knight, Sir Owen of the Mountains with the giant Guylon, were all gentle sports and holiday recreations. At length the valiant Peter, watching his opportunity, aimed a fearful blow, with the full intention of cleaving his adversary to the very chin; but Risingh, nimbly raising his sword, warded it off so narrowly that, glancing on one side, it shaved away a huge canteen that he always carried swung on one side; thence pursuing its trenchant course, it severed off a deep coat-pocket, stored with bread and cheese—all which dainties, rolling among the armies, occasioned a fearful scrambling between the Swedes and Dutchmen, and made the general battle to wax ten times more furious than ever.

Enraged to see his military stores thus wofully laid waste, the stout Risingh, collecting all his forces, aimed a mighty blow full at the hero's crest. In vain did his fierce little cocked hat oppose its course; the biting steel clove through the stubborn ram-beaver, and would infallibly have cracked the crown, but that the skull was of such adamantine hardness that the brittle weapon shivered into pieces, shedding a thousand sparks, like beams of glory, round his grisly visage.

Stunned with the blow, the valiant Peter reeled, turned up his eyes, and beheld fifty thousand suns, besides moons and stars, dancing about the firmament—at length, missing his footing, by reason of his wooden leg, down he came, on his seat of honor, with a crash that shook the surrounding hills, and would infallibly have wrecked his anatomical system had he not been received into a cushion softer than velvet, which Providence, or Minerva, or St. Nicholas, or some kindly cow, had benevolently prepared for his reception.

The furious Risingh, in despite of that noble maxim cherished by all true knights, that "fair play is a jewel," hastened to take advantage of the hero's fall; but just as he was stooping to give the fatal blow, the ever-vigilant Peter bestowed him a sturdy thwack over the sconce with his wooden leg that set some dozen chimes of bells ringing triple bob-majors in his cerebellum. The bewildered Swede staggered with the blow, and in the meantime the wary Peter, espying a pocket-pistol lying hard by (which had dropped from the wallet of his faithful squire and trumpeter, Van Corlear, during his furious encounter with the drummer), discharged it full at the head of the reeling Risingh.—Let not my reader mistake—it was not a murderous weapon loaded with powder and ball, but a little sturdy stone pottle, charged to the muzzle with a double dram of true Dutch courage, which the knowing Van Corlear always carried about him by way of replenishing his valor. The hideous missive sung through the air, and true to its course, as was the mighty fragment of a rock discharged at Hector by bully Ajax, encountered the huge head of the gigantic Swede with matchless violence.

This heaven-directed blow decided the eventful battle. The ponderous pericranium of General Jan Risingh sunk upon his breast; his knees tottered under him; a deathlike torpor seized upon his giant frame, and he tumbled to the earth with such tremendous violence that old Pluto started with affright, lest he should have broken through the roof of his infernal palace.

His fall was the signal of defeat and victory.—The Swedes gave way—the Dutch pressed forward; the former took to their heels, the latter hotly pursued—some entered with them, pell-mell, through the sallyport—others stormed the bastion, and others scrambled over the curtain. Thus, in a little while, the impregnable fortress of Fort Christina, which like another Troy had stood a siege of full ten hours, was finally carried by assault, without the loss of a single man on either side. Victory, in the likeness of a gigantic ox-fly, sat perched upon the cocked hat of the gallant Stuyvesant; and it was universally declared, by all the writers whom he hired to write the history of his expedition, that on this memorable day he gained a sufficient quantity of glory to immortalize a dozen of the greatest heroes in Christendom!

CHAPTER EIGHT

IN WHICH THE AUTHOR AND THE READER, WHILE REPOSING AFTER THE BATTLE, FALL INTO A VERY GRAVE DISCOURSE—AFTER WHICH IS RECORDED THE CONDUCT OF PETER STUYVESANT AFTER HIS VICTORY

THANKS to St. Nicholas, we have safely finished this tremendous battle; let us sit down, my worthy reader, and cool ourselves, for I am in a prodigious sweat and agitation.— Truly this fighting of battles is hot work! and if your great commanders did but know what trouble they give their historians, they would not have the conscience to achieve so many horrible victories. But methinks I hear my reader complain that, throughout this boasted battle, there is not the least slaughter, nor a single individual maimed, if we except the unhappy Swede who was shorn of his queue by the trenchant blade of Peter Stuyvesant; all which, he observes, is a great outrage on probability, and highly injurious to the interest of the narration.

This is certainly an objection of no little moment; but it arises entirely from the obscurity that envelops the remote periods of time about which I have undertaken to write. Thus, though doubtless, from the importance of the object, and the prowess of the parties concerned, there must have been terrible carnage, and prodigies of valor displayed, before the walls of Christina, yet, notwithstanding that I have consulted every history, manuscript and tradition touching this memorable though long forgotten battle, I cannot find mention made of a single man killed or wounded in the whole affair.

This is, without doubt, owing to the extreme modesty of our forefathers, who, like their descendants, were never prone to vaunt of their achievements; but it is a virtue that places their historian in a most embarrassing predicament; for, having promised my readers a hideous and unparalleled battle, and having worked them up into a warlike and bloodthirsty state of mind, to put them off without any havoc and slaughter was as bitter a disappointment as to summon a multitude of good people to attend an execution, and then cruelly balk them by a reprieve.

Had the inexorable fates only allowed me some half a score of dead men, I had been content; for I would have made them such heroes as abounded in the olden time, but whose race is now unfortunately extinct—any one of whom, if we may believe those authentic writers, the poets, could drive great armies like sheep before him, and conquer and desolate whole cities by his single arm.

But seeing that I had not a single life at my disposal, all that was left me was to make the most I could of my battle, by means of kicks, and cuffs, and bruises, and such like ignoble wounds. And here I cannot but compare my dilemma, in some sort, to that of the divine Milton, who, having arrayed with sublime preparation his immortal hosts against each other, is sadly put to it how to manage them, and how he shall make the end of his battle answer to the beginning; inasmuch as, being mere spirits, he cannot deal a mortal blow, nor even give a flesh wound to any of his combatants. For my part, the greatest difficulty I found was, when I had once put my warriors in a passion, and let them loose into the midst of the enemy, to keep them from doing mischief. Many a time had I to restrain the sturdy Peter from cleaving a gigantic Swede to the very waistband, or spitting half a dozen little fellows on his sword, like so many sparrows; and when I had set some hundreds of missives flying in the air, I did not dare to suffer one of them to reach the ground lest it should have put an end to some unlucky Dutchman.

The reader cannot conceive how mortifying it is to a writer thus in a manner to have his hands tied, and how many tempting opportunities I had to wink at, where I might have made as fine a death-blow as any recorded in history or song.

From my own experience, I begin to doubt most potently of the authenticity of many of Homer's stories. I verily believe that when he had once lanched one of his favorite heroes among a crowd of the enemy, he cut down many an honest fellow, without any authority for so doing excepting that he presented a fair mark—and that often a poor devil was sent to grim Pluto's domains merely because he had a name that would give a sounding turn to a period. But I disclaim all such unprincipled liberties—let me but have truth and the law on my side, and no man would fight harder than myself: but since the various records I consulted did not warrant it, I had too much conscience to kill a single soldier. By St. Nicholas, but it would have been a pretty piece of business! My enemies, the critics, who I foresee will be ready enough to lay any crime they can discover at my door, might have charged me with murder outright—and I should have esteemed myself lucky to escape with no harsher verdict than manslaughter!

And now, gentle reader, that we are tranquilly sitting

down here, smoking our pipes, permit me to indulge in a melancholy reflection, which at this moment passes across my mind.—How vain, how fleeting, how uncertain are all those gaudy bubbles after which we are panting and toiling in this world of fair delusion! The wealth which the miser has amassed with so many weary days, so many sleepless nights, a spendthrift heir may squander away in joyless prodigality; the noblest monuments which pride has ever reared to perpetuate a name the hand of time will shortly tumble into ruins—and even the brightest laurels gained by feats of arms may wither and be forever blighted by the chilling neglect of mankind. — "How many illustrious heroes," says the good Boetius, "who were once the pride and glory of the age, hath the silence of historians buried in eternal oblivion!" And this it was that induced the Spartans, when they went to battle, solemnly to sacrifice to the muses, supplicating that their achievements should be worthily recorded. Had not Homer tuned his lofty lyre, observes the elegant Cicero, the valor of Achilles had remained unsung. And such, too, after all the toils and perils he had braved, after all the gallant actions he had achieved, such too had nearly been the fate of the chivalric Peter Stuyvesant, but that I fortunately stepped in and engraved his name on the indelible tablet of history, just as the caitiff Time was silently brushing it away forever.

The more I reflect, the more am I astonished at the important character of the historian. He is the sovereign censor to decide upon the renown or infamy of his fellowmen— he is the patron of kings and conquerors, on whom it depends whether they shall live in after ages, or be forgotten, as were their ancestors before them. The tyrant may oppress while the object of his tyranny exists, but the historian possesses superior might, for his power extends even beyond the grave. The shades of departed and long-forgotten heroes anxiously bend down from above, while he writes, watching each movement of his pen, whether it shall pass by their names with neglect or inscribe them on the deathless pages of renown.

Even the drop of ink that hangs trembling on his pen, which he may either dash upon the floor or waste in idle scrawlings —that very drop, which to him is not worth the twentieth part of a farthing, may be of incalculable value to some departed worthy—may elevate half a score, in one moment, to immortality, who would have given worlds, had they possessed them, to insure the glorious meed.

Let not my readers imagine, however, that I am indulging in vainglorious boastings, or am anxious to blazon forth the importance of my tribe. On the contrary, I shrink when I reflect on the awful responsibility we historians assume—I shudder to think what direful commotions and calamities we occasion in the world—I swear to thee, honest reader, as I am a man, I weep at the very idea! Why, let me ask, are so many illustrious men daily tearing themselves away from the embraces of their families—slighting the smiles of beauty —despising the allurements of fortune, and exposing themselves to the miseries of war?—Why are kings desolating empires and depopulating whole countries? In short, what induces all great men, of all ages and countries, to commit so many victories and misdeeds, and inflict so many miseries upon mankind and on themselves, but the mere hope that some historian will kindly take them into notice, and admit them into a corner of his volume. For, in short, the mighty object of all their toils, their hardships, and privations, is nothing but *immortal fame*—and what is immortal fame?— why, half a page of dirty paper!—Alas! alas! how humiliating the idea—that the renown of so great a man as Peter Stuyvesant should depend upon the pen of so little a man as Diedrich Knickerbocker!

And now, having refreshed ourselves after the fatigues and perils of the field, it behooves us to return once more to the scene of conflict, and inquire what were the results of this renowned conquest. The fortress of Christina being the fair metropolis, and in a manner the key to New Sweden, its capture was speedily followed by the entire subjugation of the province. This was not a little promoted by the gallant and courteous deportment of the chivalric Peter. Though a man terrible in battle, yet in the hour of victory was he endued with a spirit generous merciful, and humane—he vaunted not over his enemies, nor did he make defeat more galling by unmanly insults; for like that mirror of knightly virtue, the renowned Paladin Orlando, he was more anxious to do great actions than to talk of them after they were done. He put no man to death; ordered no houses to be burned down; permitted no ravages to be perpetrated on the property of the vanquished, and even gave one of his bravest officers a severe admonishment with his walking-staff, for having been detected in the act of sacking a hen-roost.

He moreover issued a proclamation, inviting the inhabitants to submit to the authority of their High Mightinesses; but declaring, with unexampled clemency, that whoever refused should be lodged, at the public expense, in a goodly castle provided for the purpose, and have an armed retinue to wait on them in the bargain. In consequence of these beneficent terms, about thirty Swedes stepped manfully forward and took the oath of allegiance; in reward for which they were graciously permitted to remain on the banks of the Delaware, where their descendants reside at this very day. But I am told by divers observant travelers that they have never been able to get over the chapfallen looks of their ancestors, and do still unaccountably transmit from father to son manifest marks of the sound drubbing given them by the sturdy Amsterdamers.

The whole country of New Sweden, having thus yielded to the arms of the triumphant Peter, was reduced to a colony, called South River, and placed under the superintendence of a lieutenant-governor; subject to the control of the supreme government at New Amsterdam. This great dignitary was called Mynheer William Beekman, or rather *Beek*man, who derived his surname, as did Ovidius Naso of yore, from the lordly dimensions of his nose, which projected from the center of his countenance like the beak of a parrot. He was the great progenitor of the tribe of the Beekmans, one of the most ancient and honorable families of the province, the members of which do gratefully commemorate the origin of their dignity, not as your noble families in England would do, by having a glowing proboscis emblazoned in their escutcheon, but by one and all wearing a right goodly nose stuck in the very middle of their faces.

Thus was this perilous enterprise gloriously terminated with the loss of only two men—Wolfert Van Horne, a tall, spare man, who was knocked overboard by the boom of a sloop in a flaw of wind; and fat Brom Van Bummel, who was suddenly carried off by an indigestion; both, however, were immortalized as having bravely fallen in the service of their country. True it is, Peter Stuyvesant had one of his limbs terribly fractured, being shattered to pieces in the act of storming the fortress; but as it was fortunately his wooden leg, the wound was promptly and effectually healed.

And now nothing remains to this branch of my history, but to mention that this immaculate hero and his victorious army returned joyously to the Manhattoes, where they made a solemn and triumphant entry, bearing with them the conquered Risingh, and the remnant of his battered crew, who had refused allegiance; for it appears that the gigantic Swede had only fallen into a swoon at the end of the battle, from whence he was speedily restored by a wholesome tweak of the nose.

These captive heroes were lodged, according to the promise of the governor, at the public expense, in a fair and spacious castle; being the prison of state, of which Stoffel Brinkerhoff, the immortal conqueror of Oyster Bay, was appointed governor; and which has ever since remained in the possession of his descendants.*

It was a pleasant and goodly sight to witness the joy of the people of New Amsterdam at beholding their warriors once more return from this war in the wilderness. The old

---

* This castle, though very much altered and modernized, is still in being, and stands at the corner of Pearl street, facing Coenties' Slip.

women thronged round Antony Van Corlear, who gave the whole history of the campaign with matchless accuracy; saving that he took the credit of fighting the whole battle himself, and especially of vanquishing the stout Risingh, which he considered himself as clearly entitled to, seeing that it was effected by his own stone pottle.

The schoolmasters throughout the town gave holiday to their little urchins, who followed in droves after the drums, with paper caps on their heads, and sticks in their breeches, thus taking the first lesson in the art of war. As to the sturdy rabble, they thronged at the heels of Peter Stuyvesant wherever he went, waving their greasy hats in the air, and shouting "Hardkoppig Piet forever!"

It was, indeed, a day of roaring rout and jubilee. A huge dinner was prepared at the Stadt-house in honor of the conquerors, where were assembled, in one glorious constellation, the great and the little luminaries of New Amsterdam. There were the lordly Schout and his obsequious deputy—the burgomasters with their officious schepens at their elbows—the subaltern officers at the elbows of the schepens, and so on to the lowest hanger-on of police; every Tag having his Rag at his side, to finish his pipe, drink off his heel-taps, and laugh at his flights of immortal dullness. In short—for a city feast is a city feast all the world over, and has been a city feast ever since the creation—the dinner went off much the same as do our great corporation junketings and Fourth of July banquets. Loads of fish, flesh and fowl were devoured, oceans of liquor drunk, thousands of pipes smoked, and many a dull joke honored with much obstreperous fat-sided laughter.

I must not omit to mention that to this far-famed victory Peter Stuyvesant was indebted for another of his many titles —for so hugely delighted were the honest burghers with his achievements that they unanimously honored him with the name of *Pietre de Groodt*, that is to say Peter the Great, or, as it was translated by the people of New Amsterdam, *Piet de Pig*—an appellation which he maintained even unto the day of his death.

BOOK SEVEN

*CONTAINING THE THIRD PART OF THE REIGN OF PETER
THE HEADSTRONG—HIS TROUBLES WITH THE BRITISH
NATION, AND THE DECLINE AND FALL OF THE DUTCH
DYNASTY*

CHAPTER ONE

HOW PETER STUYVESANT RELIEVED THE SOVEREIGN PEO-
    PLE FROM THE BURDEN OF TAKING CARE OF THE
    NATION—WITH SUNDRY PARTICULARS OF HIS CONDUCT
    IN TIME OF PEACE

THE history of the reign of Peter Stuyvesant furnishes a
melancholy picture of the incessant cares and vexations in-
separable from government; and may serve as a solemn
warning to all who are ambitious of attaining the seat of
power. Though crowned with victory, enriched by conquest, and returning in triumph to his metropolis, his exultation was checked by beholding the sad abuses that had taken
place during the short interval of his absence.

The populace, unfortunately for their own comfort, had
taken a deep draught of the intoxicating cup of power, during the reign of William the Testy; and though, upon the
accession of Peter Stuyvesant, they felt, with a certain in-
stinctive perception, which mobs as well as cattle possess,
that the reins of government had passed into stronger hands,
yet could they not help fretting and chafing and champing
upon the bit in restive silence.

It seems, by some strange and inscrutable fatality, to be
the destiny of most countries (and more especially of your
enlightened republics) always to be governed by the most incompetent man in the nation—so that you will scarcely find

an individual throughout the whole community who cannot point out innumerable errors in administration, and convince you, in the end, that had *he* been at the head of affairs, matters would have gone on a thousand times more prosperously. Strange! that government, which seems to be so generally understood, should invariably be so erroneously administered—strange that the talent of legislation, so prodigally bestowed, should be denied to the only man in the nation to whose station it is requisite!

Thus it was in the present instance; not a man of all the herd of pseudo politicians in New Amsterdam but was an oracle on topics of state, and could have directed public affars incomparably better than Peter Stuyvesant. But so severe was the old governor in his disposition that he would never suffer one of the multitude of able counselors by whom he was surrounded to intrude his advice and save the country from destruction.

Scarcely, therefore, had he departed on his expedition against the Swedes than the old factions of William Kieft's reign began to thrust their heads above water, and to gather together in political meetings, to discuss "the state of the nation." At these assemblages, the busy burgomasters and their officious schepens made a very considerable figure. These worthy dignitaries were no longer the fat, well-fed, tranquil magistrates that presided in the peaceful days of Wouter Van Twiller—on the contrary, being elected by the people, they formed in a manner a sturdy bulwark between the mob and the administration. They were great candidates for popularity, and strenuous advocates for the rights of the rabble; resembling in disinterested zeal the widemouthed tribunes of ancient Rome, or those virtuous patriots of modern days emphatically denominated "the friends of the people."

Under the tuition of these profound politicians, it is astonishing how suddenly enlightened the swinish multitude became in matters above their comprehensions. Cobblers, tinkers and tailors all at once felt themselves inspired, like

those religious idiots in the glorious times of monkish illumination; and, without any previous study or experience, became instantly capable of directing all the movements of
government. Nor must I neglect to mention a number of
superannuated, wrong-headed old burghers, who had come
over, when boys, in the crew of the "Goede Vrouw," and
were held up as infallible oracles by the enlightened mob.
To suppose that a man who had helped to discover a country
did not know how it ought to be governed was preposterous
in the extreme. It would have been deemed as much a
heresy as at the present day to question the political talents
and universal infallibility of our old "heroes of '76"—and to
doubt that he who had fought for a government, however
stupid he might naturally be, was not competent to fill any
station under it.

But as Peter Stuyvesant had a singular inclination to
govern his province without the assistance of his subjects
he felt highly incensed on his return to find the factious appearance they had assumed during his absence. His first
measure, therefore, was to restore perfect order, by prostrat-
ing the dignity of the sovereign people.

He accordingly watched his opportunity, and one evening, when the enlightened mob was gathered together, listening to a patriotic speech from an inspired cobbler, the intrepid
Peter all at once appeared among them, with a countenance
sufficient to petrify a mill-stone. The whole meeting was
thrown into consternation—the orator seemed to have received a paralytic stroke in the very middle of a sublime
sentence, and stood aghast with open mouth and trembling
knees, while the words horror! tyranny! liberty! rights!
taxes! death! destruction! and a deluge of other patriotic
phrases came roaring from his throat before he had power
to close his lips. The shrewd Peter took no notice of the
skulking throng around him, but advancing to the brawling
bully-ruffian, and drawing out a huge silver watch which
might have served in times of yore as a town clock, and
which is still retained by his descendants as a family curi-

osity, requested the orator to mend it and set it going. The
orator humbly confessed it was utterly out of his power, as
he was unacquainted with the nature of its construction.
"Nay, but," said Peter, "try your ingenuity, man; you see
all the springs and wheels, and how easily the clumsiest hand
may stop it and pull it to pieces; and why should it not be
equally easy to regulate as to stop it?" The orator declared
that his trade was wholly different—that he was a poor cobbler, and had never meddled with a watch in his life—that
there were men skilled in the art, whose business it was to
attend to those matters, but for his part he should only mar
the workmanship and put the whole in confusion.—"Why,
harkee, master of mine," cried Peter, turning suddenly upon
him, with a countenance that almost petrified the patcher of
shoes into a perfect lap-stone—"dost thou pretend to meddle
with the movements of government—to regulate, and correct, and patch, and cobble a complicated machine, the principles of which are above thy comprehension, and its simplest
operations too subtle for thy understanding; when thou canst
not correct a trifling error in a common piece of mechanism,
the whole mystery of which is open to thy inspection?—Hence
with thee to the leather and stone, which are emblems of
thy head; cobble thy shoes, and confine thyself to the voca-
tion for which Heaven has fitted thee.—But," elevating his
voice until it made the welkin ring, "if ever I catch thee or
any of thy tribe meddling again with affairs of government,
by St. Nicholas, but I'll have every mother's bastard of ye
flay'd alive, and your hides stretched for drum-heads, that
ye may thenceforth make a noise to some purpose!"

This threat, and the tremendous voice in which it was
uttered, caused the whole multitude to quake with fear.
The hair of the orator arose on his head like his own swine's
bristles, and not a knight of the thimble present but his heart
died within him, and he felt as though he could have verily
escaped through the eye of a needle.

But though this measure produced the desired effect in
reducing the community to order, yet it tended to injure the

popularity of the great Peter among the enlightened vulgar.
Many accused him of entertaining highly aristocratic sentiments, and of leaning too much in favor of the patricians.
Indeed, there appeared to be some ground for such an accusation, as he always carried himself with a very lofty, soldier-
like port, and was somewhat particular in his dress; dressing
himself, when not in uniform, in simple, but rich apparel,
and was especially noted for having his sound leg (which
was a very comely one) always arrayed in a red stocking
and high-heeled shoe. Though a man of great simplicity of
manners, yet there was something about him that repelled
rude familiarity, while it encouraged frank and even social
intercourse.

He likewise observed some appearance of court ceremony
and etiquette. He received the common class of visitors on
the *stoop** before his door, according to the custom of our
Dutch ancestors. But when visitors were formally received
in his parlor, it was expected they would appear in clean
linen, by no means to be barefooted, and always to take
their hats off. On public occasions he appeared with great
pomp of equipage (for, in truth, his station required a little
show and dignity) and always rode to church in a yellow
wagon with flaming red wheels.

These symptoms of state and ceremony occasioned considerable discontent among the vulgar. They had been
accustomed to find easy access to their former governors,
and in particular had lived on terms of extreme familiarity
with William the Testy. They therefore were very impatient
of these dignified precautions which discouraged intrusion.
But Peter Stuyvesant had his own way of thinking in these
matters, and was a stanch upholder of the dignity of office.

He always maintained that government to be the least
popular which is most open to popular access and control;
and that the very brawlers against court ceremony, and the

---

* Properly spelled *stoeb*—the porch commonly built in front of
Dutch houses, with benches on each side.

reserve of men in power, would soon despise rulers among whom they found even themselves to be of consequence. Such, at least, had been the case with the administration of William the Testy; who, bent on making himself popular, had listened to every man's advice, suffered everybody to have admittance to his person at all hours, and, in a word, treated every one as his thorough equal. By this means, every scrub politician and public busybody was enabled to measure wits with him, and to find out the true dimensions, not only of his person, but of his mind.—And what great man can stand such scrutiny?—It is the mystery that envelops great men that gives them half their greatness. We are always inclined to think highly of those who hold themselves aloof from our examination. There is likewise a kind of superstitious reverence for office, which leads us to exaggerate the merits and abilities of men in power, and to suppose that they must be constituted different from other men. And, indeed, faith is as necessary in politics as in religion. It certainly is of the first importance that a country should be governed by wise men; but then it is almost equally important that the people should believe them to be wise; for this belief alone can produce willing subordination.

To keep up, therefore, this desirable confidence in rulers, the people should be allowed to see as little of them as possible. He who gains access to cabinets soon finds out by what foolishness the world is governed. He discovers that there is quackery in legislation, as well as in everything else; that many a measure, which is supposed by the million to be the result of great wisdom and deep deliberation, is the effect of mere chance, or, perhaps, of harebrained experiment—that rulers have their whims and errors as well as other men, and after all are not so wonderfully superior to their fellow-creatures as he at first imagined; since he finds that even his own opinions have had some weight with them. Thus awe subsides into confidence, confidence inspires familiarity, and familiarity produces contempt. Peter Stuyvesant, on the contrary, by conducting himself with dignity and loftiness,

was looked up to with great reverence. As he never gave
his reasons for anything he did, the public always gave him
credit for very profound ones—every movement, however
intrinsically unimportant, was a matter of speculation, and
his very red stockings excited some respect, as being different
from the stockings of other men.

To these times may we refer the rise of family pride and
aristocratic distinctions;* and indeed I cannot but look back
with reverence to the early planting of those mighty Dutch
families which have taken such vigorous root and branched
out so luxuriantly in our state. The blood which has flowed
down uncontaminated through a succession of steady, virtuous generations since the times of the patriarchs of Communipaw, must certainly be pure and worthy. And if so,
then are the Van Rensselaers, the Van Zandts, the Van
Hornes, the Rutgers, the Bensons, the Brinkerhoffs, the
Schermerhornes, and all the true descendants of the ancient
Pavonians, the only legitimate nobility and real lords of the
soil.

I have been led to mention thus particularly the well-
authenticated claims of our genuine Dutch families, because
I have noticed, with great sorrow and vexation, that they
have been somewhat elbowed aside in latter days by foreign
intruders. It is really astonishing to behold how many great
families have sprung up of late years, who pride themselves
excessively on the score of ancestry. Thus he who can look
up to his father without humiliation assumes not a little
importance—he who can safely talk of his grandfather is
still more vainglorious—but he who can look back to his
great-grandfather without blushing is absolutely intolerable
in his pretensions to family—bless us! what a piece of work

---

* In a work published many years after the time here treated of
(in 1701, by C. W. A. M.), it is mentioned that Frederick Philipse was
counted the richest Mynheer in New York, and was said to have *whole
hogsheads of Indian money or wampum;* and had a son and daughter,
who, according to the Dutch custom, should divide it equally.

is here, between these mushrooms of an hour and these mushrooms of a day!

But from what I have recounted in the former part of this chapter, I would not have my reader imagine that the great Peter was a tyrannical governor, ruling his subjects with a rod of iron; on the contrary, where the dignity of authority was not implicated, he abounded with generosity and courteous condescension. In fact, he really believed, though I fear my more enlightened republican readers will consider it a proof of his ignorance and illiberality, that in preventing the cup of social life from being dashed with the intoxicating ingredient of politics he promoted the tranquillity and happiness of the people—and by detaching their minds from subjects which they could not understand, and which only tended to inflame their passions, he enabled them to attend more faithfully and industriously to their proper callings; becoming more useful citizens and more attentive to their families and fortunes.

So far from having any unreasonable austerity, he delighted to see the poor and the laboring man rejoice, and for this purpose was a great promoter of holidays and public amusements. Under his reign was first introduced the custom of cracking eggs at Paas, or Easter. New Year's Day was also observed with extravagant festivity, and ushered in by the ringing of bells and firing of guns. Every house was a temple to the jolly god—oceans of cherry brandy, true Hollands, and mulled cider, were set afloat on the occasion; and not a poor man in town but made it a point to get drunk out of a principle of pure economy—taking in liquor enough to serve him for half a year afterward.

It would have done one's heart good, also, to have seen the valiant Peter, seated among the old burghers and their wives of a Saturday afternoon, under the great trees that spread their shade over the Battery, watching the young men and women as they danced on the green. Here he would smoke his pipe, crack his joke, and forget the rugged toils of war in the sweet oblivious festivities of peace. He would

occasionally give a nod of approbation to those of the young
men who shuffled and kicked most vigorously, and now and
then give a hearty smack, in all honesty of soul, to the
buxom lass that held out longest and tired down all her competitors, which he considered as infallible proofs of her being
the best dancer. Once, it is true, the harmony of the meeting was rather interrupted. A young vrouw, of great figure
in the gay world, and who, having lately come from Holland, of course lead the fashions in the city, made her appearance in not more than half-a-dozen petticoats, and these
too of most alarming shortness. A universal whisper ran
through the assembly, the old ladies all felt shocked in the
extreme, the young ladies blushed and felt excessively for
the "poor thing," and even the governor himself was observed to be a little troubled in mind. To complete the astonishment of the good folks, she undertook, in the course of
a jig, to describe some astonishing figures in algebra, which
she had learned from a dancing-master at Rotterdam.
Whether she was too animated in flourishing her feet, or
whether some vagabond zephyr took the liberty of obtruding
his services, certain it is that in the course of a grand evolu-
tion which would not have disgraced a modern ballroom,
she made a most unexpected display—whereat the whole
assembly was thrown into great admiration, several grave
country members were not a little moved, and the good Peter
himself, who was a man of unparalleled modesty, felt himself grievously scandalized.

The shortness of the female dresses, which had continued
in fashion ever since the days of William Kieft, had long
offended his eye, and though extremely averse to meddling
with the petticoats of the ladies, yet he immediately recommended that every one should be furnished with a flounce to
the bottom. He likewise ordered that the ladies, and indeed
the gentlemen, should use no other step in dancing than
shuffle-and-turn, and double-trouble; and forbade, under
pain of his high displeasure, any young lady thenceforth to
attempt what was termed "exhibiting the graces."

These were the only restrictions he ever imposed upon the sex, and these were considered by them as tyrannical oppressions, and resisted with that becoming spirit always manifested by the gentle sex whenever their privileges are invaded.—In fact, Peter Stuyvesant plainly perceived that if he attempted to push the matter any further there was danger of their leaving off petticoats altogether; so like a wise man, experienced in the ways of women, he held his peace, and suffered them ever after to wear their petticoats and cut their capers as high as they pleased.

CHAPTER TWO

HOW PETER STUYVESANT WAS MUCH MOLESTED BY THE MOSSTROOPERS OF THE EAST AND THE GIANTS OF MER-RYLAND—AND HOW A DARK AND HORRID CONSPIRACY WAS CARRIED ON IN THE BRITISH CABINET AGAINST THE PROSPERITY OF THE MANHATTOES

WE are now approaching toward the crisis of our work, and if I be not mistaken in my forebodings we shall have a world of business to dispatch in the ensuing chapters.

It is with some communities, as it is with certain meddle-some individuals, they have a wonderful facility at getting into scrapes; and I have always remarked that those are most liable to get in who have the least talent at getting out again. This is, doubtless, owing to the excessive valor of those states; for I have likewise noticed that this rampant and ungovernable quality is always most unruly where most confined; which accounts for its vaporing so amazingly in little states, little men, and ugly little women especially.

Thus, when one reflects that the province of the Man-hattoes, though of prodigious importance in the eyes of its inhabitants and its historian, was really of no very great consequence in the eyes of the rest of the world; that it had but little wealth or other spoils to reward the trouble of assailing it, and that it had nothing to expect from running wantonly into war, save an exceeding good beating.—On pondering these things, I say, one would utterly despair of finding in its history either battles or bloodshed, or any other of those calamities which give importance to a nation and entertainment to the reader. But, on the contrary, we find, so valiant is this province, that it has already drawn upon itself a host of enemies; has had as many buffetings as would gratify the ambition of the most warlike nation; and is, in sober sadness, a very forlorn, distressed, and woebegone little province!—all which was, no doubt, kindly ordered by Providence, to give interest and sublimity to this pathetic history.

But I forbear to enter into a detail of the pitiful maraudings and harassments that, for a long while after the victory on the Delaware, continued to insult the dignity, and disturb the repose, of the Nederlanders. Suffice it in brevity to say, that the implacable hostility of the people of the east, which had so miraculously been prevented from breaking out, as my readers must remember, by the sudden prevalence of witchcraft, and the dissensions in the council of Amphyctions, now again displayed itself in a thousand grievous and bitter scourings upon the borders.

Scarcely a month passed but what the Dutch settlements on the frontiers were alarmed by the sudden appearance of an invading army from Connecticut. This would advance resolutely through the country, like a puissant caravan of the deserts, the women and children mounted in carts loaded with pots and kettles, as though they meant to boil the honest Dutchmen alive and devour them like so many lobsters. At the tails of these carts would stalk a crew of long-limbed, lank-sided varlets, with axes on their shoulders and packs on their backs, resolutely bent upon *improving* the country in despite of its proprietors. These, settling themselves down, would in a short time completely dislodge the unfortunate Nederlanders; elbowing them out of those rich bottoms and fertile valleys in which our Dutch yeomanry are so famous for nestling themselves. For it is notorious, that wherever these shrewd men of the east get a footing the honest Dutchmen do gradually disappear, retiring slowly, like the Indians before the whites; being totally discomfited by the talking, chaffering, swapping, bargaining disposition of their new neighbors.

All these audacious infringements on the territories of their High Mightinesses were accompanied, as has before been hinted, by a world of rascally brawls, ribroastings, and bundlings, which would doubtless have incensed the valiant Peter to wreak immediate chastisement had he not at the very same time been perplexed by distressing accounts from Mynheer Beckman, who commanded the territories at South River.

The restless Swedes, who had so graciously been suffered to remain about the Delaware, already began to show signs of mutiny and disaffection. But what was worse, a peremptory claim was laid to the whole territory, as the rightful property of Lord Baltimore, by Fendal, a chieftain who ruled over the colony of Maryland, or Merryland, as it was anciently called, because that the inhabitants, not having the fear of the Lord before their eyes, were notoriously prone to get fuddled and make merry with mint-julep and appletoddy. Nay, so hostile was this bully Fendal that he threatened, unless his claim was instantly complied with, to march incontinently at the head of a potent force of the roaring boys of Merryland, together with a great and mighty train of giants who infested the banks of the Susquehanna*—and

---

* We find very curious and wonderful accounts of these strange people (who were doubtless the ancestors of the present Marylanders) made by Master Hariot, in his interesting history. "The Susquesahanocks," observes he, "are a giantly people, strange in proportion, behaviour, and attire—their voice sounding from them as if out of a cave. Their tobacco-pipes were three-quarters of a yard long, carved at the great end with a bird, beare, or other device, sufficient to beat out the braines of a horse (and how many asses braines are beaten out, or rather men's braines smoked out, and asses braines haled in, by our lesser pipes at home). The calfe of one of their legges measured three quarters of a yard about, the rest of his limbs proportionable."—*Master Hariot's Journ. Purch. Pil.*

to lay waste and depopulate the whole country of South River.

By this it is manifest that this boasted colony, like all great acquisitions of territory, soon became a greater evil to the conqueror than the loss of it was to the conquered; and caused greater uneasiness and trouble than all the territory of the New Netherlands besides. Thus Providence wisely orders that one evil shall balance another. The conqueror who wrests the property of his neighbor, who wrongs a nation and desolates a country, though he may acquire increase of empire and immortal fame, yet insures his own inevitable punishment. He takes to himself a cause of endless anxiety—he incorporates with his late sound domain a loose part—a rotten, disaffected member; which is an exhaustless source of internal treason and disunion, and external altercation and hostility. Happy is that nation which, compact, united, loyal in all its parts, and concentrated in its strength, seeks no idle acquisition of unprofitable and ungovernable territory—which, content to be prosperous and happy, has no ambition to be great. It is like a man well organized in his system, sound in health, and full of vigor; unencumbered by useless trappings, and fixed in an unshaken attitude. But the nation insatiable of territory, whose domains are scattered, feebly united and weakly organized, is like a senseless miser sprawling among golden stores, open to every attack and unable to defend the riches he vainly endeavors to overshadow.

At the time of receiving the alarming dispatches from South River, the great Peter was busily employed in quelling certain Indian troubles that had broken out about Esopus, and was moreover meditating how to relieve his eastern borders on the Connecticut. He, however, sent word to Mynheer Beckman to be of good heart, to maintain incessant vigilance, and to let him know if matters wore a more threatening appearance; in which case he would incontinently repair with his warriors of the Hudson to spoil the merriment of these Merrylanders; for he coveted exceedingly to have

a bout, hand to hand, with some half a score of these giants
—having never encountered a giant in his whole life, unless
we may so call the stout Risingh, and he was but a little one.

Nothing further, however, occurred to molest the tranquillity of Mynheer Beckman and his colony. Fendal and
his myrmidons remained at home, carousing it soundly upon
hoe-cakes, bacon, and mint-julep, and running horses, and
fighting cocks, for which they were greatly renowned.—At
hearing of this, Peter Stuyvesant was very well pleased, for
notwithstanding his inclination to measure weapons with
these monstrous men of the Susquehanna, yet he had already as much employment nearer home as he could turn his
hands to. Little did he think, worthy soul, that this southern calm was but the deceitful prelude to a most terrible and
fatal storm, then brewing, which was soon to burst forth
and overwhelm the unsuspecting city of New Amsterdam!

Now so it was, that while this excellent governor was
giving his little senate laws, and not only giving them, but
enforcing them too—while he was incessantly traveling the
rounds of his beloved province—posting from place to place
to redress grievances, and while busy at one corner of his
dominions all the rest getting into an uproar—at this very
time, I say, a dark and direful plot was hatching against
him, in that nursery of monstrous projects, the British cabinet. The news of his achievements on the Delaware, according to a sage old historian of New Amsterdam, had
occasioned not a little talk and marvel in the courts of Europe. And the same profound writer assures us that the
cabinet of England began to entertain great jealousy and
uneasiness at the increasing power of the Manhattoes and
the valor of its sturdy yeomanry.

Agents, the same historian observes, were sent by the
Amphyctionic council of the east to entreat the assistance
of the British cabinet in subjugating this mighty province.
Lord Sterling also asserted his right to Long Island, and, at
the same time, Lord Baltimore, whose agent, as has before
been mentioned, had so alarmed Mynheer Beckman, laid his

claim before the cabinet to the lands of South River, which
he complained were unjustly and forcibly detained from him
by these daring usurpers of the Nieuw Nederlandts.

Thus did the unlucky empire of the Manhattoes stand in
imminent danger of experiencing the fate of Poland, and being torn limb from limb to be shared among its savage neighbors.   But while these rapacious powers were whetting their
fangs, and waiting for the signal to fall tooth and nail upon
this delicious little fat Dutch empire, the lordly lion, who sat
as umpire, all at once settled the claims of all parties by laying his own paw upon the spoil.   For we are told that his
majesty, Charles the Second, not to be perplexed by adjust-
ing these several pretensions, made a present of a large tract
of North America, including the province of New Netherlands, to his brother, the Duke of York—a donation truly
loyal, since none but great monarchs have a right to give
away what does not belong to them.

That this munificent gift might not be merely nominal,
his majesty, on the 12th of March, 1664, ordered that an
armament should be forthwith prepared, to invade the city
of New Amsterdam by land and water, and put his brother
in complete possession of the premises.

Thus critically are situated the affairs of the New Nether-
landers.   The honest burghers, so far from thinking of the
jeopardy in which their interests are placed, are soberly smoking their pipes, and thinking of nothing at all—the privy
counselors of the province are at this moment snoring in full
quorum, while the active Peter, who takes all the labor of
thinking and acting upon himself, is busily devising some
method of bringing the grand council of Amphyctions to
terms.   In the meanwhile, an angry cloud is darkly scowl-
ing on the horizon—soon shall it rattle about the ears of these
dozing Nederlanders, and put the mettle of their stout-hearted
governor completely to the trial.

But come what may, I here pledge my veracity that in
all warlike conflicts and subtle perplexities he shall still acquit himself with the gallant bearing and spotless honor of a

noble-minded, obstinate old cavalier.—Forward then to the
charge!—shine out, propitious stars, on the renowned city of
the Manhattoes; and may the blessing of St. Nicholas go
with thee—honest Peter Stuyvesant!

CHAPTER THREE

OF PETER STUYVESANT'S EXPEDITION INTO THE EAST
COUNTRY, SHOWING THAT, THOUGH AN OLD BIRD,
HE DID NOT UNDERSTAND TRAP

GREAT nations resemble great men in this particular, that
their greatness is seldom known until they get in trouble;
adversity, therefore, has been wisely denominated the ordeal
of true greatness, which, like gold, can never receive its real
estimation until it has passed through the furnace. In proportion, therefore, as a nation, a community, or an individual (possessing the inherent quality of greatness) is involved
in perils and misfortunes, in proportion does it rise in grandeur—and even when sinking under calamity, makes, like a
house on fire, a more glorious display than ever it did in the
fairest period of its prosperity.

The vast empire of China, though teeming with population and imbibing and concentrating the wealth of nations,
has vegetated through a succession of drowsy ages; and were
it not for its internal revolution, and the subversion of its ancient government by the Tartars, might have presented nothing but an uninteresting detail of dull, monotonous prosperity. Pompeii and Herculaneum might have passed into
oblivion, with a herd of their contemporaries, if they had
not been fortunately overwhelmed by a volcano. The renowned city of Troy has acquired celebrity only from its ten
years' distress and final conflagration—Paris rises in importance by the plots and massacres which have ended in the
exaltation of the illustrious Napoleon—and even the mighty
London itself has skulked through the records of time, cele-

* * * N

brated for nothing of moment, excepting the plague, the great fire, and Guy Faux's gunpowder plot!—Thus cities and empires seem to creep along, enlarging in silent obscurity under the pen of the historian, until at length they burst forth in some tremendous. calamity—and snatch, as it were, immortality from the explosion!

The above principle being admitted, my reader will plainly perceive that the city of New Amsterdam, and its dependent province, are on the high road to greatness. Dangers and hostilities threaten from every side, and it is really a matter of astonishment to me how so small a state has been able, in so short a time, to entangle itself in so many difficulties. Ever since the province was first taken by the nose, at the Fort of Good Hope, in the tranquil days of Wouter Van Twiller, has it been gradually increasing in historic importance; and never could it have had a more appropriate chieftain to conduct it to the pinnacle of grandeur than Peter Stuyvesant.

In the fiery heart of this iron-headed old warrior sat enthroned all those five kinds of courage described by Aristotle, and had the philosopher mentioned five hundred more to the back of them, I verily believe he would have been found master of them all. The only misfortune was that he was deficient in the better part of valor, called discretion, a cold-blooded virtue which could not exist in the tropical climate of his mighty soul. Hence it was, he was continually hurrying into those unheard-of enterprises that give an air of chivalric romance to all his history, and hence it was that he now conceived a project worthy of the hero of La Mancha himself.

This was no other than to repair in person to the great council of the Amphyctions, bearing the sword in one hand and the olive-branch in the other—to require immediate reparation for the innumerable violations of that treaty which in an evil hour he had formed—to put a stop to those repeated maraudings on the eastern borders—or else to throw his gauntlet and appeal to arms for satisfaction.

On declaring this resolution in his privy council, the venerable members were seized with vast astonishment; for once in their lives they ventured to remonstrate, setting forth the rashness of exposing his sacred person in the midst of a strange and barbarous people, with sundry other weighty remonstrances—all which had about as much influence upon the determination of the headstrong Peter as though you were to endeavor to turn a rusty weathercock with a broken-winded bellows.

Summoning, therefore, to his presence his trusty follower, Antony Van Corlear, he commanded him to hold himself in readiness to accompany him the following morning on this his hazardous enterprise. Now Antony the trumpeter was a little stricken in years, yet by dint of keeping up a good heart, and having never known care or sorrow (having never been married), he was still a hearty, jocund, rubicund, gameson wag, and of great capacity in the doublet. This last was ascribed to his living a jolly life on those domains at the Hook which Peter Stuyvesant had granted to him for his gallantry at Fort Casimir.

Be this as it may, there was nothing that more delighted Antony than this command of the great Peter, for he could have followed the stout-hearted old governor to the world's end with love and loyalty—and he moreover still remembered the frolicking, and dancing, and bundling, and other disports of the east country, and entertained dainty recollection of numerous kind and buxom lasses, whom he longed exceedingly again to encounter.

Thus, then, did this mirror of hardihood set forth, with no other attendant but his trumpeter, upon one of the most perilous enterprises ever recorded in the annals of knight-errantry. For a single warrior to venture openly among a whole nation of foes; but, above all, for a plain downright Dutchman to think of negotiating with the whole council of New England—never was there known a more desperate undertaking!—Ever since I have entered upon the chronicles of this peerless, but hitherto uncelebrated, chieftain, has he kept

me in a state of incessant action and anxiety with the toils
and dangers he is constantly encountering.—Oh! for a chapter of the tranquil reign of Wouter Van Twiller, that I might
repose on it as on a feather bed!

Is it not enough, Peter Stuyvesant, that I have once already rescued thee from the machinations of these terrible
Amphyctions, by bringing the whole powers of witchcraft to
thine aid?—Is it not enough that I have followed thee undaunted, like a guardian spirit, into the midst of the horrid
battle of Fort Christina?—That I have been put incessantly
to my trumps to keep thee safe and sound—now warding off
with my single pen the shower of dastard blows that fell
upon thy rear—now narrowly shielding thee from a deadly
thrust, by a mere tobacco-box—now casing thy dauntless
skull with adamant, when even thy stubborn ram-beaver
failed to resist the sword of the stout Risingh—and now, not
merely bringing thee off alive, but triumphant, from the
clutches of the gigantic Swede, by the desperate means of a
paltry stone pottle?—Is not all this enough, but must thou
still be plunging into new difficulties, and jeopardizing in
headlong enterprises, thyself, thy trumpeter, and thy historian?

And now the ruddy-faced Aurora, like a buxom chambermaid, draws aside the sable curtains of the night, and out
bounces from his bed the jolly red-haired Phœbus, startled
at being caught so late in the embraces of Dame Thetis.
With many a sable oath he harnesses his brazen-footed
steeds, and whips and lashes, and splashes up the firmament, like a loitering postboy, half an hour behind his time.
And now behold that imp of fame and prowess, the headstrong Peter, bestriding a raw-boned, switch-tailed charger,
gallantly arrayed in full regimentals, and bracing on his
thigh that trusty brass-hilted sword which had wrought
such fearful deeds on the banks of the Delaware.

Behold, hard after him, his doughty trumpeter Van Corlear, mounted on a broken-winded, wall-eyed, calico mare;
his stone pottle, which had laid low the mighty Risingh,

slung under his arm, and his trumpet displayed vauntingly
in his right hand, decorated with a gorgeous banner, on
which is emblazoned the great beaver of the Manhattoes.
See them proudly issuing out of the city gate like an iron-
clad hero of yore, with his faithful squire at his heels, the
populace following them with their eyes, and shouting many
a parting wish and hearty cheering.—Farewell, Hardkoppig Piet! Farewell, honest Antony!—Pleasant be your wayfaring—prosperous your return! The stoutest hero that ever
drew a sword, and the worthiest trumpeter that ever trod
shoe-leather!

Legends are lamentably silent about the events that befell
our adventurers in this their adventurous travel, excepting
the Stuyvesant manuscript, which gives the substance of a
pleasant little heroic poem, written on the occasion by Domini
Ægidius Luyck,* who appears to have been the poet laureate
of New Amsterdam. This inestimable manuscript assures
us that it was a rare spectacle to behold the great Peter and
his loyal follower hailing the morning sun, and rejoicing in
the clear countenance of nature, as they pranced it through
the pastoral scenes of Bloemen Dael;† which in those days
was a sweet and rural valley, beautified with many a bright
wild flower, refreshed by many a pure streamlet, and enlivened here and there by a delectable little Dutch cottage,
sheltered under some sloping hill, and almost buried in embowering trees.

Now did they enter upon the confines of Connecticut,
where they encountered many grievous difficulties and perils.
At one place they were assailed by a troop of country squires
and militia colonels, who, mounted on goodly steeds, hung
upon their rear for several miles, harassing them exceedingly
with guesses and questions, more especially the worthy Peter,

---

* This Luyck was, moreover, rector of the Latin School in Nieuw
Neaerlandts, 1663. There are two pieces addressed to Ægidius Luyck,
in D. Selyn's MSS. of poesies, upon his marriage with Judith Isendoorn.
—Old MS.

† Now called Blooming Dale, about four miles from New York.

whose silver-chased leg excited not a little marvel. At another place, hard by the renowned town of Stamford, they were set upon by a great and mighty legion of church deacons, who imperiously demanded of them five shillings, for traveling on Sunday, and threatened to carry them captive to a neighboring church, whose steeple peered above the trees; but these the valiant Peter put to rout with little difficulty, insomuch that they bestrode their canes and galloped off in horrible confusion, leaving their cocked hats behind in the hurry of their flight. But not so easily did he escape from the hands of a crafty man of Piquag; who, with undaunted perseverance, and repeated onsets, fairly bargained him out of his goodly switch-tailed charger, leaving in place thereof a villainous foundered Narraghanset pacer.

But, mauger all these hardships, they pursued their journey cheerily along the course of the soft flowing Connecticut, whose gentle waves, says the song, roll through many a fertile vale and sunny plain; now reflecting the lofty spires of the bustling city, and now the rural beauties of the humble hamlet; now echoing with the busy hum of commerce, and now with the cheerful song of the peasant.

At every town would Peter Stuyvesant, who was noted for warlike punctilio, order the sturdy Antony to sound a courteous salutation; though the manuscript observes that the inhabitants were thrown into great dismay when they heard of his approach. For the fame of his incomparable achievements on the Delaware had spread throughout the east country, and they dreaded lest he had come to take vengeance on their manifold transgressions.

But the good Peter rode through these towns with a smiling aspect; waving his hand with inexpressible majesty and condescension; for he verily believed that the old clothes which these ingenious people had thrust into their broken windows, and the festoons of dried apples and peaches which ornamented the fronts of their houses, were so many decorations in honor of his approach; as it was the custom, in the days of chivalry, to compliment renowned heroes by sumptuous displays of tapestry and gorgeous furniture. The women crowded to the doors to gaze upon him as he passed, so much does prowess in arms delight the gentle sex. The little children, too, ran after him in troops, staring with wonder at his regimentals, his brimstone breeches, and the silver garniture of his wooden leg. Nor must I omit to mention the joy which many strapping wenches betrayed at beholding the jovial Van Corlear, who had whilom delighted them so much with his trumpet, when he bore the great Peter's challenge to the Amphyctions. The kind-hearted Antony alighted from his calico mare and kissed them all with infinite lovingkindness—and was right pleased to see a crew of little trumpeters crowding around him for his blessing; each of whom he patted on the head, bade him be a good boy, and gave him a penny to buy molasses candy.

The Stuyvesant manuscript makes but little further mention of the governor's adventures upon this expedition, excepting that he was received with extravagant courtesy and respect by the great council of the Amphyctions, who almost talked him to death with complimentary and congratulatory harangues. I will not detain my readers by dwelling on his negotiations with the grand council. Suffice it to mention it was like all other negotiations—a great deal was said, and very little done: one conversation led to another—one conference begat misunderstandings which it took a dozen conferences to explain; at the end of which the parties found themselves just where they were at first; excepting that they had entangled themselves in a host of questions of etiquette, and conceived a cordial distrust of each other that rendered their future negotiations ten times more difficult than ever.*

In the midst of all these perplexities, which bewildered the brain and incensed the ire of the sturdy Peter, who was perhaps of all men in the world least fitted for diplomatic wiles, he privately received the first intimation of the dark

---

* For certain of the particulars of this ancient negotiation see Haz. Col. State Papers. It is singular that Smith is entirely silent with respect to this memorable expedition of Peter Stuyvesant

conspiracy which had been matured in the cabinet of England. To this was added the astounding intelligence that a hostile squadron had already sailed from England, destined to reduce the province of New Netherlands, and that the grand council of Amphyctions had engaged to co-operate, by sending a great army to invade New Amsterdam by land.

Unfortunate Peter! did I not enter with sad foreboding upon this ill-starred expedition? did I not tremble when I saw thee, with no other counselor but thine own head, with no other armor but an honest tongue, a spotless conscience, and a rusty sword! with no other protector but St. Nicholas —and no other attendant but a trumpeter—did I not tremble when I beheld thee thus sally forth to contend with all the knowing powers of New England?

Oh, how did the sturdy old warrior rage and roar when he found himself thus entrapped, like a lion in the hunter's toil! Now did he determine to draw his trusty sword, and manfully to fight his way through all the countries of the east. Now did he resolve to break in upon the council of the Amphyctions and put every mother's son of them to death. At length, as his direful wrath subsided, he resorted to safer though less glorious expedients.

Concealing from the council his knowledge of their machinations, he privately dispatched a trusty messenger, with missives to his counselors at New Amsterdam, apprising them of the impending danger, commanding them immediately to put the city in a posture of defense, while in the meantime he would endeavor to elude his enemies and come to their assistance. This done, he felt himself marvelously relieved, rose slowly, shook himself like a rhinoceros, and issued forth from his den, in much the same manner as Giant Despair is described to have issued from Doubting Castle in the chivalric history of the Pilgrim's Progress.

And now, much does it grieve me that I must leave the gallant Peter in this imminent jeopardy: but it behooves us to hurry back and see what is going on at New Amsterdam, for greatly do I fear that city is already in a turmoil. Such was ever the fate of Peter Stuyvesant; while doing one thing with heart and soul, he was too apt to leave everything else at sixes and sevens. While, like a potentate of yore, he was absent, attending to those things in person which in modern days are trusted to generals and embassadors, his little territory at home was sure to get in an uproar.—All which was owing to that uncommon strength of intellect which induced him to trust to nobody but himself, and which had acquired him the renowned appellation of Peter the Headstrong.

CHAPTER FOUR

HOW THE PEOPLE OF NEW AMSTERDAM WERE THROWN INTO A GREAT PANIC BY THE NEWS OF A THREATENED INVASION, AND THE MANNER IN WHICH THEY FORTIFIED THEMSELVES

THERE is no sight more truly interesting to a philosopher than to contemplate a community where every individual has a voice in public affairs, where every individual thinks himself the Atlas of the nation, and where every individual thinks it his duty to bestir himself for the good of his country.—I say, there is nothing more interesting to a philosopher than to see such a community in a sudden bustle of war. Such a clamor of tongues—such a bawling of patriotism— such running hither and thither—everybody in a hurry— everybody up to the ears in trouble—everybody in the way, and everybody interrupting his industrious neighbor—who is busily employed in doing nothing! It is like witnessing a great fire, where every man is at work like a hero—some dragging about empty engines—others scampering with full buckets, and spilling the contents into the boots of their neighbors—and others ringing the church bells all night, by way of putting out the fire. Little firemen, like sturdy little knights storming a breach, clambering up and down scaling-ladders, and bawling through tin trumpets by way of directing the attack.—Here one busy fellow, in his great zeal to

save the property of the unfortunate, catches up an anonymous chamber utensil, and gallants it off with an air of as
much self-importance as if he had rescued a pot of money—
another throws looking-glasses and china out of the window
to save them from the flames, while those who can do nothing else to assist the great calamity run up and down the
streets with open throats, keeping up an incessant cry of
Fire! Fire! Fire!

"When the news arrived at Sinope," says the grave and
profound Lucian—though I own the story is rather trite,
"that Philip was about to attack them, the inhabitants were
thrown into violent alarm. Some ran to furbish up their
arms; others rolled stones to build up the walls—everybody,
in short, was employed, and everybody was in the way of
his neighbor. Diogenes alone was the only man who could
find nothing to do—whereupon, determining not to be idle
when the welfare of his country was at stake, he tucked up
his robe and fell to rolling his tub with might and main up
and down the Gymnasium." In like manner did every
mother's son in the patriotic community of New Amsterdam, on receiving the missives of Peter Stuyvesant, busy
himself most mightily in putting things in confusion, and
assisting the general uproar. "Every man" — saith the
Stuyvesant manuscript—"flew to arms!" By which is
meant that not one of our honest Dutch citizens would
venture to church or to market without an old-fashioned
spit of a sword dangling at his side and a long, Dutch fowling-piece on his shoulder—nor would he go out of a night
without a lantern; nor turn a corner without first peeping
cautiously round, lest he should come unawares upon a British army.—And we are informed that Stoffel Brinkerhoff,
who was considered by the old women almost as brave a
man as the governor himself, actually had two one-pound
swivels mounted in his entry, one pointing out at the front
door and the other at the back.

But the most strenuous measure resorted to on this awful
occasion, and one which has since been found of wonderful

efficacy, was to assemble popular meetings. These brawling convocations, I have already shown, were extremely offensive to Peter Stuyvesant; but as this was a moment of unusual agitation, and as the old governor was not present to repress them, they broke out with intolerable violence. Hither, therefore, the orators and politicians repaired, and there seemed to be a competition among them who should bawl the loudest, and exceed the others in hyperbolical bursts of patriotism, and in resolutions to uphold and defend the Government. In these sage and all-powerful meetings it was determined, *nem. con.*, that they were the most enlightened, the most dignified, the most formidable, and the most ancient community upon the face of the earth. Finding that this resolution was so universally and readily carried, another was immediately proposed—whether it were not possible and politic to exterminate Great Britain? Upon which sixty-nine members spoke most eloquently in the affirmative, and only one rose to suggest some doubts; who, as a punishment for his treasonable presumption, was immediately seized by the mob and tarred and feathered—which punishment being equivalent to the Tarpeian Rock, he was afterward considered as an outcast from society, and his opinion went for nothing. The question, therefore, being unanimously carried in the affirmative, it was recommended to the grand council to pass it into a law; which was accordingly done.— By this measure the hearts of the people at large were wonderfully encouraged, and they waxed exceeding choleric and valorous. Indeed, the first paroxysm of alarm having in some measure subsided; the old women having buried all the money they could lay their hands on, and their husbands daily getting fuddled with what was left—the community began even to stand on the offensive. Songs were manufactured in Low Dutch, and sung about the streets, wherein the English were most wofully beaten, and shown no quarter; and popular addresses were made, wherein it was proved to a certainty that the fate of Old England depended upon the will of the New Amsterdamers.

Finally, to strike a violent blow at the very vitals of Great Britain, a multitude of the wiser inhabitants assembled, and having purchased all the British manufactures they could find, they made thereof a huge bonfire; and in the patriotic glow of the moment every man present, who had a hat or breeches of English workmanship, pulled it off and threw it most undauntedly into the flames—to the irreparable detriment, loss, and ruin of the English manufacturers. In commemoration of this great exploit, they erected a pole on the spot, with a device on the top intended to represent the province of Nieuw Nederlandts destroying Great Britain, under the similitude of an eagle picking the little island of Old England out of the globe; but either through the unskillfulness of the sculptor, or his ill-timed waggery, it bore a striking resemblance to a goose vainly striving to get hold of a dumpling.

CHAPTER FIVE

SHOWING HOW THE GRAND COUNCIL OF THE NEW NETHERLANDS CAME TO BE MIRACULOUSLY GIFTED WITH LONG TONGUES—TOGETHER WITH A GREAT TRIUMPH OF ECONOMY

IT will need but very little penetration in any one acquainted with the character and habits of that most potent and blustering monarch, the sovereign people, to discover that, notwithstanding all the bustle and talk of war that stunned him in the last chapter, the renowned city of New Amsterdam is in sad reality, not a whit better prepared for defense than before. Now, though the people, having gotten over the first alarm, and finding no enemy immediately at hand, had, with that valor of tongue for which your illustrious rabble is so famous, run into the opposite extreme, and, by dint of gallant vaporing and rodomontade, had actually talked themselves into the opinion that they were the bravest and most powerful people under the sun, yet were the privy counselors of Peter Stuyvesant somewhat dubious on that point. They dreaded moreover lest that stern hero should return and find that, instead of obeying his peremptory orders, they had wasted their time in listening to the hectorings of the mob, than which, they well knew, there was nothing he held in more exalted contempt.

To make up, therefore, as speedily as possible for lost time, a grand divan of the counselors and burgomasters was convened to talk over the critical state of the province, and devise measures for its safety. Two things were unanimously agreed upon in this venerable assembly: first, that the city required to be put in a state of defense; and, secondly, that, as the danger was imminent, there should be no time lost—which points being settled, they immediately fell to making long speeches, and belaboring one another in endless and intemperate disputes. For about this time was this unhappy city first visited by that talking endemic, so universally prevalent in this country, and which so invariably evinces itself wherever a number of wise men assemble together, breaking out in long, windy speeches, caused, as physicians suppose, by the foul air which is ever generated in a crowd. Now it was, moreover, that they first introduced the ingenious method of measuring the merits of a harangue by the hour-glass; he being considered the ablest orator who spoke longest on a question. For which excellent invention, it is recorded, we are indebted to the same profound Dutch critic who judged of books by their size.

This sudden passion for endless harangues, so little consonant with the customary gravity and taciturnity of our sage forefathers, was supposed, by certain learned philosophers, to have been imbibed, together with divers other barbarous propensities, from their savage neighbors; who were peculiarly noted for their *long talks* and *council fires*—who would never undertake any affair of the least importance without previous debates and harangues among their chiefs and *old men*. But the real cause was that the people, in electing their representatives to the grand council, were par-

ticular in choosing them for their talents at talking, without
inquiring whether they possessed the more rare, difficult,
and ofttimes important talent of holding their tongues. The
consequence was that this deliberative body was composed
of the most loquacious men in the community. As they
considered themselves placed there to talk, every man concluded that his duty to his constituents, and, what is more,
his popularity with them, required that he should harangue
on every subject, whether he understood it or not. There
was an ancient mode of burying a chieftain, by every soldier
throwing his shield full of earth on the corpse, until a mighty
mound was formed; so, whenever a question was brought
forward in this assembly, every member pressing forward
to throw on his quantum of wisdom, the subject was quickly
buried under a huge mass of words.

We are told that when disciples were admitted into the
school of Pythagoras they were for two years enjoined silence, and were neither permitted to ask questions nor make
remarks. After they had thus acquired the inestimable art
of holding their tongues, they were gradually permitted to
make inquiries, and finally to communicate their own opinions.

What a pity is it that, while superstitiously hoarding up
the rubbish and rags of antiquity, we should suffer these precious gems to lie unnoticed! What a beneficial effect would
this wise regulation of Pythagoras have if introduced in leg-
islative bodies—and how wonderfully would it have tended
to expedite business in the grand council of the Manhattoes!

Thus, however, did Dame Wisdom (whom the wags of
antiquity have humorously personified as a woman) seem to
take mischievous pleasure in jilting the venerable counselors
of New Amsterdam. The old factions of Long Pipes and
Short Pipes, which had been almost strangled by the herculean grasp of Peter Stuyvesant, now sprung up with tenfold
violence. Not that the original cause of difference still existed—but it has ever been the fate of party names and party
rancor to remain long after the principles that gave rise to
them have been forgotten. To complete the public confusion

and bewilderment, the fatal word *Economy*, which one would have thought was dead and buried with William the Testy, was once more set afloat, like the apple of discord, in the grand council of Nieuw Nederlandts—according to which sound principle of policy, it was deemed more expedient to throw away twenty thousand guilders upon an inefficacious plan of defense than thirty thousand on a good and substantial one—the province thus making a clear saving of ten thousand guilders.

But when they came to discuss the mode of defense, then began a war of words that baffles all description. The members being, as I observed, enlisted in opposite parties, were enabled to proceed with amazing system and regularity in the discussion of the questions before them. Whatever was proposed by a Long Pipe was opposed by the whole tribe of Short Pipes, who, like true politicians, considered it their first duty to effect the downfall of the Long Pipes—their second, to elevate themselves—and their third, to consult the welfare of the country. This at least was the creed of the most upright among the party; for as to the great mass, they left the third consideration out of the question altogether.

In this great collision of hard heads, it is astonishing the number of projects for defense that were struck out, not one of which had ever been heard of before, nor has been heard of since, unless it be in very modern days—projects that threw the windmill system of the ingenious Kieft completely in the background. Still, however, nothing could be decided on; for so soon as a formidable host of air castles were reared by one party, they were demolished by the other. The simple populace stood gazing in anxious expectation of the mighty egg that was to be hatched with all this cackling; but they gazed in vain, for it appeared that the grand council was determined to protect the province as did the noble and gigantic Pantagruel his army—by covering it with his tongue.

Indeed, there was a portion of the members, consisting of fat, self-important old burghers, who smoked their pipes and said nothing, excepting to negative every plan of defense that was offered. These were of that class of wealthy old citizens, who, having amassed a fortune, button up their pockets, shut their mouths, look rich, and are good for nothing all the rest of their lives. Like some phlegmatic oyster, which, having swallowed a pearl, closes its shell, settles down in the mud, and parts with its life sooner than its treasure. Every plan of defense seemed to these worthy old gentlemen pregnant with ruin. An armed force was a legion of locusts, preying upon the public property—to fit out a naval armament was to throw their money into the sea—to build fortifications was to bury it in the dirt. In short, they settled it as a sovereign maxim, so long as their pockets were full, no matter how much they were drubbed—A kick left no scar— a broken head cured itself—but an empty purse was of all maladies the slowest to heal, and one in which nature did nothing for the patient.

Thus did this venerable assembly of *sages* lavish away that time which the urgency of affairs rendered invaluable in empty brawls and long-winded speeches, without ever agreeing, except on the point with which they started; namely, that there was no time to be lost, and delay was ruinous. At length St. Nicholas, taking compassion on their distracted situation, and anxious to preserve them from anarchy, so ordered that in the midst of one of their most noisy debates on the subject of fortification and defense, when they had nearly fallen to loggerheads in consequence of not being able to convince each other, the question was happily settled by a messenger, who bounced into the chamber and informed them that the hostile fleet had arrived, and was actually advancing up the bay!

Thus was all further necessity of either fortifying or disputing completely obviated, and thus was the grand council saved a world of words, and the province a world of expense —a most absolute and glorious triumph of economy!

CHAPTER SIX

IN WHICH THE TROUBLES OF NEW AMSTERDAM APPEAR TO
THICKEN—SHOWING THE BRAVERY, IN TIME OF PERIL,
OF A PEOPLE WHO DEFEND THEMSELVES BY RESOLU-
TIONS

LIKE as an assemblage of politic cats, engaged in clamorous gibberings, and caterwaulings, eying one another with
hideous grimaces, spitting in each other's faces, and on the
point of breaking forth into a general clapper-clawing, are
suddenly put to scampering rout and confusion by the startling appearance of a house-dog—so was the no less vociferous council of New Amsterdam amazed, astounded, and totally dispersed by the sudden arrival of the enemy. Every
member made the best of his way home, waddling along as
fast as his short legs could fag under their heavy burden,
and wheezing as he went with corpulency and terror. When
he arrived at his castle, he barricadoed the street door, and
buried himself in the cider cellar, without daring to peep out,
lest he should have his head carried off by a cannon-ball.

The sovereign people all crowded into the market-place,
herding together with the instinct of sheep, who seek for
safety in each other's company, when the shepherd and his
dog are absent, and the wolf is prowling round the fold.
Far from finding relief, however, they only increased each
other's terrors. Each man looked ruefully in his neighbor's
face, in search of encouragement, but only found in its woe-
begone lineaments a confirmation of his own dismay. Not
a word now was to be heard of conquering Great Britain,
not a whisper about the sovereign virtues of economy—while
the old women heightened the general gloom by clamorously
bewailing their fate, and incessantly calling for protection on
Saint Nicholas and Peter Stuyvesant.

Oh, how did they bewail the absence of the lion-hearted Peter!—and how did they long for the comforting presence of Antony Van Corlear! Indeed, a gloomy uncertainty hung over the fate of these adventurous heroes. Day after day had elapsed since the alarming message from the governor, without bringing any further tidings of his safety. Many a fearful conjecture was hazarded as to what had befallen him and his loyal squire. Had they not been devoured alive by the cannibals of Marblehead and Cape Cod?—were they not put to the question by the great council of Amphyctions?—were they not smothered in onions by the terrible men of Piquag? In the midst of this consternation and perplexity, when horror, like a mighty nightmare, sat brooding upon the little, fat, plethoric city of New Amsterdam, the ears of the multitude were suddenly startled by a strange and distant sound—it approached—it grew louder and louder —and now it resounded at the city gate. The public could not be mistaken in the well-known sound—a shout of joy burst from their lips as the gallant Peter, covered with dust and followed by his faithful trumpeter, came galloping into the market-place.

The first transports of the populace having subsided, they gathered round the honest Antony, as he dismounted from his horse, overwhelming him with greetings and congratulations. In breathless accents he related to them the marvelous adventures through which the old governor and himself had gone, in making their escape from the clutches of the terrible Amphyctions. But though the Stuyvesant manuscript, with its customary minuteness where anything touching the great Peter is concerned, is very particular as to the incidents of this masterly retreat, yet the particular state of the public affairs will not allow me to indulge in a full recital thereof. Let it suffice to say, that while Peter Stuyvesant was anxiously revolving in his mind how he could make good his escape with honor and dignity, certain of the ships sent out for the conquest of the Manhattoes touched at the eastern ports, to obtain needful supplies, and to call on the

grand council of the league for its promised co-operation.
Upon hearing of this, the vigilant Peter, perceiving that a
moment's delay were fatal, made a secret and precipitate
decampment, though much did it grieve his lofty soul to be
obliged to turn his back even upon a nation of foes. Many
hair-breadth 'scapes and divers perilous mishaps did they
sustain, as they scoured, without sound of trumpet, through
the fair regions of the east. Already was the country in an
uproar with hostile preparation, and they were obliged to
take a large circuit in their flight, lurking along through the
woody mountains of the Devil's Back-bone; from whence
the valiant Peter sallied forth one day, like a lion, and put to
rout a whole region of squatters, consisting of three generations of a prolific family, who were already on their way to
take possession of some corner of the New Netherlands.
Nay, the faithful Antony had great difficulty at sundry times
to prevent him, in the excess of his wrath, from descending
down from the mountains, and falling, sword in hand, upon
certain of the border towns, who were marshaling forth their
draggle-tailed militia.

The first movements of the governor on reaching his
dwelling was to mount the roof, from whence he contemplated, with rueful aspect, the hostile squadron. This had
already come to anchor in the bay, and consisted of two stout
frigates, having on board, as John Josselyn, Gent., informs
us, "three hundred valiant red-coats." Having taken this
survey, he sat himself down and wrote an epistle to the commander, demanding the reason of his anchoring in the harbor
without obtaining previous permission so to do. This letter
was couched in the most dignified and courteous tones,
though I have it from undoubted authority that his teeth
were clinched, and he had a bitter sardonic grin upon his
visage all the while he wrote. Having dispatched his letter,
the grim Peter stumped to and fro about the town, with a
most war-betokening countenance, his hands thrust into his
breeches pockets, and whistling a Low Dutch psalm tune,
which bore no small resemblance to the music of a northeast

wind, when a storm is brewing. The very dogs, as they eyed him, skulked away in dismay—while all the old and ugly women of New Amsterdam ran howling at his heels, imploring him to save them from murder, robbery, and pitiless ravishment!

The reply of Colonel Nichols, who commanded the invaders, was couched in terms of equal courtesy with the letter of the governor—declaring the right and title of his British Majesty to the province; where he affirmed the Dutch to be mere interlopers; and demanding that the town, forts, etc., should be forthwith rendered into his majesty's obedience and protection—promising, at the same time, life, liberty, estate, and free trade, to every Dutch denizen who should readily submit to his majesty's government.

Peter Stuyvesant read over this friendly epistle with some such harmony of aspect as we may suppose a crusty farmer, who has long been fattening upon his neighbor's soil, reads the loving letter of John Stiles, that warns him of an action of ejectment. The old governor, however, was not to be taken by surprise, but thrusting the summons into his breeches pocket, he stalked three times across the room, took a pinch of snuff with great vehemence, and then loftily waving his hand promised to send an answer the next morning. In the meantime, he called a general council of war of his privy counselors and burgomasters, not for the purpose of asking their advice, for that, as has already been shown, he valued not a rush; but to make known unto them his sovereign determination, and require their prompt adherence.

Before, however, he convened his council, he resolved upon three important points; *first*, never to give up the city without a little hard fighting, for he deemed it highly derogatory to the dignity of so renowned a city to suffer itself to be captured and stripped, without receiving a few kicks into the bargain—*secondly*, that the majority of his grand council was composed of arrant poltroons, utterly destitute of true bottom—and, *thirdly*, that he would not therefore suffer them to see the summons of Colonel Nichols, lest the easy

terms it held out might induce them to clamor for a surrender.

His orders being duly promulgated, it was a piteous sight
to behold the late valiant burgomasters, who had demolished
the whole British empire in their harangues, peeping ruefully
out of their hiding-places, and then crawling cautiously
forth; dodging through narrow lanes and alleys; starting at
every little dog that barked, as though it had been a discharge of artillery—mistaking lamp-posts for British grena-
diers, and, in the excess of their panic, metamorphosing
pumps into formidable soldiers leveling blunderbusses at
their bosoms! Having, however, in despite of numerous
perils and difficulties of the kind, arrived safe, without the
loss of a single man, at the hall of assembly, they took their
seats and awaited in fearful silence the arrival of the governor. In a few moments the wooden leg of the intrepid
Peter was heard in regular and stout-hearted thumps upon
the staircase. He entered the chamber arrayed in a full suit
of regimentals, and carrying his trusty toledo, not girded on
his thigh, but tucked under his arm. As the governor never
equipped himself in this portentous manner unless something of a martial nature were working within his fearless
pericranium, his council regarded him ruefully, as if they
saw fire and sword in his iron countenance, and forgot to
light their pipes in breathless suspense.

The great Peter was as eloquent as he was valorous—
indeed, these two rare qualities seemed to go hand in hand
in his composition; and, unlike most great statesmen, whose
victories are only confined to the bloodless field of argument,
he was always ready to enforce his hardy words by no less
hardy deeds. His speeches were generally marked by a
simplicity approaching to bluntness, and by a truly categorical decision. Addressing the grand council, he touched
briefly upon the perils and hardships he had sustained in
escaping from his crafty foes. He next reproached the
council for wasting, in idle debate and party feuds, that time
which should have been devoted to their country. He was

particularly indignant at those brawlers, who, conscious of
individual security, had disgraced the councils of the province
by impotent hectorings and scurrilous invectives against a
noble and powerful enemy—those cowardly curs who were
incessant in their barkings and yelpings at the lion, while
distant or asleep, but the moment he approached were the
first to skulk away. He now called on those who had been
so valiant in their threats against Great Britain to stand
forth and support their vauntings by their actions; for it was
deeds, not *words*, that bespoke the spirit of a nation. He
proceeded to recall the golden days of former prosperity,
which were only to be regained by manfully withstanding
their enemies; for the peace, he observed, which is effected
by force of arms, is always more sure and durable than that
which is patched up by temporary accommodations. He
endeavored, moreover, to arouse their martial fire by remind-
ing them of the time when, before the frowning walls of
Fort Christina, he had led them on to victory. He strove
likewise to awaken their confidence, by assuring them of the
protection of St. Nicholas, who had hitherto maintained them
in safety, amid all the savages of the wilderness, the witches
and squatters of the east, and the giants of Merryland.
Finally, he informed them of the insolent summons he had
received to surrender, but concluded by swearing to defend
the province as long as Heaven was on his side, and he had
a wooden leg to stand upon—which noble sentence he em-
phasized by a tremendous thwack with the broadside of his
sword upon the table that totally electrified his auditors.

The privy counselors, who had long been accustomed to
the governor's way, and in fact had been brought into as
perfect discipline as were ever the soldiers of the great
Frederick, saw that there was no use in saying a word—so
lighted their pipes and smoked away in silence, like fat and
discreet counselors. But the burgomasters, being less under
the governor's control, considering themselves as representatives of the sovereign people, and being moreover inflated
with considerable importance and self-sufficiency, which they

had acquired at those notable schools of wisdom and morality, the popular meetings, were not so easily satisfied. Mustering up fresh spirit, when they found there was some chance of escaping from their present jeopardy without the disagreeable alternative of fighting, they requested a copy of the summons to surrender, that they might show it to a general meeting of the people.

So insolent and mutinous a request would have been enough to have roused the gorge of the tranquil Van Twiller himself—what, then, must have been its effect upon the great Stuyvesant, who was not only a Dutchman, a governor, and a valiant wooden-legged soldier to boot, but withal a man of the most stomachful and gunpowder disposition? He burst forth into a blaze of noble indignation—swore not a mother's son of them should see a syllable of it—that they deserved, every one of them, to be hanged, drawn and quartered, for traitorously daring to question the infallibility of government—that as to their advice or concurrence, he did not care a whiff of tobacco for either—that he had long been harassed and thwarted by their cowardly counsels; but that they might thenceforth go home, and go to bed like old women; for he was determined to defend the colony himself, without the assistance of them or their adherents. So saying, he tucked his sword under his arm, cocked his hat upon his head, and girding up his loins stumped indignantly out of the council chamber—everybody making room for him as he passed.

No sooner had he gone than the busy burgomasters called a public meeting in front of the Stadt-house, where they appointed as chairman one Dofue Roerback, a mighty gingerbread-baker in the land and formerly of the cabinet of William the Testy. He was looked up to with great reverence by the populace, who considered him a man of dark knowledge, seeing he was the first that imprinted new year cakes with the mysterious hieroglyphics of the Cock and Breeches, and such like magical devices.

This great burgomaster, who still chewed the cud of ill-will against the valiant Stuyvesant, in consequence of having

been ignominiously kicked out of his cabinet at the time or
his taking the reins of government—addressed the greasy
multitude in what is called a patriotic speech, in which he
informed them of the courteous summons to surrender—of
the governor's refusal to comply therewith—of his denying
the public a sight of the summons, which, he had no doubt,
contained conditions highly to the honor and advantage of
the province.

He then proceeded to speak of his excellency in high-
sounding terms, suitable to the dignity and grandeur of his
station, comparing him to Nero, Caligula, and those other
great men of yore, who are generally quoted by popular
orators on similar occasions; assuring the people that the
history of the world did not contain a despotic outrage to
equal the present for atrocity, cruelty, tyranny, and blood-
thirstiness—that it would be recorded in letters of fire on
the blood-stained tablet of history! that ages would roll back
with sudden horror when they came to view it! that the
womb of time—(by the way, your orators and writers take
strange liberties with the womb of time, though some would
fain have us believe that time is an old gentleman)—that the
womb of time, pregnant as it was with direful horrors, would
never produce a parallel enormity!—With a variety of other
heart-rending, soul-stirring tropes and figures which I cannot
enumerate—neither, indeed, need I, for they were exactly
the same that are used in all popular harangues and patriotic orations at the present day, and may be classed in
rhetoric under the general title of RIGMAROLE.

The speech of this inspired burgomaster being finished,
the meeting fell into a kind of popular fermentation, which
produced not only a string of right wise resolutions, but likewise a most resolute memorial, addressed to the governor,
remonstrating at his conduct—which was no sooner handed
to him than he handed it into the fire; and thus deprived
posterity of an invaluable document that might have served
as a precedent to the enlightened cobblers and tailors of the
present day, in their sage intermeddlings with politics.

CHAPTER SEVEN

CONTAINING A DOLEFUL DISASTER OF ANTONY THE TRUM-
PETER—AND HOW PETER STUYVESANT, LIKE A SECOND
CROMWELL, SUDDENLY DISSOLVED A RUMP PARLIA-
MENT

Now did the high-minded Pieter de Groodt shower down
a pannier-load of benedictions upon his burgomasters, for a
set of self-willed, obstinate, headstrong varlets, who would
neither be convinced nor persuaded; and determined thenceforth to have nothing more to do with them, but to consult
merely the opinion of his privy counselors, which he knew
from experience to be the best in the world—inasmuch as it
never differed from his own. Nor did he omit, now that his
hand was in, to bestow some thousand left-handed compliments upon the sovereign people; whom he railed at for a
herd of poltroons, who had no relish for the glorious hardships and illustrious misadventures of battle—but would
rather stay at home, and eat and sleep in ignoble ease, than
gain immortality and a broken head by valiantly fighting in
a ditch.

Resolutely bent, however, upon defending his beloved
city, in despite even of itself, he called unto him his trusty
Van Corlear, who was his right-hand man in all times of
emergency. Him did he adjure to take his war-denouncing
trumpet, and, mounting his horse, to beat up the country,
night and day. Sounding the alarm along the pastoral borders of the Bronx—starting the wild solitudes of Croton—
arousing the rugged yeomanry of Weehawk and Hoboken
—the mighty men of battle of Tappan Bay*—and the brave
boys of Tarry Town and Sleepy Hollow—together with all

---

* A corruption of Top-paun; so called from a tribe of Indians which
boasted a hundred and fifty fighting men. See Ogilby's History.

the other warriors of the country round about; charging them one and all to sling their powder-horns, shoulder their fowling-pieces, and march merrily down to the Manhattoes.

Now there was nothing in all the world, the divine sex excepted, that Antony Van Corlear loved better than errands of this kind. So, just stopping to take a lusty dinner, and bracing to his side his junk bottle, well charged with heart inspiring Hollands, he issued jollily from the city gate that looked out upon what is at present called Broadway; sounding as usual a farewell strain that rung in sprightly echoes through the winding streets of New Amsterdam.—Alas! never more were they to be gladdened by the melody of their favorite trumpeter!

It was a dark and stormy night when the good Antony arrived at the famous creek (sagely denominated Haerlem *river*) which separates the island of Manna-hata from the main land. The wind was high, the elements were in an uproar, and no Charon could be found to ferry the adventurous sounder of brass across the water. For a short time he vapored like an impatient ghost upon the brink, and then, bethinking himself of the urgency of his errand, took a hearty embrace of his stone bottle, swore most valorously that he would swim across, *en spijt den Duyvel* (in spite of the devil!), and daringly plunged into the stream.—Luckless Antony! scarce had he buffeted half-way over when he was observed to struggle violently, as if battling with the spirit of the waters—instinctively he put his trumpet to his mouth, and giving a vehement blast, sunk forever to the bottom.

The potent clangor of his trumpet, like the ivory horn of the renowned Paladin Orlando, when expiring in the glorious field of Roncesvalles, rung far and wide through the country, alarming the neighbors round, who hurried in amazement to the spot. Here an old Dutch burgher, famed for his veracity, and who had been a witness of the fact, related to them the melancholy affair; with the fearful addition (to which I am slow of giving belief) that he saw the duyvel, in the shape of a huge moss-bonker, seize the sturdy Antony by the leg and drag him beneath the waves. Certain it is, the place, with the adjoining promontory, which projects into the Hudson, has been called *Spijt den duyvel*, or *Spiking Devil*, ever since—the restless ghost of the unfortunate Antony still haunts the surrounding solitudes, and his trumpet has often been heard by the neighbors, of a stormy night, mingling with the howling of the blast. Nobody ever attempts to swim over the creek after dark; on the contrary, a bridge has been built to guard against such melancholy accidents in future—and as to moss-bonkers, they are held in such abhorrence that no true Dutchman will admit them to his table, who loves good fish and hates the devil.

Such was the end of Antony Van Corlear—a man deserving of a better fate. He lived roundly and soundly, like a true and jolly bachelor, until the day of his death; but though he was never married, yet did he leave behind some two or three dozen children in different parts of the country—fine, chubby, brawling, flatulent little urchins, from whom, if legends speak true (and they are not apt to lie), did descend the innumerable race of editors who people and defend this country, and who are bountifully paid by the people for keeping up a constant alarm—and making them miserable. Would that they inherited the worth, as they do the wind, of their renowned progenitor!

The tidings of this lamentable catastrophe imparted a severer pang to the bosom of Peter Stuyvesant than did even the invasion of his beloved Amsterdam. It came ruthlessly home to those sweet affections that grow close around the heart, and are nourished by its warmest current. As some lorn pilgrim, while the tempest whistles through his locks, and dreary night is gathering around, sees stretched, cold and lifeless, his faithful dog—the sole companion of his journeying, who had shared his solitary meal, and so often licked his hand in humble gratitude—so did the generous-hearted hero of the Manhattoes contemplate the untimely end of his faithful Antony. He had been the humble at-

tendant of his footsteps—he had cheered him in many a
heavy hour by his honest gayety, and had followed him in
loyalty and affection through many a scene of direful peril
and mishap; he was gone forever—and that, too, at a moment when every mongrel cur seemed skulking from his
side. This—Peter Stuyvesant—this was the moment to try
thy fortitude; and this was the moment when thou didst
indeed shine forth—Peter *the Headstrong!*

The glare of day had long dispelled the horrors of the last
stormy night; still all was dull and gloomy. The late jovial
Apollo hid his face behind lugubrious clouds, peeping out
now and then, for an instant, as if anxious, yet fearful, to
see what was going on in his favorite city. This was the
eventful morning when the great Peter was to give his reply
to the summons of the invaders. Already was he closeted
with his privy council, sitting in grim state, brooding over
the fate of his favorite trumpeter, and anon boiling with
indignation as the insolence of his recreant burgomasters
flashed upon his mind. While in this state of irritation, a
courier arrived in all haste from Winthrop, the subtle Governor of Connecticut, counseling him in the most affectionate
and disinterested manner to surrender the province, and
magnifying the dangers and calamities to which a refusal
would subject him. What a moment was this to intrude
officious advice upon a man who never took advice in his
whole life!—The fiery old governor strode up and down the
chamber, with a vehemence that made the bosoms of his
counselors to quake with awe—railing at his unlucky fate,
that thus made him the constant butt of facetious subjects
and jesuitical advisers.

Just at this ill-chosen juncture the officious burgomasters,
who were now completely on the watch, and had heard of
the arrival of mysterious dispatches, came marching in a
resolute body into the room, with a legion of schepens and
toad-eaters at their heels, and abruptly demanded a perusal
of the letter. Thus to be broken in upon by what he esteemed
a "rascal rabble," and that, too, at the very moment he was

grinding under an irritation from abroad, was too much for
the spleen of the choleric Peter.   He tore the letter in a
thousand pieces*—threw it in the face of the nearest burgomaster—broke his pipe over the head of the next—hurled his
spitting-box at an unlucky schepen who was just making a
masterly retreat out at the door, and finally prorogued the
whole meeting *sine die*, by kicking them downstairs with
his wooden leg.

As soon as the burgomasters could recover from the confusion into which their sudden exit had thrown them, and
had taken a little time to breathe, they protested against the
conduct of the governor, which they did not hesitate to pronounce tyrannical, unconstitutional, highly indecent, and
somewhat disrespectful.   They then called a public meeting
where they read the protest, and addressing the assembly in
a set speech, related at full length, and with appropriate
coloring and exaggeration, the despotic and vindictive deportment of the governor; declaring that, for their own
parts, they did not value a straw the being kicked, cuffed,
and mauled by the timber toe of his excellency, but they felt
for the dignity of the sovereign people, thus rudely insulted
by the outrage committed on the seat of honor of their representatives.   The latter part of the harangue had a violent
effect upon the sensibility of the people, as it came home at
once to that delicacy of feeling and jealous pride of character
vested in all true mobs; who, though they may bear injuries
without a murmur, yet are marvelously jealous of their sovereign dignity—and there is no knowing to what act of
resentment they might have been provoked against the
redoubtable Peter, had not the greasy rogues been somewhat more afraid of their sturdy old governor than they
were of St. Nicholas, the English—or the D——l himself.

---

* Smith's History of New York.

CHAPTER EIGHT

HOW PETER STUYVESANT DEFENDED THE CITY OF NEW
AMSTERDAM, FOR SEVERAL DAYS, BY DINT OF THE
STRENGTH OF HIS HEAD

THERE is something exceedingly sublime and melancholy
in the spectacle which the present crisis of our history presents. An illustrious and venerable little city—the metropolis of an immense extent of uninhabited country—garrisoned by a doughty host of orators, chairmen, committee-
men, burgomasters, schepens, and old women—governed by
a determined and strong-headed warrior, and fortified by
mud batteries, palisadoes and resolutions—blockaded by sea,
beleaguered by land, and threatened with direful desolation
from without; while its very vitals are torn with internal
faction and commotion! Never did historic pen record a
page of more complicated distress, unless it be the strife that
distracted the Israelites during the siege of Jerusalem—where
discordant parties were cutting each other's throats at the
moment when the victorious legions of Titus had toppled
down their bulwarks, and were carrying fire and sword into
the very sanctum sanctorum of the temple.

Governor Stuyvesant, having triumphantly, as has been
recorded, put his grand council to the rout, and thus delivered
himself from a multitude of impertinent advisers, dispatched
a categorical reply to the commanders of the invading squadron; wherein he asserted the right and title of their High
Mightinesses the Lords States-General to the province of New
Netherlands, and, trusting in the righteousness of his cause,
set the whole British nation at defiance! My anxiety to
extricate my readers and myself from these disastrous scenes
prevents me from giving the whole of this gallant letter,
which concluded in these manly and affectionate terms:

"As touching the threats in your conclusion, we have nothing to answer, only that we fear nothing but what God (who is as just as merciful) shall lay upon us; all things being in His gracious disposal, and we may as well be preserved by Him with small forces as by a great army; which makes us to wish you all happiness and prosperity, and recommend you to His protection.—My lords, your thrice humble and affectionate servant and friend,

"P. STUYVESANT."

Thus having resolutely thrown his gauntlet, the brave Peter stuck a pair of horse-pistols in his belt, girded an immense powder-horn on his side, thrust his sound leg into a Hessian boot, and, clapping his fierce little war hat on the top of his head, paraded up and down in front of his house, determined to defend his beloved city to the last.

While all these woful struggles and dissensions were prevailing in the unhappy city of New Amsterdam, and while its worthy but ill-starred governor was framing the above-quoted letter, the English commanders did not remain idle. They had agents secretly employed to foment the fears and clamors of the populace; and moreover circulated far and wide, through the adjacent country, a proclamation, repeating the terms they had already held out in their summons to surrender, and beguiling the simple Nederlanders with the most crafty and conciliating professions. They promised that every man who voluntarily submitted to the authority of his British Majesty should retain peaceable possession of his house, his vrouw, and his cabbage-garden. That he should be suffered to smoke his pipe, speak Dutch, wear as many breeches as he pleased, and import bricks, tiles, and stone jugs from Holland, instead of manufacturing them on the spot. That he should on no account be compelled to learn the English language, or keep accounts in any other way than by casting them up on his fingers, and chalking them down upon the crown of his hat; as is still observed among the Dutch yeomanry at the present day.

That every man should be allowed quietly to inherit his father's hat, coat, shoe-buckles, pipe, and every other personal appendage, and that no man should be obliged to conform to any improvements, inventions, or any other modern innovations; but, on the contrary, should be permitted to build his house, follow his trade, manage his farm, rear his hogs, and educate his children, precisely as his ancestors did before him since time immemorial. Finally, that he should have all the benefits of free trade, and should not be required to acknowledge any other saint in the calendar than St. Nicholas, who should thenceforward, as before, be considered the tutelar saint of the city.

These terms, as may be supposed, appeared very satisfactory to the people, who had a great disposition to enjoy their property unmolested, and a most singular aversion to engage in a contest where they could gain little more than honor and broken heads—the first of which they held in philosophic indifference, the latter in utter detestation. By these insidious means, therefore, did the English succeed in alienating the confidence and affections of the populace from their gallant old governor, whom they considered as obstinately bent upon running them into hideous misadventures; and did not hesitate to speak their minds freely, and abuse him most heartily—behind his back.

Like as a mighty grampus, who, though assailed and buffeted by roaring waves and brawling surges, still keeps on an undeviating course; and, though overwhelmed by boisterous billows, still emerges from the troubled deep, spouting and blowing with tenfold violence—so did the inflexible Peter pursue, unwavering, his determined career, and rise, contemptuous, above the clamors of the rabble.

But when the British warriors found, by the tenor of his reply, that he set their power at defiance, they forthwith dispatched recruiting officers to Jamaica, and Jericho, and Nineveh, and Quag, and Patchog, and all those towns on Long Island which had been subdued of yore by the immortal Stoffel Brinkerhoff; stirring up the valiant progeny of Pre-

served Fish, and Determined Cock, and those other illustrious squatters, to assail the city of New Amsterdam by land.
In the meanwhile, the hostile ships made awful preparation
to commence an assault by water.

The streets of New Amsterdam now presented a scene
of wild dismay and consternation. In vain did the gallant
Stuyvesant order the citizens to arm and assemble in the
public square or market-place. The whole party of Short
Pipes in the course of a single night had changed into arrant
old women—a metamorphosis only to be paralleled by the
prodigies recorded by Livy as having happened at Rome on
the approach of Hannibal, when statues sweated in pure
affright, goats were converted into sheep, and cocks turning
into hens ran cackling about the streets.

The harassed Peter, thus menaced from without and tor-
mented from within, baited by the burgomasters and hooted
at by the rabble, chafed and growled and raged like a furious bear tied to a stake and worried by a legion of scoundrel
curs. Finding, however, that all further attempts to defend
the city were vain, and hearing that an irruption of borderers
and mosstroopers was ready to deluge him from the east, he
was at length compelled, in spite of his proud heart, which
swelled in his throat until it had nearly choked him, to consent to a treaty of surrender.

Words cannot express the transports of the people on receiving this agreeable intelligence; had they obtained a conquest over their enemies they could not have indulged greater
delight. The streets resounded with their congratulations—
they extolled their governor as the father and deliverer of
his country—they crowded to his house to testify their gratitude, and were ten times more noisy in their plaudits than
when he returned, with victory perched upon his beaver,
from the glorious capture of Fort Christina. But the indignant Peter shut his doors and windows, and took refuge in
the innermost recesses of his mansion, that he might not hear
the ignoble rejoicings of the rabble.

In consequence of this consent of the governor, a parley

was demanded of the besieging forces to treat of the terms of surrender. Accordingly, a deputation of six commissioners was appointed on both sides; and on the 27th of August, 1664, a capitulation highly favorable to the province, and honorable to Peter Stuyvesant, was agreed to by the enemy, who had conceived a high opinion of the valor of the Manhattoes, and the magnanimity and unbounded discretion of their governor.

One thing alone remained, which was, that the articles of surrender should be ratified and signed by the governor. When the commissioners respectfully waited upon him for this purpose, they were received by the hardy old warrior with the most grim and bitter courtesy. His warlike accouterments were laid aside—an old India nightgown was wrapped about his rugged limbs, a red nightcap overshadowed his frowning brow, and an iron-gray beard, of three days' growth, gave additional grimness to his visage. Thrice did he seize a little worn-out stump of a pen and essay to sign the loathsome paper—thrice did he clinch his teeth and make a most horrible countenance, as though a pestiferous dose of rhubarb, senna, and ipecacuanha, had been offered to his lips; at length, dashing it from him, he seized his brass-hilted sword, and jerking it from the scabbard, swore by St. Nicholas he'd sooner die than yield to any power under heaven.

In vain was every attempt to shake this sturdy resolution —menaces, remonstrances, revilings, were exhausted to no purpose—for two whole days was the house of the valiant Peter besieged by the clamorous rabble, and for two whole days did he partake himself to his arms, and persist in a magnanimous refusal to ratify the capitulation.

At length the populace, finding that boisterous measures did but incense more determined opposition, bethought themselves of a humble expedient, by which, happily, the governor's ire might be soothed and his resolution undermined. And now a solemn and mournful procession, headed by the burgomasters and schepens, and followed by the populace,

moves slcwly to the governor's dwelling, bearing the capitulation. Here they found the stout old hero, drawn up like a
giant in his castle, the doors strongly barricadoed, and himself in full regimentals, with his cocked hat on his head,
firmly posted with a blunderbuss at the garret-window.

There was something in this formidable position that
struck even the ignoble vulgar with awe and admiration.
The brawling multitude could not but reflect with self-abasement upon their own pusillanimous conduct, when they beheld their hardy but deserted old governor thus faithful to
his post, like a forlorn hope, and fully prepared to defend his
ungrateful city to the last. These compunctions, however,
were soon overwhelmed by the recurring tide of public apprehension. The populace arranged themselves before the
house, taking off their hats with most respectful humility.—
Burgomaster Roerback, who was of that popular class of
orators described by Sallust as being "talkative rather than
eloquent," stepped forth and addressed the governor in a
speech of three hours' length; detailing in the most pathetic
terms the calamitous situation of the province, and urging
him in a constant repetition of the same arguments and words
to sign the capitulation.

The mighty Peter eyed him from his little garret-window
in grim silence—now and then his eye would glance over the
surrounding rabble, and an indignant grin, like that of an
angry mastiff, would mark his iron visage. But though he
was a man of most undaunted mettle—though he had a heart
as big as an ox, and a head that would have set adamant to
scorn—yet after all he was a mere mortal: wearied out by
these repeated oppositions and this eternal haranguing, and
perceiving that, unless he complied, the inhabitants would
follow their own inclinations, or rather their fears, without
waiting for his consent, he testily ordered them to hand up
the paper. It was accordingly hoisted to him on the end of
a pole, and having scrawled his name at the bottom of it, he
anathematized them all for a set of cowardly, mutinous, degenerate poltroons—threw the capitulation at their heads,

slammed down the window, and was heard stumping downstairs with the most vehement indignation. The rabble incontinently took to their heels; even the burgomasters were
not slow in evacuating the premises, fearing lest the sturdy
Peter might issue from his den and greet them with some
unwelcome testimonial of his displeasure.

Within three hours after the surrender, a legion of British beef-fed warriors poured into New Amsterdam, taking
possession of the fort and batteries. And now might be
heard from all quarters the sound of hammers, made by the
old Dutch burghers, who were busily employed in nailing up
their doors and windows, to protect their vrouws from these
fierce barbarians, whom they contemplated in silent sullen-
ness from the garret-windows, as they paraded through the
streets.

Thus did Col. Richard Nichols, the commander of the
British forces, enter into quiet possessions of the conquered
realm, as *locum tenens* for the Duke of York. The victory
was attended with no other outrage than that of changing
the name of the province and its metropolis, which thenceforth were denominated NEW YORK, and so have continued
to be called unto the present day. The inhabitants, according to treaty, were allowed to maintain quiet possession of
their property; but so inveterately did they retain their abhorrence of the British nation that in a private meeting of the
leading citizens it was unanimously determined never to ask
any of their conquerors to dinner.

CHAPTER NINE

CONTAINING THE DIGNIFIED RETIREMENT AND MORTAL SUR-
RENDER OF PETER THE HEADSTRONG

THUS, then, have I concluded this great historical enterprise; but before I lay aside my weary pen there yet remains to be performed one pious duty. If, among the va-

riety of readers that may peruse this book, there should
haply be found any of those souls of true nobility which
glow with celestial fire at the history of the generous and the
brave, they will doubtless be anxious to know the fate of the
gallant Peter Stuyvesant. To gratify one such sterling heart
of gold, I would go more lengths than to instruct the cold-
blooded curiosity of a whole fraternity of philosophers.

No sooner had that high-mettled cavalier signed the
articles of capitulation than, determined not to witness the
humiliation of his favorite city, he turned his back on its
walls and made a growling retreat to his *Bouwery*, or country-seat, which was situated about two miles off; where he
passed the remainder of his days in patriarchal retirement.
There he enjoyed that tranquillity of mind which he had
never known amid the distracting cares of government; and
tasted the sweets of absolute and uncontrolled authority,
which his factious subjects had so often dashed with the
bitterness of opposition.

No persuasions could ever induce him to revisit the city—
on the contrary, he would always have his great armchair
placed with its back to the windows which looked in that
direction; until a thick grove of trees, planted by his own
hand, grew up and formed a screen that effectually excluded
it from the prospect. He railed continually at the degenerate innovations and improvements introduced by the conquerors—forbade a word of their detested language to be
spoken in his family—a prohibition readily obeyed, since
none of the household could speak anything but Dutch—
and even ordered a fine avenue to be cut down in front of
his house, because it consisted of English cherry-trees.

The same incessant vigilance that blazed forth when he
had a vast province under his care now showed itself with
equal vigor, though in narrower limits. He patroled with
unceasing watchfulness around the boundaries of his little
territory; repelled every encroachment with intrepid promptness; punished every vagrant depredation upon his orchard
or his farmyard with inflexible severity—and conducted every

stray hog or cow in triumph to the pound. But to the indigent neighbor, the friendless stranger, or the weary wanderer, his spacious doors were ever open, and his capacious fireplace, that emblem of his own warm and generous heart, had always a corner to receive and cherish them. There was an exception to this, I must confess, in case the ill-starred applicant was an Englishman or a Yankee, to whom, though he might extend the hand of assistance, he never could be brought to yield the rites of hospitality. Nay, if peradventure some straggling merchant of the east should stop at his door, with his cartload of tinware or wooden bowls, the fiery Peter would issue forth like a giant from his castle, and make such a furious clattering among his pots and kettles that the vender of *"notions"* was fain to betake himself to instant flight.

His handsome suit of regimentals, worn threadbare by the brush, was carefully hung up in the state bed-chamber, and regularly aired on the first fair day of every month—and his cocked hat and trusty sword were suspended in grim repose over the parlor mantel-piece, forming supporters to a full-length portrait of the renowned Admiral Van Tromp. In his domestic empire he maintained strict discipline and a well-organized, despotic government; but, though his own will was the supreme law, yet the good of his subjects was his constant object. He watched over, not merely their immediate comforts, but their morals and their ultimate welfare; for he gave them abundance of excellent admonition, nor could any of them complain that, when occasion required, he was by any means niggardly in bestowing wholesome correction.

The good old Dutch festivals, those periodical demonstrations of an overflowing heart and a thankful spirit, which are falling into sad disuse among my fellow-citizens, were faithfully observed in the mansion of Governor Stuyvesant. New Year was truly a day of open-handed liberality, of jocund revelry, and warm-hearted congratulation—when the bosom seemed to swell with genial good-fellowship—and the plenteous table was attended with an unceremonious freedom, and honest, broad-mouthed merriment, unknown in these days of degeneracy and refinement. Pas and Pinxter were scrupulously observed throughout his dominions; nor was the day of St. Nicholas suffered to pass by without making presents, hanging the stocking in the chimney, and complying with all its other ceremonies.

Once a year, on the first day of April, he used to array himself in full regimentals, being the anniversary of his triumphal entry into New Amsterdam, after the conquest of New Sweden. This was always a kind of saturnalia among the domestics, when they considered themselves at liberty, in some measure, to say and do what they pleased; for on this day their master was always observed to unbend, and become exceeding pleasant and jocose, sending the old gray-headed negroes on April fool's errands for pigeon's milk; not one of whom but allowed himself to be taken in, and humored his old master's jokes, as became a faithful and well-disciplined dependent. Thus did he reign, happily and peacefully, on his own land—injuring no man—envying no man —molested by no outward strifes—perplexed by no internal commotions; and the mighty monarchs of the earth, who were vainly seeking to maintain peace and promote the welfare of mankind, by war and desolation, would have done well to have made a voyage to the little island of Mannahata, and learned a lesson in government from the domestic economy of Peter Stuyvesant.

In process of time, however, the old governor, like all other children of mortality, began to exhibit tokens of decay. Like an aged oak, which, though it long has braved the fury of the elements, and still retains its gigantic proportions, yet begins to shake and groan with every blast—so was it with the gallant Peter; for, though he still bore the port and semblance of what he was in the days of his hardihood and chivalry, yet did age and infirmity begin to sap the vigor of his frame—but his heart, that most unconquerable citadel, still triumphed unsubdued. With matchless avidity would he

listen to every article of intelligence concerning the battles
between the English and Dutch—still would his pulse beat
high, whenever he heard of the victories of De Ruyter—and
his countenance lower, and his eyebrows knit, when fortune
turned in favor of the English. At length, as on a certain
day he had just smoked his fifth pipe, and was napping after
dinner in his armchair, conquering the whole British nation
in his dreams, he was suddenly aroused by a fearful ringing
of bells, rattling of drums, and roaring of cannon, that put
all his blood in a ferment. But when he learned that these
rejoicings were in honor of a great victory obtained by the
combined English and French fleets over the brave De Ruyter and the younger Van Tromp, it went so much to his
heart that he took to his bed, and, in less than three days,
was brought to death's door by a violent cholera morbus!
But, even in this extremity, he still displayed the unconquerable spirit of Peter *the Headstrong;* holding out, to the last
gasp, with the most inflexible obstinacy, against a whole
army of old women, who were bent upon driving the enemy
out of his bowels, after a true Dutch mode of defense, by
inundating the seat of war with catnip and pennyroyal.

While he thus lay, lingering on the verge of dissolution,
news was brought him that the brave De Ruyter had suffered
but little loss—had made good his retreat—and meant once
more to meet the enemy in battle. The closing eye of the
old warrior kindled at the words—he partly raised himself
in bed—a flash of martial fire beamed across his visage—he
clinched his withered hand, as if he felt within his grip that
sword which waved in triumph before the walls of Fort Christina, and, giving a grim smile of exultation, sunk back upon
his pillow and expired.

Thus died Peter Stuyvesant, a valiant soldier—a loyal
subject—an upright governor, and an honest Dutchman—
who wanted only a few empires to desolate to have been
immortalized as a hero.

His funeral obsequies were celebrated with the utmost
grandeur and solemnity. The town was perfectly emptied

of its inhabitants, who crowded in throngs to pay the last
sad honors to their good old governor.   All his sterling qualities rushed in full tide upon their recollections, while the
memory of his foibles and his faults had expired with him.
The ancient burghers contended who should have the privilege of bearing the pall; the populace strove who should walk
nearest to the bier—and the melancholy procession was closed
by a number of gray-headed negroes, who had wintered and
summered in the household of their departed master for the
greater part of a century.

With sad and gloomy countenances the multitude gathered around the grave.   They dwelt with mournful hearts
on the sturdy virtues, the signal services, and the gallant exploits of the brave old worthy.   They recalled, with secret
upbraidings, their own factious opposition to his government
—and many an ancient burgher, whose phlegmatic features
had never been known to relax, nor his eyes to moisten, was
now observed to puff a pensive pipe, and the big drop to steal
down his cheek—while he muttered, with affectionate accent
and melancholy shake of the head—"Well den!—Hardkoppig Peter ben gone at last!"

His remains were deposited in the family vault, under a
chapel which he had piously erected on his estate and dedicated to St. Nicholas—and which stood on the identical spot
at present occupied by St. Mark's church, where his tombstone is still to be seen.   His estate, or *Bouwery*, as it was
called, has ever continued in the possession of his descendants, who, by the uniform integrity of their conduct, and
their strict adherence to the customs and manners that prevailed in the *"good old times,"* have proved themselves
worthy of their illustrious ancestor.   Many a time and oft
has the farm been haunted, at night, by enterprising money-
diggers in quest of pots of gold, said to have been buried by
the old governor—though I cannot learn that any of them
have ever been enriched by their researches; and who is
there, among my native-born fellow-citizens, that does not
remember, when, in the mischievous days of his boyhood,

he conceived it a great exploit to rob "Stuyvesant's orchard" on a holiday afternoon?

At this stronghold of the family may still be seen certain memorials of the immortal Peter. His full-length portrait frowns in martial terrors from the parlor wall—his cocked hat and sword still hang up in the best bedroom—his brimstone-colored breeches were for a long while suspended in the hall, until some years since they occasioned a dispute between a new married couple—and his silver-mounted wooden leg is still treasured up in the storeroom as an invaluable relic.

CHAPTER TEN

THE AUTHOR'S REFLECTIONS UPON WHAT HAS BEEN SAID

AMONG the numerous events which are each in their turn the most direful and melancholy of all possible occurrences, in your interesting and authentic history, there is none that occasion such deep and heartrending grief as the decline and fall of your renowned and mighty empires. Where is the reader who can contemplate, without emotion, the disastrous events by which the great dynasties of the world have been extinguished? While wandering, in imagination, among the gigantic ruins of states and empires, and marking the tremendous convulsions that wrought their overthrow, the bosom of the melancholy inquirer swells with sympathy commensurate to the surrounding desolation. Kingdoms, principalities, and powers, have each had their rise, their progress, and their downfall—each in its turn has swayed a potent scepter, each has returned to its primeval nothingness. And thus did it fare with the empire of their High Mightinesses, at the Manhattoes, under the peaceful reign of Walter the Doubter—the fretful reign of William the Testy—and the chivalric reign of Peter the Headstrong.

Its history is fruitful of instruction, and worthy of being pondered over attentively; for it is by thus raking among

the ashes of departed greatness that the sparks of true knowledge are found, and the lamp of wisdom illumined. Let,
then, the reign of Walter the Doubter warn against yielding
to that sleek, contented security, that overweening fondness
for comfort and repose, that are produced by a state of prosperity and peace. These tend to unnerve a nation; to destroy its pride of character; to render it patient of insult,
deaf to the calls of honor and of justice; and cause it to cling
to peace, like the sluggard to his pillow, at the expense of
every valuable duty and consideration. Such supineness insures the very evil from which it shrinks. One right, yielded
up, produces the usurpation of a second; one encroachment,
passively suffered, makes way for another; and the nation
that thus, through a doting love of peace, has sacrificed honor
and interest, will at length have to fight for existence.

Let the disastrous reign of William the Testy serve as a
salutary warning against that fitful, feverish mode of legislation that acts without system; depends on shifts and projects, and trusts to lucky contingencies; that hesitates, and
wavers, and at length decides with the rashness of ignorance
and imbecility; that stoops for popularity by courting the
prejudices and flattering the arrogance, rather than commanding the respect, of the rabble; that seeks safety in a
multitude of counselors, and distracts itself by a variety of
contradictory schemes and opinions; that mistakes procrasti-
nation for deliberate wariness—hurry for decision—starveling parsimony for wholesome economy—bustle for business,
and vaporing for valor; that is violent in council, sanguine
in expectation, precipitate in action, and feeble in execution;
that undertakes enterprises without forethought, enters upon
them without preparation, conducts them without energy,
and ends them in confusion and defeat.

Let the reign of the good Stuyvesant show the effects of
vigor and decision, even when destitute of cool judgment
and surrounded by perplexities. Let it show how frankness,
probity and high-souled courage will command respect and
secure honor, even where success is unattainable. But, at

the same time, let it caution against a too ready reliance on the good faith of others and a too honest confidence in the loving professions of powerful neighbors, who are most friendly when they most mean to betray. Let it teach a judicious attention to the opinions and wishes of the many, who, in times of peril, must be soothed and led, or apprehension will overpower the deference to authority. Let the empty wordiness of his factious subjects, their intemperate harangues, their violent "resolutions," their hectorings against an absent enemy, and their pusillanimity on his approach, teach us to distrust and despise those clamorous patriots whose courage dwells but in the tongue. Let them serve as a lesson to repress that insolence of speech, destitute of real force, which too often breaks forth in popular bodies, and bespeaks the vanity rather than the spirit of a nation. Let them caution us against vaunting too much of our own power and prowess, and reviling a noble enemy. True gallantry of soul would always lead us to treat a foe with courtesy and proud punctilio; a contrary conduct but takes from the merit of victory, and renders defeat doubly disgraceful.

But I cease to dwell on the stores of excellent examples to be drawn from the ancient chronicles of the Manhattoes. He who reads attentively will discover the threads of gold which run throughout the web of history, and are invisible to the dull eye of ignorance. But, before I conclude, let me point out a solemn warning, furnished in the subtle chain of events by which the capture of Fort Casimir has produced the present convulsions of our globe.

Attend, then, gentle reader, to this plain deduction, which, if thou art a king, an emperor, or other powerful potentate, I advise thee to treasure up in thy heart—though little expectation have I that my work will fall into such hands; for well I know the care of crafty ministers to keep all grave and edifying books of the kind out of the way of unhappy monarchs—lest peradventure they should read them and learn wisdom.

By the treacherous surprisal of Fort Casimir, then, did

the crafty Swedes enjoy a transient triumph; but drew upon their heads the vengeance of Peter Stuyvesant, who wrested all New Sweden from their hands. By the conquest of New Sweden, Peter Stuyvesant aroused the claims of Lord Baltimore; who appealed to the cabinet of Great Britain; who subdued the whole province of New Netherlands. By this great achievement, the whole extent of North America, from Nova Scotia to the Floridas, was rendered one entire dependency upon the British crown—but mark the consequence: The hitherto scattered colonies being thus consolidated, and having no rival colonies to check or keep them in awe, waxed great and powerful, and finally, becoming too strong for the mother country, were enabled to shake off its bonds, and by a glorious revolution became an independent empire. But the chain of effects stopped not here; the successful revolution in America produced the sanguinary revolution in France, which produced the puissant Bonaparte, who produced the French despotism, which has thrown the whole world in confusion!—Thus have these great powers been successively punished for their ill-starred conquests; and thus, as I asserted, have all the present convulsions, revolutions and disasters that overwhelm mankind originated in the capture of the little Fort Casimir, as recorded in this eventful history.

And now, worthy reader, ere I take a sad farewell—which, alas! must be forever—willingly would I part in cordial fellowship, and bespeak thy kind-hearted remembrance. That I have not written a better history of the days of the patriarchs is not my fault—had any other person written one as good I should not have attempted it at all. That many will hereafter spring up and surpass me in excellence I have very little doubt and still less care; well knowing, when the great Christovallo Colon (who is vulgarly called Columbus) had once stood his egg upon its end, every one at the table could stand his up a thousand times more dexterously. Should any reader find matter of offense in this history, I should heartily grieve, though I would on no account question his penetration by telling him he is mistaken—his good nature, by telling him he is captious—or his pure conscience, by telling him he is startled at a shadow. Surely if he is so ingenious in finding offense where none is intended it were a thousand pities he should not be suffered to enjoy the benefit of his discovery.

I have too high an opinion of the understanding of my fellow-citizens to think of yielding them any instruction; and I covet too much their good-will to forfeit it by giving them good advice. I am none of those cynics who despise the world because it despises them—on the contrary, though but low in its regard, I look up to it with the most perfect good nature, and my only sorrow is that it does not prove itself more worthy of the unbounded love I bear it.

If, however, in this my historic production—the scanty fruit of a long and laborious life—I have failed to gratify the dainty p late of the age, I can only lament my misfortune—for it is too late in the season for me even to hope to repair it. Already has withering age showered his sterile snows upon my brow; in a little while, and this genial warmth, which still lingers around my heart, and throbs—worthy reader—throbs kindly toward thyself, will be chilled forever. Haply this frail compound of dust, which while alive may have given birth to naught but unprofitable weeds, may form a humble sod of the valley, from whence may spring many a sweet wild flower to adorn my beloved island of Manna-hata!

END OF "A HISTORY OF NEW YORK"

MISCELLANIES

CONTRIBUTED TO THE KNICKERBOCKER MAGAZINE

BY GEOFFREY CRAYON

A CHRONICLE OF WOLFERT'S ROOST

TO THE EDITOR OF THE KNICKERBOCKER

SIR—I have observed that as a man advances in life he is subject to a kind of plethora of the mind, doubtless occasioned by the vast accumulation of wisdom and experience upon the brain. Hence he is apt to become narrative and admonitory, that is to say, fond of telling long stories, and of doling out advice, to the small profit and great annoyance of his friends. As I have a great horror of becoming the oracle, or, more technically speaking, the "bore" of the domestic circle, and would much rather bestow my wisdom and tediousness upon the world at large, I have always sought to ease off this surcharge of the intellect by means of my pen, and hence have inflicted divers gossiping volumes upon the patience of the public. I am tired, however, of writing volumes; they do not afford exactly the relief I require; there is too much preparation, arrangement, and parade, in this set form of coming before the public. I am growing too indolent and unambitious for anything that requires labor or display. I have thought, therefore, of securing to myself a snug corner in some periodical work where I might, as it were, loll at my ease in my elbow-chair and chat sociably with the public, as with an old friend, on any chance subject that might pop into my brain.

In looking around, for this purpose, upon the various excellent periodicals with which our country abounds, my eye was struck by the title of your work—"THE KNICKER-BOCKER." My heart leaped at the sight.

DIEDRICH KNICKERBOCKER, sir, was one of my earliest and most valued friends, and the recollection of him is associated with some of the pleasantest scenes of my youthful days. To explain this, and to show how I came into possession of sundry of his posthumous works, which I have from time to time given to the world, permit me to relate a few particulars of our early intercourse. I give them with the more confidence as I know the interest you take in that departed worthy, whose name and effigy are stamped upon your title-page, and as they will be found important to the better understanding and relishing divers communications I may have to make to you.

My first acquaintance with that great and good man, for such I may venture to call him, now that the lapse of some thirty years has shrouded his name with venerable antiquity, and the popular voice has elevated him to the rank of the classic historian of yore, my first acquaintance with him was formed on the banks of the Hudson, not far from the wizard region of Sleepy Hollow. He had come there in the course of his researches among the Dutch neighborhoods for materials for his immortal history. For this purpose he was ransacking the archives of one of the most ancient and historical mansions in the country. It was a lowly edifice, built in the time of the Dutch dynasty, and stood on a green bank overshadowed by trees, from which it peeped forth upon the great Tappan Zee, so famous among early Dutch navigators. A bright pure spring welled up at the foot of the green bank; a wild brook came babbling down a neighboring ravine and threw itself into a little woody cove in front of the mansion. It was indeed as quiet and sheltered a nook as the heart of man could require in which to take refuge from the cares and troubles of the world; and as such it had been chosen, in old times, by Wolfert Acker, one of the privy counselors of the renowned Peter Stuyvesant.

This worthy but ill-starred man had led a weary and worried life throughout the stormy reign of the chivalric Peter, being one of those unlucky wights with whom the world is ever at variance, and who are kept in a continual fume and fret by the wickedness of mankind. At the time of the subjugation of the province by the English he retired hither in high dudgeon; with the bitter determination to bury himself from the world, and live here in peace and quietness for the remainder of his days. In token of this fixed resolution he inscribed over his door the favorite Dutch motto, "Lust in Rust" (pleasure in repose). The mansion was thence called "Wolfert's Rust"—Wolfert's Rest; but in process of time the name was vitiated into Wolfert's Roost, probably from its quaint cock-loft look, or from its having a weather-cock perched on every gable. This name it continued to bear, long after the unlucky Wolfert was driven forth once more upon a wrangling world, by the tongue of a termagant wife; for it passed into a proverb throughout the neighborhood, and has been handed down by tradition, that the cock of the Roost was the most henpecked bird in the country.

This primitive and historical mansion has since passed through many changes and trials, which it may be my lot hereafter to notice. At the time of the sojourn of Diedrich Knickerbocker it was in possession of the gallant family of the Van Tassels, who have figured so conspicuously in his writings. What appears to have given it peculiar value, in his eyes, was the rich treasury of historical facts here secretly hoarded up, like buried gold; for it said that Wolfert Acker, when he retreated from New Amsterdam, carried off with him many of the records and journals of the province pertaining to the Dutch dynasty; swearing that they should never fall into the hands of the English. These, like the lost books of Livy, had baffled the research of former historians;

but these did I find the indefatigable Diedrich diligently deciphering. He was already a sage in years and experience, I but an idle stripling; yet he did not despise my youth and ignorance, but took me kindly by the hand, and led me gently into those paths of local and traditional lore which he was so fond of exploring. I sat with him in his little chamber at the Roost, and watched the antiquarian patience and perseverance with which he deciphered those venerable Dutch documents, worse than Herculean manuscripts. I sat with him by the spring at the foot of the green bank, and listened to his heroic tales about the worthies of the olden time, the paladins of New Amsterdam. I accompanied him in his legendary researches about Tarrytown and Sing Sing, and explored with him the spellbound recesses of Sleepy Hollow. I was present at many of his conferences with the good old Dutch burghers and their wives, from whom he derived many of those marvelous facts not laid down in books or records, and which give such superior value and authenticity to his history over all others that have been written concerning the New Netherlands.

But let me check my proneness to dilate upon this favorite theme; I may recur to it hereafter. Suffice it to say, the intimacy thus formed continued for a considerable time; and, in company with the worthy Diedrich I visited many of the places celebrated by his pen. The currents of our lives at length diverged. He remained at home to complete his mighty work, while a vagrant fancy led me to wander about the world. Many, many years elapsed before I returned to the parent soil. In the interim, the venerable historian of the New Netherlands had been gathered to his fathers, but his name had risen to renown. His native city, that city in which he so much delighted, had decreed all manner of costly honors to his memory. I found his effigy imprinted upon New Year cakes, and devoured with eager relish by holiday urchins; a great oyster-house bore the name of "Knickerbocker Hall"; and I narrowly escaped the pleasure of being run over by a Knickerbocker omnibus!

Proud of having associated with a man who had achieved such greatness, I now recalled our early intimacy with tenfold pleasure, and sought to revisit the scenes we had trodden together. The most important of these was the mansion of the Van Tassels, the Roost of the unfortunate Wolfert. Time, which changes all things, is but slow in its operations upon a Dutchman's dwelling. I found the venerable and quaint little edifice much as I had seen it during the sojourn of Diedrich. There stood his elbow-chair in the corner of the room he had occupied; the old-fashioned Dutch writing-desk at which he had pored over the chronicles of the Manhattoes; there was the old wooden chest, with the archives left by Wolfert Acker, many of which, however, had been fired off as wadding from the long duck gun of the Van Tassels. The scene around the mansion was still the same: the green bank; the spring beside which I had listened to the legendary narratives of the historian; the wild brook babbling down to the woody cove, and the overshadowing locust trees, half shutting out the prospect of the great Tappan Zee.

As I looked round upon the scene my heart yearned at the recollection of my departed friend, and I wistfully eyed the mansion which he had inhabited, and which was fast mouldering to decay. The thought struck me to arrest the desolating hand of Time; to rescue the historic pile from utter ruin, and to make it the closing scene of my wanderings; a quiet home, where I might enjoy "lust in rust" for the remainder of my days. It is true, the fate of the unlucky Wolfert passed across my mind; but I consoled myself with the reflection that I was a bachelor, and that I had n termagant wife to dispute the sovereignty of the Roost with me.

I have become possessor of the Roost! I have repaired and renovated it with religious care, in the genuine Dutch style, and have adorned and illustrated it with sundry relics of the glorious days of the New Netherlands. A venerable weather-cock, of portly Dutch dimensions, which once battled with the wind on the top of the Stadt-house of New Amsterdam, in the time of Peter Stuyvesant, now erects its crest on the gable end of my edifice; a gilded horse in full gallop, once the weather-cock of the great Vander Heyden Palace of Albany, now glitters in the sunshine and veers with every breeze on the peaked turret over my portal; my sanctum sanctorum is the chamber once honored by the illustrious Diedrich, and it is from his elbow-chair, and his identical old Dutch writing-desk, that I pen this rambling epistle.

Here, then, have I set up my rest, surrounded by the recollections of early days and the mementos of the historian of the Manhattoes, with that glorious river before me which flows with such majesty through his works and which has ever been to me a river of delight.

I thank God I was born on the banks of the Hudson! I think it an invaluable advantage to be born and brought up in the neighborhood of some grand and noble object in nature; a river, a lake, or a mountain. We make a friendship with it, we in a manner ally ourselves to it for life. It remains an object of our pride and affections, a rallying point, to call us home again after all our wanderings. "The things which we have learned in our childhood," says an old writer, "grow up with our souls, and unite themselves to it." So it is with the scenes among which we have passed our early days; they influence the whole course of our thoughts and feelings; and I fancy I can trace much of what is good and pleasant in my own heterogeneous compound to my early companionship with this glorious river. In the warmth of my youthful enthusiasm I used to clothe it with moral attributes, and almost to give it a soul. I admired its frank, bold, honest character; its noble sincerity and perfect truth. Here was no specious, smiling surface, covering the dangerous sand-bar or perfidious rock; but a stream deep as it was broad, and bearing with honorable faith the bark that trusted to its waves. I gloried in this simple, quiet, majestic, epic flow; ever straight forward. Once, indeed, it turns aside for a moment, forced from its course by opposing mountains, but it struggles bravely through them, and immediately resumes its straightforward march. Behold, thought I, an emblem of a good man's course through life; ever simple, open and direct; or if, overpowered by adverse circumstances, he deviate into error, it is but momentary; he soon recovers his onward and honorable career, and continues it to the end of his pilgrimage.

Excuse this rhapsody, into which I have been betrayed by a revival of early feelings. The Hudson is, in a manner, my first and last love; and after all my wanderings and seeming infidelities, I return to it with a heartfelt preference over all the other rivers in the world. I seem to catch new life as I bathe in its ample billows and inhale the pure breezes of its hills. It is true, the romance of youth is past, that once spread illusions over every scene. I can no longer picture an Arcadia in every green valley; nor a fairyland among the distant mountains; nor a peerless beauty in every villa gleaming among the trees; but though the illusions of youth have faded from the landscape, the recollections of departed years and departed pleasures shed over it the mellow charm of evening sunshine.

Permit me, then, Mr. Editor, through the medium of your work, to hold occasional discourse from my retreat with the busy world I have abandoned. I have much to say about what I have seen, heard, felt, and thought through the course of a varied and rambling life, and some lucubrations that have long been encumbering my portfolio; together with divers reminiscences of the venerable historian of the New Netherlands, that may not be unacceptable to those who have taken an interest in his writings, and are desirous of anything that may cast a light back upon our early history. Let your readers rest assured of one thing, that, though retired from the world, I am not disgusted with it; and that if in my communings with it I do not prove very wise, I trust I shall at least prove very good-natured.

Which is all at present from

Yours, etc., GEOFFREY CRAYON.

TO THE EDITOR OF THE KNICKERBOCKER

WORTHY SIR—In a preceding communication, I have given you some brief notice of Wolfert's Roost, the mansion where I first had the good fortune to become acquainted with the venerable historian of the New Netherlands. As this ancient edifice is likely to be the place whence I shall date many of my lucubrations, and as it is really a very remarkable little pile, intimately connected with all the great epochs of our local and national history, I have thought it but right to give some further particulars concerning it. Fortunately, in rummaging a ponderous Dutch chest of drawers, which serves as the archives of the Roost, and in which are preserved many inedited manuscripts of Mr. Knickerbocker, together with the precious records of New Amsterdam brought hither by Wolfert Acker at the downfall of the Dutch dynasty, as has been already mentioned, I found in one corner, among dried pumpkin-seeds, bunches of thyme, and pennyroyal, and crumbs of New Year cakes, a manuscript, carefully wrapped up in the fragment of an old parchment deed, but much blotted, and the ink grown foxy by time, which, on inspection, I discovered to be a faithful chronicle of the Roost. The handwriting, and certain internal evidences, leave no doubt in my mind that it is a genuine production of the venerable historian of the New Netherlands, written, very probably, during his residence at the Roost, in gratitude for the hospitality of its proprietor. As such, I submit it for publication. As the entire chronicle is too long for the pages of your Magazine, and as it contains many minute particulars, which might prove tedious to the general reader, I have abbreviated and occasionally omitted some of its details; but may hereafter furnish them separately, should they seem to be required by the curiosity of an enlightened and document-hunting public.

Respectfully yours,

GEOFFREY CRAYON.

A CHRONICLE OF WOLFERT'S ROOST

FOUND AMONG THE PAPERS OF THE LATE DIEDRICH KNICKERBOCKER

ABOUT five-and-twenty miles from the ancient and renowned city of Manhattan, formerly called New Amsterdam, and vulgarly called New York, on the eastern bank of that expansion of the Hudson known among Dutch mariners of yore as the Tappan Zee, being in fact the great Mediterranean Sea of the New Netherlands, stands a little old-fashioned stone mansion, all made up of gable-ends, and as full of angles and corners as an old cocked hat. Though but of small dimensions, yet, like many small people, it is of mighty spirit, and values itself greatly on its antiquity, being one of the oldest edifices, for its size, in the whole country. It claims to be an ancient seat of empire, I may rather say an empire in itself, and, like all empires, great and small, has had its grand historical epochs. In speaking of this doughty and valorous little pile, I shall call it by its usual appellation of "The Roost"; though that is a name given to it in modern days, since it became the abode of the white man.

Its origin, in truth, dates far back in that remote region commonly called the fabulous age, in which vulgar fact becomes mystified and tinted up with delectable fiction. The eastern shore of the Tappan Sea was inhabited in those days by an unsophisticated race, existing in all the simplicity of nature; that is to say, they lived by hunting and fishing, and recreated themselves occasionally with a little tomahawking and scalping. Each stream that flows down from the hills into the Hudson had its petty sachem, who ruled over a hand-breadth of forest on either side, and had his seat of government at its mouth. The chieftain who ruled at the Roost was not merely a great warrior but a medicine-man, or prophet, or conjurer, for they all mean the same thing in Indian parlance. Of his fighting propensities evidences still remain in various arrow-heads of flint, and stone battle-axes, occasionally dug up about the Roost: of his wizard powers we have a token in a spring which wells up at the foot of the bank, on the very margin of the river, which, it is said, was gifted by him with rejuvenating powers, something like the renowned Fountain of Youth in the Floridas, so anxiously but vainly sought after by the veteran Ponce de Leon. This story, however, is stoutly contradicted by an old Dutch matter-of-fact tradition, which declares that the spring in question was smuggled over from Holland in a churn by Femmetie Van Slocum, wife of Goosen Garret Van Slocum, one of the first settlers, and that she took it up by night, unknown to her husband, from beside their farmhouse near Rotterdam; being sure she should find no water equal to it in the new country—and she was right.

The wizard sachem had a great passion for discussing territorial questions, and settling boundary lines; this kept him in continual feud with the neighboring sachems, each of whom stood up stoutly for his hand-breadth of territory; so that there is not a petty stream nor ragged hill in the neighborhood that has not been the subject of long talks and hard battles. The sachem, however, as has been observed, was a medicine-man as well as warrior, and vindicated his claims by arts as well as arms; so that, by dint of a little hard fighting here, and hocus-pocus there, he managed to extend his boundary-line from field to field and stream to stream, until he found himself in legitimate possession of that region of hills and valleys, bright fountains and limpid brooks, locked in by the mazy windings of the Neperan and the Pocantico.*

* As every one may not recognize these boundaries by their original Indian names, it may be well to observe that the Neperan is that beautiful stream, vulgarly called the Saw-Mill River, which, after winding gracefully for many miles through a lovely valley, shrouded by groves and dotted by Dutch farmhouses, empties itself into the Hudson at the ancient dorp of Yonkers. The Pocantico is that hitherto nameless

This last-mentioned stream, or rather the valley through which it flows, was the most difficult of all his acquisitions. It lay half way to the stronghold of the redoubtable sachem of Sing Sing, and was claimed by him as an integral part of his domains. Many were the sharp conflicts between the rival chieftains for the sovereignty of this valley, and many the ambuscades, surprisals, and deadly onslaughts that took place among its fastnesses, of which it grieves me much that I cannot furnish the details for the gratification of those gentle but bloody-minded readers of both sexes, who delight in the romance of the tomahawk and scalping knife. Suffice it to say that the wizard chieftain was at length victorious, though his victory is attributed in Indian tradition to a great medicine or charm by which he laid the sachem of Sing Sing and his warriors asleep among the rocks and recesses of the valley, where they remain asleep to the present day with their bows and war clubs beside them. This was the origin of that potent and drowsy spell which still prevails over the valley of the Pocantico, and which has gained it the well-merited appellation of Sleepy Hollow. Often, in secluded and quiet parts of that valley, where the stream is overhung by dark woods and rocks, the plowman, on some calm and sunny day as he shouts to his oxen, is surprised at hearing faint shouts from the hillsides in reply; being, it is said, the spellbound warriors, who half start from their rocky couches and grasp their weapons, but sink to sleep again.

The conquest of the Pocantico was the last triumph of the wizard sachem. Notwithstanding all his medicine and charms, he fell in battle in attempting to extend his bound-

brook, that, rising among woody hills, winds in many a wizard maze through the sequestered haunts of Sleepy Hollow. We owe it to the indefatigable researches of Mr. Knickerbocker that those beautiful streams are rescued from modern commonplace and reinvested with their ancient Indian names. The correctness of the venerable historian may be ascertained by reference to the records of the original Indian grants to the Herr Frederick Philipsen, preserved in the County Clerk's office at White Plains.

ary line to the east so as to take in the little wild valley of
the Sprain, and his grave is still shown near the banks of
that pastoral stream. He left, however, a great empire to
his successors, extending along the Tappan Sea, from Yonkers quite to Sleepy Hollow; all which delectable region, if
every one had his right, would still acknowledge allegiance
to the lord of the Roost—whoever he might be.*

The wizard sachem was succeeded by a line of chiefs of
whom nothing remarkable remains on record. The last who
makes any figure in history is the one who ruled here at the
time of the discovery of the country by the white man. This
sachem is said to have been a renowned trencherman, who
maintained almost as potent a sway by dint of good feeding
as his warlike predecessor had done by hard fighting. He
diligently cultivated the growth of oysters along the aquatic
borders of his territories, and founded those great oyster-beds
which yet exist along the shores of the Tappan Sea. Did
any dispute occur between him and a neighboring sachem,
he invited him and all his principal sages and fighting-men
to a solemn banquet, and seldom failed of feeding them into
terms. Enormous heaps of oyster-shells, which encumber
the lofty banks of the river, remain as monuments of his
gastronomical victories, and have been occasionally adduced
through mistake by amateur geologists from town as additional proofs of the deluge. Modern investigators, who are
making such indefatigable researches into our early history,
have even affirmed that this sachem was the very individual
on whom Master Hendrick Hudson and his mate, Robert

---

*In recording the contest for the sovereignty of Sleepy Hollow, I
have called one sachem by the modern name of his castle or stronghold;
viz., Sing Sing. This, I would observe for the sake of historical exact-
ness, is a corruption of the old Indian name O-sin-sing, or rather O-sin-
song; that is to say, a place where anything may be had for a song—a
great recommendation for a market-town. The modern and melodious
alteration of the name to Sing Sing is said to have been made in compliment to an eminent Methodist singing-master, who first introduced
into the neighborhood the art of singing through the nose.   D. K.

Juet, made that sage and astounding experiment so gravely
recorded by the latter in his narrative of the voyage: "Our
master and his mate determined to try some of the cheefe
men of the country whether they had any treacherie in them.
So they took them down into the cabin and gave them so
much wine and aqua vitæ that they were all very merrie;
one of them had his wife with him, which sate so modestly
as any of our countrywomen would do in a strange place.
In the end one of them was drunke; and that was strange
to them, for they could not tell how to take it." *

How far Master Hendrick Hudson and his worthy mate
carried their experiment with the sachem's wife is not recorded, neither does the curious Robert Juet make any mention of the after-consequences of this grand moral test; tradition, however, affirms that the sachem on landing gave his
modest spouse a hearty rib-roasting, according to the con-
nubial discipline of the aboriginals; it further affirms that
he remained a hard drinker to the day of his death, trading
away all his lands, acre by acre, for aqua vitæ; by which
means the Roost and all its domains, from Yonkers to Sleepy
Hollow, came, in the regular course of trade and by right of
purchase, into the possession of the Dutchmen.

Never has a territorial right in these new countries been
more legitimately and tradefully established; yet, I grieve
to say, the worthy government of the New Netherlands was
not suffered to enjoy this grand acquisition unmolested; for,
in the year 1654, the losel Yankees of Connecticut—those
swapping, bargaining, squatting enemies of the Manhattoes
—made a daring inroad into this neighborhood and founded
a colony called Westchester, or, as the ancient Dutch records
term it, Vest Dorp, in the right of one Thomas Pell, who pretended to have purchased the whole surrounding country of
the Indians, and stood ready to argue their claims before any
tribunal of Christendom.

This happened during the chivalrous reign of Peter Stuyve-

---

* See Juet's Journal, Purchas Pilgrim.

sant, and it roused the ire of that gunpowder old hero; who, without waiting to discuss claims and titles, pounced at once upon the nest of nefarious squatters, carried off twenty-five of them in chains to the Manhattoes, nor did he stay his hand, nor give rest to his wooden leg, until he had driven every Yankee back into the bounds of Connecticut, or obliged him to acknowledge allegiance to their High Mightinesses. He then established certain outposts, far in the Indian country, to keep an eye over these debatable lands; one of these border-holds was the Roost, being accessible from New Amsterdam by water, and easily kept supplied. The Yankees, however, had too great a hankering after this delectable region to give it up entirely. Some remained and swore allegiance to the Manhattoes; but, while they kept this open semblance of fealty, they went to work secretly and vigorously to intermarry and multiply, and by these nefarious means artfully propagated themselves into possession of a wide tract of those open, arable parts of Westchester County, lying along the Sound, where their descendants may be found at the present day; while the mountainous regions along the Hudson, with the valleys of the Neperan and the Pocantico, are tenaciously held by the lineal descendants of the Copperheads.

————

THE chronicle of the venerable Diedrich here goes on to relate how that, shortly after the above-mentioned events, the whole province of the New Netherlands was subjugated by the British; how that Wolfert Acker, one of the wrangling councilors of Peter Stuyvesant, retired indudge on to this fastness in the wilderness, determining to enjoy "lust in rust" for the remainder of his days, whence the place first received its name of Wolfert's Roost. As these and sundry other matters have been laid before the public in a preceding article, I shall pass them over, and resume the chronicle where it treats of matters not hitherto recorded:

LIKE many men who retire from a worrying world, says Diedrich Knickerbocker, to enjoy quiet in the country, Wolfert Acker soon found himself up to the ears in trouble. He had a termagant wife at home, and there was what is profanely called "the deuce to pay" abroad. The recent irruption of the Yankees into the bounds of the New Netherlands had left behind it a doleful pestilence such as it apt to follow the steps of invading armies. This was the deadly plague of witchcraft, which had long been prevalent to the eastward. The malady broke out at Vest Dorp, and threatened to spread throughout the country. The Dutch burghers along the Hudson, from Yonkers to Sleepy Hollow, hastened to nail horseshoes to their doors, which have ever been found of sovereign virtue to repel this awful visitation. This is the origin of the horseshoes which may still be seen nailed to the doors of barns and farmhouses in various parts of this sage and sober-thoughted region.

The evil, however, bore hard upon the Roost; partly, perhaps, from its having in old times been subject to supernatural influences during the sway of the Wizard Sachem; but it has always, in fact, been considered a fated mansion. The unlucky Wolfert had no rest day nor night. When the weather was quiet all over the country, the wind would howl and whistle round his roof; witches would ride and whirl upon his weathercocks and scream down his chimneys. His cows gave bloody milk, and his horses broke bounds and scampered into the woods. There were not wanting evil tongues to whisper that Wolfert's termagant wife had some tampering with the enemy; and that she even attended a witches' Sabbath in Sleepy Hollow; nay, a neighbor, who lived hard by, declared that he saw her harnessing a rampant broomstick, and about to ride to the meeting; though others presume it was merely flourished in the course of one of her curtain lectures to give energy and emphasis to a period. Certain it is that Wolfert Acker nailed a horseshoe to the front door, during one of her nocturnal excursions, to prevent her return; but as she re-entered the house without any difficulty, it is probable she was not so much of a witch as she was represented.*

After the time of Wolfert Acker, a long interval elapses, about which but little is known. It is hoped, however, that the antiquarian researches so diligently making in every part of this new country may yet throw some light upon what may be termed the Dark Ages of the Roost.

The next period at which we find this venerable and eventful pile rising to importance, and resuming its old belligerent character, is during the revolutionary war. It was at that time owned by Jacob Van Tassel, or Van Texel, as the name was originally spelled, after the place in Holland which gave birth to this heroic line. He was strong-built, long-limbed, and as stout in soul as in body; a fit successor to the warrior sachem of yore, and, like him, delighting in extravagant enterprises and hardy deeds of arms. But, before I enter upon the exploits of this worthy cock of the Roost, it is fitting I should throw some light upon the state of the mansion and of the surrounding country at the time.

The situation of the Roost is in the very heart of what

---

* HISTORICAL NOTE.—The annexed extracts from the early colonial records relate to the irruption of witchcraft into Westchester County, as mentioned in the chronicle:

"July 7, 1670.—Katharine Harryson, accused of witchcraft on complaint of Thomas Hunt and Edward Waters, in behalf of the town, who pray that she may be driven from the town of Westchester. The woman appears before the council. . . . . She was a native of England, and had lived a year in Weathersfield, Connecticut, where she had been tried for witchcraft, found guilty by the jury, acquitted by the bench, and released out of prison upon condition she would remove. Affair adjourned.

"August 24.—Affair taken up again, when, being heard at large, it was referred to the general court of assize. Woman ordered to give security for good behavior," etc.

In another place is the following entry:

"Order given for Katharine Harryson, charged with witchcraft, to leave Westchester, as the inhabitants are uneasy at her residing the e, and she is ordered to go off."

was the debatable ground between the American and British lines during the war. The British held possession of the city of New York, and the island of Manhattan on which it stands. The Americans drew up toward the Highlands, holding their headquarters at Peekskill. The intervening country, from Croton River to Spiting Devil Creek, was the debatable land, subject to be harried by friend and foe, like the Scottish borders of yore. It is a rugged country, with a line of rocky hills extending through it, like a backbone, sending ribs on either side; but among these rude hills are beautiful winding valleys, like those watered by the Pocantico and the Neperan. In the fastnesses of these hills, and along these valleys, exist a race of hard-headed, hard-handed, stout-hearted Dutchmen, descendants of the primitive Nederlanders. Most of these were strong Whigs throughout the war, and have ever remained obstinately attached to the soil, and neither to be fought nor bought out of their paternal acres. Others were Tories, and adherents to the old kingly rule; some of whom took refuge within the British lines, joined the royal bands of refugees, a name odious to the American ear, and occasionally returned to harass their ancient neighbors.

In a little while this debatable land was overrun by predatory bands from either side; sacking henroosts, plundering farmhouses, and driving off cattle. Hence arose those two great orders of border chivalry, the Skinners and the Cowboys, famous in the heroic annals of Westchester County. The former fought, or rather marauded, under the American, the latter under the British banner; but both, in the hurry of their military ardor, were apt to err on the safe side, and rob friend as well as foe. Neither of them stopped to ask the politics of horse or cow which they drove into captivity; nor, when they wrung the neck of a rooster, did they trouble their heads to ascertain whether he were crowing for Congress or King George.

While this marauding system prevailed on shore, the great Tappan Sea, which washes this belligerent region, was domineered over by British frigates and other vessels of war, anchored here and there to keep an eye upon the river, and maintain a communication between the various military posts. Stout galleys, also, armed with eighteen-pounders, and navigated with sails and oars, cruised about like hawks, ready to pounce upon their prey.

All these were eyed with bitter hostility by the Dutch yeomanry along shore, who were indignant at seeing their great Mediterranean plowed by hostile prows; and would occasionally throw up a mud breastwork on a point or promontory, mount an old iron field-piece, and fire away at the enemy, though the greatest harm was apt to happen to themselves from the bursting of their ordnance; nay, there was scarce a Dutchman along the river that would hesitate to fire with his long duck gun at any British cruiser that came within reach, as he had been accustomed to fire at water-fowl.

I have been thus particular in my account of the times and neighborhood, that the reader might the more readily comprehend the surrounding dangers in this the Heroic Age of the Roost.

It was commanded at the time, as I have already observed, by the stout Jacob Van Tassel. As I wish to be extremely accurate in this part of my chronicle, I beg that this Jacob Van Tassel of the Roost may not be confounded with another Jacob Van Tassel, commonly known in border story by the name of "Clump-footed Jake," a noted Tory, and one of the refugee band of Spiting Devil. On the contrary, he of the Roost was a patriot of the first water, and, if we may take his own word for granted, a thorn in the side of the enemy. As the Roost, from its lonely situation on the water's edge, might be liable to attack, he took measures for defense. On a row of hooks above his fireplace reposed his great piece of ordnance, ready charged and primed for action. This was a duck, or rather goose-gun, of unparalleled longitude, with which it was said he could kill a wild goose, though half way across the Tappan Sea. Indeed, there are as many wonders told of this renowned gun as of the enchanted weapons of the heroes of classic story.

In different parts of the stone walls of his mansion he had made loopholes, through which he might fire upon an assailant. His wife was stout-hearted as himself, and could load as fast as he could fire; and then he had an ancient and redoubtable sister, Nochie Van Wurmer, a match, as he said, for the stoutest man in the country. Thus garrisoned, the little Roost was fit to stand a siege, and Jacob Van Tassel was the man to defend it to the last charge of powder.

He was, as I have already hinted, of pugnacious propensities; and, not content with being a patriot at home, and fighting for the security of his own fireside, he extended his thoughts abroad, and entered into a confederacy with certain of the bold, hard-riding lads of Tarrytown, Petticoat Lane, and Sleepy Hollow, who formed a kind of Holy Brotherhood, scouring the country to clear it of Skinner and Cowboy, and all other border vermin. The Roost was one of their rallying points. Did a band of marauders from Manhattan island come sweeping through the neighborhood, and driving off cattle, the stout Jacob and his compeers were soon clattering at their heels, and fortunate did the rogues esteem themselves if they could but get a part of their booty across the lines, or escape themselves without a rough handling. Should the mosstroopers succeed in passing with their cavalgada, with thundering tramp and dusty whirlwind, across Kingsbridge, the Holy Brotherhood of the Roost would rein up at that perilous pass, and, wheeling about, would indemnify themselves by foraging the refugee region of Morrisania.

When at home at the Roost, the stout Jacob was not idle; but was prone to carry on a petty warfare of his own, for his private recreation and refreshment. Did he ever chance to espy, from his lookout place, a hostile ship or galley anchored or becalmed near shore, he would take down his long goose-gun from the hooks over the fireplace, sally out alone, and lurk along shore, dodging behind rocks and trees, and watch-

ing for hours together, like a veteran mouser intent on a rat-
hole. So sure as a boat put off for shore, and came within
shot, bang! went the great goose-gun; a shower of slugs
and buckshot whistled about the ears of the enemy, and before the boat could reach the shore, Jacob had scuttled up
some woody ravine, and left no trace behind.

About this time the Roost experienced a vast accession of
warlike importance, in being made one of the stations of the
water-guard. This was a kind of aquatic corps of observation, composed of long, sharp, canoe-shaped boats, technically called whale-boats, that lay lightly on the water and
could be rowed with great rapidity. They were manned by
resolute fellows, skilled at pulling an oar or handling a musket.
These lurked about in nooks and bays, and behind those
long promontories which run out into the Tappan Sea, keeping a lookout, to give notice of the approach or movements
of hostile ships. They roved about in pairs; sometimes at
night, with muffled oars, gliding like specters about frigates
and guardships riding at anchor, cutting off any boats that
made for shore, and keeping the enemy in constant uneasiness. These mosquito-cruisers generally kept aloof by day,
so that their harboring places might not be discovered, but
would pull quietly along, under shadow of the shore, at
night, to take up their quarters at the Roost. Hither, at
such time, would also repair the hard-riding lads of the hills,
to hold secret councils of war with the "ocean chivalry";
and in these nocturnal meetings were concerted many of
those daring forays, by land and water, that resounded
throughout the border.

————

THE chronicle here goes on to recount divers wonderful
stories of the wars of the Roost, from which it would seem
that this little warrior-nest carried the terror of its arms into
every sea, from Spiting Devil Creek to Antony's Nose; that
it even bearded the stout island of Manhattan, invading it at

night, penetrating to its center, and burning down the famous
Delancey house, the conflagration of which makes such a
blaze in revolutionary history. Nay more, in their extravagant daring, these cocks of the Roost meditated a nocturnal
descent upon New York itself, to swoop upon the British
commanders, Howe and Clinton, by surprise, bear them off
captive, and perhaps put a triumphant close to the war!

All these and many similar exploits are recorded by the
worthy Diedrich, with his usual minuteness and enthusiasm,
whenever the deeds in arms of his kindred Dutchmen are in
question; but though most of these warlike stories rest upon
the best of all authority, that of the warriors themselves, and
though many of them are still current among the revolutionary patriarchs of this heroic neighborhood, yet I dare not expose them to the incredulity of a tamer and less chivalric age.
Suffice it to say the frequent gatherings at the Roost, and the
hardy projects set on foot there, at length drew on it the
fiery indignation of the enemy; and this was quickened by
the conduct of the stout Jacob Van Tassel; with whose
valorous achievements we resume the course of the chronicle.

THIS doughty Dutchman, continues the sage Diedrich
Knickerbocker, was not content with taking a share in all
the magnanimous enterprises concocted at the Roost, but still
continued his petty warfare along shore. A series of exploits
at length raised his confidence in his prowess to such a
height that he began to think himself and his goose-gun a
match for anything. Unluckily, in the course of one of his
prowlings, he descried a British transport aground, not far
from shore, with her stern swung toward the land, within
pointblank shot. The temptation was too great to be resisted; bang! as usual, went the great goose-gun, shivering
the cabin windows, and driving all hands forward. Bang!
bang! the shots were repeated. The reports brought several
sharpshooters of the neighborhood to the spot; before the

transport could bring a gun to bear, or land a boat, to take revenge, she was soundly peppered and the coast evacuated. This was the last of Jacob's triumphs. He fared like some heroic spider that has unwittingly ensnared a hornet, to his immortal glory, perhaps, but to the utter ruin of his web.

It was not long after this, during the absence of Jacob Van Tassel on one of his forays, and when no one was in garrison but his stout-hearted spouse, his redoubtable sister, Nochie Van Wurmer, and a strapping negro wench, called Dinah, that an armed vessel came to anchor off the Roost, and a boat full of men pulled to shore. The garrison flew to arms, that is to say, to mops, broomsticks, shovels, tongs, and all kinds of domestic weapons; for, unluckily, the great piece of ordnance, the goose-gun, was absent with its owner. Above all, a vigorous defense was made with that most potent of female weapons, the tongue. Never did invaded henroost make a more vociferous outcry. It was all in vain. The house was sacked and plundered, fire was set to each corner, and in a few moments its blaze shed a baleful light far over the Tappan Sea. The invaders then pounced upon the blooming Laney Van Tassel, the beauty of the Roost, and endeavored to bear her off to the boat. But here was the real tug of war. The mother, the aunt, and the strapping negro wench, all flew to the rescue. The struggle continued down to the very water's edge; when a voice from the armed vessel at anchor ordered the spoilers to let go their hold; they relinquished their prize, jumped into their boats and pulled off, and the heroine of the Roost escaped with a mere rumpling of the feathers.

————

THE fear of tiring my readers, who may not take such an interest as myself in these heroic themes, induces me to close here my extracts from this precious chronicle of the venerable Diedrich. Suffice it briefly to say, that shortly after the catastrophe of the Roost, Jacob Van Tassel, in the course

of one of his forays, fell into the hands of the British; was
sent prisoner to New York, and was detained in captivity
for the greater part of the war. In the meantime, the Roost
remained a melancholy ruin; its stone walls and brick chimneys alone standing, blackened by fire, and the resort of bats
and owlets. It was not until the return of peace, when this
belligerent neighborhood once more resumed its quiet agri-
cultural pursuits, that the stout Jacob sought the scene of
his triumphs and disasters; rebuilt the Roost, and reared
again on high its glittering weather-cocks.

Does any one want further particulars of the fortunes of
this eventful little pile? Let him go to the fountain-head,
and drink deep of historic truth. Reader! the stout Jacob
Van Tassel still lives, a venerable, gray-headed patriarch of
the revolution, now in his ninety-fifth year! He sits by his
fireside, in the ancient city of the Manhattoes, and passes the
long winter evenings, surrounded by his children, and grandchildren, and great-grandchildren, all listening to his tales of
the border wars, and the heroic days of the Roost. His
great goose-gun, too, is still in existence, having been preserved for many years in a hollow tree, and passed from
hand to hand among the Dutch burghers, as a precious relic
of the revolution. It is now actually in possession of a con-
temporary of the stout Jacob, one almost his equal in years,
who treasures it up at his house in the Bowerie of New Amsterdam, hard by the ancient rural retreat of the chivalric
Peter Stuyvesant. I am not without hopes of one day seeing
this formidable piece of ordnance restored to its proper station in the arsenal of the Roost.

Before closing this historic document, I cannot but advert to certain notions and traditions concerning the venerable pile in question. Old time edifices are apt to gather odd
fancies and superstitions about them, as they do moss and
weather-stains; and this is in a neighborhood a little given to
old-fashioned notions, and who look upon the Roost as somewhat of a fated mansion. A lonely, rambling, down-hill
lane leads to it. overhung with trees, with a wild brook

dashing along, and crossing and re-crossing it. This lane I found some of the good people of the neighborhood shy of treading at night; why, I could not for a long time ascertain; until I learned that one or two of the rovers of the Tappan Sea, shot by the stout Jacob during the war, had been buried hereabout, in unconsecrated ground.

Another local superstition is of a less gloomy kind, and one which I confess I am somewhat disposed to cherish. The Tappan Sea, in front of the Roost, is about three miles wide, bordered by a lofty line of waving and rocky hills. Often, in the still twilight of a summer evening, when the sea is like glass, with the opposite hills throwing their purple shadows half across it, a low sound is heard, as of the steady, vigorous pull of oars, far out in the middle of the stream, though not a boat is to be descried. This I should have been apt to ascribe to some boat rowed along under the shadows of the western shore, for sounds are conveyed to a great distance by water at such quiet hours, and I can distinctly hear the baying of the watch-dogs at night, from the farms on the sides of the opposite mountains. The ancient traditionists of the neighborhood, however, religiously ascribed these sounds to a judgment upon one Rumbout Van Dam, of Spiting Devil, who danced and drank late one Saturday night, at a Dutch quilting frolic, at Kakiat, and set off alone for home in his boat, on the verge of Sunday morning; swearing he would not land till he reached Spiting Devil, if it took him a month of Sundays. He was never seen afterward, but is often heard plying his oars across the Tappan Sea, a Flying Dutchman on a small scale, suited to the size of his cruising-ground; being doomed to ply between Kakiat and Spiting Devil till the day of judgment, but never to reach the land.

There is one room in the mansion which almost overhangs the river, and is reputed to be haunted by the ghost of a young lady who died of love and green apples. I have been awakened at night by the sound of oars and the tinkling of guitars beneath the window; and seeing a boat loitering in the moonlight, have been tempted to believe it the Flying Dutchman of Spiting Devil, and to try whether a silver bullet might not put an end to his unhappy cruisings; but, happening to recollect that there was a living young lady in the haunted room, who might be terrified by the report of fire-arms, I have refrained from pulling trigger.

As to the enchanted fountain, said to have been gifted by the wizard sachem with supernatural powers, it still wells up at the foot of the bank, on the margin of the river, and goes by the name of the Indian spring; but I have my doubts as to its rejuvenating powers, for though I have drank oft and copiously of it, I cannot boast that I find myself growing younger.   GEOFFREY CRAYON.

SLEEPY HOLLOW

BY GEOFFREY CRAYON, GENT.

HAVING pitched my tent, probably for the remainder of my days, in the neighborhood of Sleepy Hollow, I am tempted to give some few particulars concerning that spell-bound region; especially as it has risen to historic importance under the pen of my revered friend and master, the sage-historian of the New Netherlands. Besides, I find the very existence of the place has been held in question by many; who, judging from its odd name and from the odd stories current among the vulgar concerning it, have rashly deemed the whole to be a fanciful creation, like the Lubber Land of mariners. I must confess there is some apparent cause for doubt, in consequence of the coloring given by the worthy Diedrich to his descriptions of the Hollow; who, in this instance, has departed a little from his usually sober if not severe style; beguiled, very probably, by his predilection for the haunts of his youth, and by a certain lurking taint of romance whenever anything connected with the Dutch was to be described.

I shall endeavor to make up for this amiable error on the part of my venerable and venerated friend by presenting the reader with a more precise and statistical account of the Hollow; though I am not sure that I shall not be prone to lapse in the end into the very error I am speaking of, so potent is the witchery of the theme.

I believe it was the very peculiarity of its name and the idea of something mystic and dreamy connected with it that first led me in my boyish ramblings into Sleepy Hollow. The character of the valley seemed to answer to the name; the slumber of past ages apparently reigned over it; it had not awakened to the stir of improvement which had put all the rest of the world in a bustle. Here reigned good, old long-forgotten fashions; the men were in homespun garbs, evidently the product of their own farms and the manufacture of their own wives; the women were in primitive short gowns and petticoats, with the venerable sunbonnets of Holland origin. The lower part of the valley was cut up into small farms, each consisting of a little meadow and cornfield; an orchard of sprawling, gnarled apple-trees, and a garden, where the rose, the marigold, and the hollyhock were permitted to skirt the domains of the capacious cabbage, the aspiring pea, and the portly pumpkin. Each had its prolific little mansion teeming with children; with an old hat nailed against the wall for the housekeeping wren; a motherly hen, under a coop on the grass-plot, clucking to keep around her a brood of vagrant chickens; a cool, stone well, with the moss-covered bucket suspended to the long balancing-pole, according to the antediluvian idea of hydraulics; and its spinning-wheel humming within doors the patriarchal music of home manufacture.

The Hollow at that time was inhabited by families which had existed there from the earliest times, and which, by frequent intermarriage, had become so interwoven as to make a kind of natural commonwealth. As the families had grown larger the farms had grown smaller; every new generation requiring a new subdivision, and few thinking of swarming from the native hive. In this way that happy golden mean had been produced, so much extolled by the poets, in which there was no gold and very little silver. One thing which doubtless contributed to keep up this amiable mean was a general repugnance to sordid labor. The sage inhabitants of Sleepy Hollow had read in their Bible, which was the only book they studied, that labor was originally inflicted upon man as a punishment of sin; they regarded it, therefore, with pious abhorrence, and never humiliated themselves to it but in cases of extremity. There seemed, in fact, to be a league and covenant against it throughout the Hollow as against a common enemy. Was any one compelled by dire necessity to repair his house, mend his fences, build a barn, or get in a harvest, he considered it a great evil that entitled him to call in the assistance of his friends. He accordingly proclaimed a "bee" or rustic gathering, whereupon all his neighbors hurried to his aid like faithful allies; attacked the task with the desperate energy of lazy men eager to overcome a job; and, when it was accomplished, fell to eating and drinking, fiddling and dancing for very joy that so great an amount of labor had been vanquished with so little sweating of the brow.

Yet, let it not be supposed that this worthy community was without its periods of arduous activity. Let but a flock of wild pigeons fly across the valley and all Sleepy Hollow was wide awake in an instant. The pigeon season had arrived! Every gun and net was forthwith in requisition. The flail was thrown down on the barn floor; the spade rusted in the garden; the plow stood idle in the furrow; every one was to the hill-side and stubble-field at daybreak to shoot or entrap the pigeons in their periodical migrations.

So, likewise, let but the word be given that the shad were ascending the Hudson, and the worthies of the Hollow were to be seen launched in boats upon the river, setting great stakes and stretching their nets like gigantic spider-webs half across the stream, to the great annoyance of navigators. Such are the wise provisions of Nature, by which she equalizes rural affairs. A laggard at the plow is often extremely industrious with the fowling-piece and fishing net; and, whenever a man is an indifferent farmer, he is apt to be a first-rate sportsman. For catching shad and wild pigeons there were none throughout the country to compare with the lads of Sleepy Hollow.

As I have observed, it was the dreamy nature of the name that first beguiled me in the holiday rovings of boyhood into this sequestered region. I shunned, however, the populous parts of the Hollow, and sought its retired haunts far in the foldings of the hills, where the Pocantico "winds its wizard stream" sometimes silently and darkly through solemn woodlands, sometimes sparkling between grassy borders in fresh, green meadows, sometimes stealing along the feet of rugged heights under the balancing sprays of beech and chestnut trees. A thousand crystal springs, with which this neighborhood abounds, sent down from the hillsides their whimpering rills, as if to pay tribute to the Pocantico. In this stream I first essayed my unskillful hand at angling. I loved to loiter along it with rod in hand, watching my float as it whirled amid the eddies or drifted into dark holes under twisted roots and sunken logs, where the largest fish are apt to lurk. I delighted to follow it into the brown recesses of the woods; to throw by my fishing-gear and sit upon rocks beneath towering oaks and clambering grape-vines; bathe my feet in the cool current, and listen to the summer breeze playing among the treetops. My boyish fancy clothed all nature around me with ideal charms, and peopled it with the fairy beings I had read of in poetry and fable. Here it was I gave full scope to my incipient habit of day-dreaming, and to a certain propensity to weave up and tint sober realities with my own whims and imaginings, which has sometimes made life a little too much like an Arabian tale to me, and this "working-day world" rather like a region of romance.

The great gathering-place of Sleepy Hollow in those days was the church. It stood outside of the Hollow, near the great highway, on a green bank shaded by trees, with the Pocantico sweeping round it and emptying itself into a spacious mill-pond. At that time the Sleepy Hollow church was the only place of worship for a wide neighborhood. It was a venerable edifice, partly of stone and partly of brick, the latter having been brought from Holland in the early days of the province, before the arts in the New Netherlands could aspire to such a fabrication. On a stone above the porch were inscribed the names of the founders, Frederick Filipsen, a mighty patroon of the olden time, who reigned over a wide extent of this neighborhood and held his seat of power at Yonkers; and his wife, Katrina Van Courtlandt, of the no less potent line of the Van Courtlandts of Croton, who lorded it over a great part of the Highlands.

The capacious pulpit, with its widespreading sounding-board, were likewise early importations from Holland; as also the communion-table, of massive form and curious fabric. The same might be said of a weather-cock perched on top of the belfry, and which was considered orthodox in all windy matters, until a small pragmatical rival was set up on the other end of the church above the chancel. This latter bore, and still bears, the initials of Frederick Filipsen, and assumed great airs in consequence. The usual contradiction ensued that always exists among church weathercocks, which can never be brought to agree as to the point from which the wind blows, having doubtless acquired, from their position, the Christian propensity to schism and controversy.

Behind the church, and sloping up a gentle acclivity, was its capacious burying-ground, in which slept the earliest fathers of this rural neighborhood. Here were tombstones of the rudest sculpture; on which were inscribed, in Dutch, the names and virtues of many of the first settlers, with their portraitures curiously carved in similitude of cherubs. Long rows of gravestones, side by side, of similar names, but various dates, showed that generation after generation of the same families had followed each other and been garnered together in this last gathering-place of kindred.

Let me speak of this quiet graveyard with all due reverence, for I owe it amends for the heedlessness of my boyish
days. I blush to acknowledge the thoughtless frolic with
which, in company with other whipsters, I have sported
within its sacred bounds during the intervals of worship;
chasing butterflies, plucking wild flowers, or vying with
each other who could leap over the tallest tombstones, until
checked by the stern voice of the sexton.

The congregation was, in those days, of a really rural
character. City fashions were as yet unknown, or unre-
garded, by the country people of the neighborhood. Steamboats had not as yet confounded town with country. A
weekly market-boat from Tarrytown, the "Farmers' Daughter," navigated by the worthy Gabriel Requa, was the only
communication between all these parts and the metropolis.
A rustic belle in those days considered a visit to the city in
much the same light as one of our modern fashionable ladies
regards a visit to Europe; an event that may possibly take
place once in the course of a lifetime, but to be hoped for
rather than expected. Hence the array of the congregation
was chiefly after the primitive fashions existing in Sleepy
Hollow; or if, by chance, there was a departure from the
Dutch sunbonnet, or the apparition of a bright gown of flow-
ered calico, it caused quite a sensation throughout the church.
As the dominie generally preached by the hour, a bucket of
water was providently placed on a bench near the door, in
summer, with a tin cup beside it, for the solace of those who
might be athirst, either from the heat of the weather or the
drought of the sermon.

Around the pulpit, and behind the communion-table, sat
the elders of the church, reverend gray-headed, leathern-
visaged men, whom I regarded with awe, as so many apos-
tles. They were stern in their sanctity, kept a vigilant eye
upon my giggling companions and myself, and shook a
rebuking finger at any boyish device to relieve the tediousness of compulsory devotion. Vain, however, were all their
efforts at vigilance. Scarcely had the preacher held forth

for half an hour, on one of his interminable sermons, than it
seemed as if the drowsy influence of Sleepy Hollow breathed
into the place; one by one the congregation sank into slumber; the sanctified elders leaned back in their pews, spreading their handkerchiefs over their faces, as if to keep off the
flies; while the locusts in the neighboring trees would spin
out their sultry summer notes, as if in imitation of the sleep-
provoking tones of the dominie.

I have thus endeavored to give an idea of Sleepy Hollow
and its church, as I recollect them to have been in the days
of my boyhood. It was in my stripling days, when a few
years had passed over my head, that I revisited them, in
company with the venerable Diedrich. I shall never forget
the antiquarian reverence with which that sage and excellent
man contemplated the church. It seemed as if all his pious
enthusiasm for the ancient Dutch dynasty swelled within his
bosom at the sight. The tears stood in his eyes, as he regarded the pulpit and the communion-table; even the very
bricks that had come from the mother country seemed to
touch a filial chord within his bosom. He almost bowed in
deference to the stone above the porch, containing the names
of Frederick Filipsen and Katrina Van Courtlandt, regarding
it as the linking together of those patronymic names, once so
famous along the banks of the Hudson; or rather as a keystone, binding that mighty Dutch family connection of yore,
one foot of which rested on Yonkers and the other on the
Croton. Nor did he forbear to notice with admiration the
windy contest which had been carried on, since time immemorial, and with real Dutch perseverance, between the
two weather-cocks; though I could easily perceive he coin-
cided with the one which had come from Holland.

Together we paced the ample churchyard. With deep
veneration would he turn down the weeds and brambles that
obscured the modest brown gravestones, half sunk in earth,
on which were recorded, in Dutch, the names of the patriarchs of ancient days, the Ackers, the Van Tassels, and the
Van Warts. As we sat on one of the tombstones, he re-

counted to me the exploits of many of these worthies; and my heart smote me, when I heard of their great doings in days of yore, to think how heedlessly I had once sported over their graves.

From the church, the venerable Diedrich proceeded in his researches up the Hollow. The genius of the place seemed to hail its future historian. All nature was alive with gratulation. The quail whistled a greeting from the cornfield; the robin caroled a song of praise from the orchard; the loquacious catbird flew from bush to bush, with restless wing, proclaiming his approach in every variety of note, and anon would whisk about, and perk inquisitively into his face, as if to get a knowledge of his physiognomy; the woodpecker, also, tapped a tattoo on the hollow apple-tree, and then peered knowingly round the trunk, to see how the great Diedrich relished his salutation; while the ground-squirrel scampered along the fence, and occasionally whisked his tail over his head, by way of a huzza!

The worthy Diedrich pursued his researches in the valley with characteristic devotion; entering familiarly into the various cottages, and gossiping with the simple folk, in the style of their own simplicity. I confess my heart yearned with admiration to see so great a man, in his eager quest after knowledge, humbly demeaning himself to curry favor with the humblest; sitting patiently on a three-legged stool, patting the children, and taking a purring grimalkin on his lap, while he conciliated the good-will of the old Dutch housewife, and drew from her long ghost stories, spun out to the humming accompaniment of her wheel.

His greatest treasure of historic lore, however, was discovered in an old goblin-looking mill, situated among rocks and waterfalls, with clanking wheels, and rushing streams, and all kinds of uncouth noises. A horseshoe, nailed to the door to keep off witches and evil spirits, showed that this mill was subject to awful visitations. As we approached it, an old negro thrust his head, all dabbled with flour, out of a hole above the water-wheel, and grinned, and rolled his eyes, and looked like the very hobgoblin of the place. The illustrious Diedrich fixed upon him, at once, as the very one to give him that invaluable kind of information never to be acquired from books. He beckoned him from his nest, sat with him by the hour on a broken millstone, by the side of the waterfall, heedless of the noise of the water and the clatter of the mill; and I verily believe it was to his conference with this African sage, and the precious revelations of the good dame of the spinning-wheel, that we are indebted for the surprising though true history of Ichabod Crane and the headless horseman, which has since astounded and edified the world.

But I have said enough of the good old times of my youthful days; let me speak of the Hollow as I found it, after an absence of many years, when it was kindly given me once more to revisit the haunts of my boyhood. It was a genial day, as I approached that fated region. The warm sunshine was tempered by a slight haze, so as to give a dreamy effect to the landscape. Not a breath of air shook the foliage. The broad Tappan Sea was without a ripple, and the sloops, with drooping sails, slept on its glassy bosom. Columns of smoke, from burning brushwood, rose lazily from the folds of the hills, on the opposite side of the river, and slowly expanded in midair. The distant lowing of a cow, or the noontide crowing of a cock, coming faintly to the ear, seemed to illustrate, rather than disturb, the drowsy quiet of the scene.

I entered the Hollow with a beating heart. Contrary to my apprehensions, I found it but little changed. The march of intellect, which had made such rapid strides along every river and highway, had not yet, apparently, turned down into this favored valley. Perhaps the wizard spell of ancient days still reigned over the place, binding up the faculties of the inhabitants in happy contentment with things as they had been handed down to them from yore. There were the same little farms and farmhouses, with their old hats for the housekeeping wren: their stone wells, moss-covered buckets, and long balancing poles. There were the same little rills, whimpering down to pay their tributes to the Pocantico; while that wizard stream still kept on its course, as of old, through solemn woodlands and fresh green meadows: nor were there wanting joyous holiday boys to loiter along its banks, as I had done; throw their pin-hooks in the stream, or launch their mimic barks. I watched them with a kind of melancholy pleasure, wondering whether they were under the same spell of the fancy that once rendered this valley a fairyland to me. Alas! alas! to me everything now stood revealed in its simple reality. The echoes no longer answered with wizard tongues; the dream of youth was at an end; the spell of Sleepy Hollow was broken!

I sought the ancient church on the following Sunday. There it stood, on its green bank, among the trees; the Pocantico swept by it in a deep dark stream, where I had so often angled; there expanded the mill-pond, as of old, with the cows under the willows on its margin, knee-deep in water, chewing the cud, and lashing the flies from their sides with their tails. The hand of improvement, however, had been busy with the venerable pile. The pulpit, fabricated in Holland, had been superseded by one of modern construction, and the front of the semi-Gothic edifice was decorated by a semi-Grecian portico. Fortunately, the two weather-cocks remained undisturbed on their perches at each end of the church, and still kept up a diametrical opposition to each other on all points of windy doctrine.

On entering the church the changes of time continued to be apparent. The elders round the pulpit were men whom I had left in the gamesome frolic of their youth, but who had succeeded to the sanctity of station of which they once had stood so much in awe. What most struck my eye was the change in the female part of the congregation. Instead of the primitive garbs of homespun manufacture and antique Dutch fashion, I beheld French sleeves, French capes, and French collars, and a fearful fluttering of French ribbons.

When the service was ended I sought the churchyard, in

which I had sported in my unthinking days of boyhood.
Several of the modest brown stones, on which were recorded
in Dutch the names and virtues of the patriarchs, had disappeared, and had been succeeded by others of white marble,
with urns and wreaths, and scraps of English tombstone
poetry, marking the intrusion of taste and literature and the
English language in this once unsophisticated Dutch neighborhood.

As I was stumbling about among these silent yet eloquent
memorials of the dead, I came upon names familiar to me;
of those who had paid the debt of nature during the long interval of my absence. Some, I remembered, my companions
in boyhood, who had sported with me on the very sod under
which they were now mouldering; others who in those days
had been the flower of the yeomanry, figuring in Sunday
finery on the church green; others, the white-haired elders
of the sanctuary, once arrayed in awful sanctity around the
pulpit, and ever ready to rebuke the ill-timed mirth of the
wanton stripling who, now a man, sobered by years and
schooled by vicissitudes, looked down pensively upon their
graves. "Our fathers," thought I, "where are they!—and
the prophets, can they live forever!"

I was disturbed in my meditations by the noise of a troop
of idle urchins, who came gamboling about the place where
I had so often gamboled. They were checked, as I and my
playmates had often been, by the voice of the sexton, a man
staid in years and demeanor. I looked wistfully in his face;
had I met him anywhere else, I should probably have passed
him by without remark; but here I was alive to the traces
of former times, and detected in the demure features of this
guardian of the sanctuary the lurking lineaments of one of
the very playmates I have alluded to. We renewed our
acquaintance. He sat down beside me, on one of the tombstones over which we had leaped in our juvenile sports, and
we talked together about our boyish days, and held edifying
discourse on the instability of all sublunary things, as in-
stanced in the scene around us. He was rich in historic

lore as to the events of the last thirty years and the circum-
ference of thirty miles, and from him I learned the appalling
revolution that was taking place throughout the neighborhood. All this I clearly perceived he attributed to the
boasted march of intellect, or rather to the all-pervading
influence of steam. He bewailed the times when the only
communication with town was by the weekly market-boat,
the "Farmers' Daughter," which, under the pilotage of the
worthy Gabriel Requa, braved the perils of the Tappan Sea.
Alas! Gabriel and the "Farmers' Daughter" slept in peace.
Two steamboats now splashed and paddled up daily to the
little rural port of Tarrytown. The spirit of speculation and
improvement had seized even upon that once quiet and unambitious little dorp. The whole neighborhood was laid out
into town lots. Instead of the little tavern below the hill,
where the farmers used to loiter on market days and indulge
in cider and gingerbread, an ambitious hotel, with cupola and
verandas, now crested the summit, among churches built in
the Grecian and Gothic styles, showing the great increase
of piety and polite taste in the neighborhood. As to Dutch
dresses and sunbonnets, they were no longer tolerated, or
even thought of; not a farmer's daughter but now went to
town for the fashions; nay, a city milliner had recently set
up in the village, who threatened to reform the heads of the
whole neighborhood.

I had heard enough! I thanked my old playmate for his
intelligence, and departed from the Sleepy Hollow church
with the sad conviction that I had beheld the last lingerings
of the good old Dutch times in this once favored region. If
anything were wanting to confirm this inpression, it would
be the intelligence which has just reached me that a bank is
about to be established in the aspiring little port just mentioned. The fate of the neighborhood is therefore sealed. I
see no hope of averting it. The golden mean is at an end.
The country is suddenly to be deluged with wealth. The
late simple farmers are to become bank directors and drink
claret and champagne; and their wives and daughters to

figure in French hats and feathers; for French wines and French fashions commonly keep pace with paper money. How can I hope that even Sleepy Hollow can escape the general inundation? In a little while, I fear the slumber of ages will be at end; the strum of the piano will succeed to the hum of the spinning wheel; the trill of the Italian opera to the nasal quaver of Ichabod Crane; and the antiquarian visitor to the Hollow, in the petulance of his disappointment, may pronounce all that I have recorded of that once favored region a fable.   GEOFFREY CRAYON.

THE BIRDS OF SPRING

BY GEOFFREY CRAYON, GENT.

My quiet residence in the country, aloof from fashion, politics, and the money market, leaves me rather at a loss for important occupation, and drives me to the study of nature, and other low pursuits. Having few neighbors, also, on whom to keep a watch and exercise my habits of observation, I am fain to amuse myself with prying into the domestic concerns and peculiarities of the animals around me; and, during the present season, have derived considerable entertainment from certain sociable little birds, almost the only visitors we have during this early part of the year.

Those who have passed the winter in the country are sensible of the delightful influences that accompany the earliest indications of spring; and of these none are more delightful than the first notes of the birds. There is one modest little sad-colored bird, much resembling a wren, which came about the house just on the skirts of winter, when not a blade of grass was to be seen, and when a few prematurely warm days had given a flattering foretaste of soft weather. He sang early in the dawning, long before sunrise, and late in

the evening, just before the closing in of night, his matin and
his vesper hymns.   It is true, he sang occasionally throughout the day; but at these still hours his song was more remarked.   He sat on a leafless tree, just before the window,
and warbled forth his notes, free and simple, but singularly
sweet, with something of a plaintive tone that heightened
their effect.

The first morning that he was heard was a joyous one
among the young folks of my household.   The long, deathlike sleep of winter was at an end; nature was once more
awakening; they now promised themselves the immediate
appearance of buds and blossoms.   I was reminded of the
tempest-tossed crew of Columbus, when, after their long
dubious voyage, the field birds came singing round the ship,
though still far at sea, rejoicing them with the belief of the
immediate proximity of land.   A sharp return of winter almost silenced my little songster, and dashed the hilarity of
the household; yet still he poured forth, now and then, a few
plaintive notes, between the frosty pipings of the breeze, like
gleams of sunshine between wintry clouds.

I have consulted my book of ornithology in vain to find
out the name of this kindly little bird, who certainly deserves
honor and favor far beyond his modest pretensions.   He
comes like the lowly violet, the most unpretending, but wel-
comest of flowers, breathing the sweet promise of the early
year.

Another of our feathered visitors, who follows close upon
the steps of winter, is the Pe-wit, or Pe-wee, or Phœbe-bird;
for he is called by each of these names, from a fancied resemblance to the sound of his monotonous note.   He is a
sociable little being, and seeks the habitation of man.   A
pair of them have built beneath my porch, and have reared
several broods there for two years past, their nest being never
disturbed.   They arrive early in the spring, just when the
crocus and the snowdrop begin to peep forth.   Their first chirp
spreads gladness through the house.   "The Phœbe-birds have
come!" is heard on all sides; they are welcomed back like

members of the family; and speculations are made upon
where they have been, and what countries they have seen
during their long absence. Their arrival is the more cheering, as it is pronounced, by the old weather-wise people of
the country, the sure sign that the severe frosts are at an
end, and that the gardener may resume his labors with confidence.

About this time, too, arrives the blue-bird, so poetically
yet truly described by Wilson. His appearance gladdens the
whole landscape. You hear his soft warble in every field.
He sociably approaches your habitation, and takes up his residence in your vicinity. But why should I attempt to describe
him, when I have Wilson's own graphic verses to place him
before the reader?

> "When winter's cold tempests and snows are no more,
>   Green meadows and brown furrowed fields reappearing;
> The fishermen hauling their shad to the shore,
>   And cloud-cleaving geese to the lakes are a-steering;
> When first the lone butterfly flits on the wing,
>   When red grow the maples, so fresh and so pleasing,
> O then comes the blue-bird, the herald of spring,
>   And hails with his warblings the charms of the season.

> "The loud-piping frogs make the marshes to ring;
>   Then warm glows the sunshine, and warm glows the
>   weather;
> The blue woodland flowers just beginning to spring,
>   And spice-wood and sassafras budding together;
> O then to your gardens, ye housewives, repair,
>   Your walks border up, sow and plant at your leisure;
> The blue-bird will chant from his box such an air
>   That all your hard toils will seem truly a pleasure!

> "He flits through the orchard, he visits each tree,
>   The red flowering peach, and the apple's sweet blossoms,
> He snaps up destroyers, wherever they be,
>   And seizes the caitiffs that lurk in their bosoms;
> He drags the vile grub from the corn it devours,
>   The worms from the webs where they riot and welter;
> His song and his services freely are ours,
>   And all that he asks is, in summer a shelter.

"The plowman is pleased when he gleans in his train,
    Now searching the furrows, now mounting to cheer **him;**
The gard'ner delights in his sweet, simple strain,
    And leans on his spade to survey and to hear him.
The slow lingering school-boys forget they'll be chid,
    While gazing intent, as he warbles before them,
In mantle of sky-blue, and bosom so red,
    That each little loiterer seems to adore him."

The happiest bird of our spring, however, and one that
rivals the European lark, in my estimation, is the Boblincon,
or Boblink, as he is commonly called. He arrives at that
choice portion of our year which, in this latitude, answers
to the description of the month of May, so often given by the
poets. With us, it begins about the middle of May and lasts
until nearly the middle of June. Earlier than this, winter is
apt to return on its traces, and to blight the opening beauties
of the year; and later than this, begin the parching, and
panting, and dissolving heats of summer. But in this genial interval, nature is in all her freshness and fragrance:
"the rains are over and gone, the flowers appear upon the
earth, the time of the singing of birds is come, and the voice
of the turtle is heard in the land." The trees are now in
their fullest foliage and brightest verdure; the woods are
gay with the clustered flowers of the laurel; the air is per-
fumed by the sweet-brier and the wild rose; the meadows
are enameled with clover-blossoms; while the young apple,
the peach, and the plum, begin to swell, and the cherry to
glow, among the green leaves.

This is the chosen season of revelry of the Boblink. He
comes amid the pomp and fragrance of the season; his life
seems all sensibility and enjoyment, all song and sunshine.
He is to be found in the soft bosoms of the freshest and sweetest meadows; and is most in song when the clover is in
blossom. He perches on the topmost twig of a tree, or on
some long flaunting weed, and as he rises and sinks with the
breeze pours forth a succession of rich tinkling notes; crowding one upon another, like the outpouring melody of the sky-
lark, and possessing the same rapturous character. Some-

times he pitches from the summit of a tree, begins his song
as soon as he gets upon the wing, and flutters tremulously
down to the earth, as if overcome with ecstasy at his own
music. Sometimes he is in pursuit of his paramour; always
in full song, as if he would win her by his melody; and always with the same appearance of intoxication and delight.

Of all the birds of our groves and meadows, the Boblink
was the envy of my boyhood. He crossed my path in the
sweetest weather, and the sweetest season of the year, when
all nature called to the fields, and the rural feeling throbbed
in every bosom; but when I, luckless urchin! was doomed
to be mewed up, during the livelong day, in that purgatory
of boyhood, a schoolroom. It seemed as if the little varlet
mocked at me, as he flew by in full song, and sought to taunt
me with his happier lot. Oh, how I envied him! No lessons, no tasks, no hateful school; nothing but holiday, frolic,
green fields, and fine weather. Had I been then more versed
in poetry, I might have addressed him in the words of Logan
to the cuckoo:

> "Sweet bird! thy bower is ever green,
>   Thy sky is ever clear;
> Thou hast no sorrow in thy note,
>   No winter in thy year.
>
> "Oh! could I fly, I'd fly with thee;
>   We'd make, on joyful wing,
> Our annual visit round the globe,
>   Companions of the spring!"

Further observation and experience have given me a different idea of this little feathered voluptuary, which I will
venture to impart, for the benefit of my schoolboy readers,
who may regard him with the same unqualified envy and
admiration which I once indulged. I have shown him only
as I saw him at first, in what I may call the poetical part
of his career, when he in a manner devoted himself to elegant pursuits and enjoyments, and was a bird of music, and
song, and taste, and sensibility, and refinement. While this
lasted, he was sacred from injury; the very schoolboy would

not fling a stone at him, and the merest rustic would pause to listen to his strain. But mark the difference. As the year advances, as the clover-blossoms disappear, and the spring fades into summer, his notes cease to vibrate on the ear. He gradually gives up his elegant tastes and habits, doffs his poetical and professional suit of black, assumes a russet or rather dusty garb, and enters into the gross enjoyments of common, vulgar birds. He becomes a bon-vivant, a mere gourmand; thinking of nothing but good cheer, and gormandizing on the seeds of the long grasses on which he lately swung, and chanted so musically. He begins to think there is nothing like "the joys of the table," if I may be allowed to apply that convivial phrase to his indulgences. He now grows discontented with plain, every-day fare, and sets out on a gastronomical tour, in search of foreign luxuries. He is to be found in myriads among the reeds of the Delaware, banqueting on their seeds; grows corpulent with good feeding, and soon acquires the unlucky renown of the ortolan. Wherever he goes, pop! pop! pop! the rusty firelocks of the country are cracking on every side; he sees his companions falling by thousands around him; he is the *reed-bird*, the much-sought-for tidbit of the Pennsylvanian epicure.

Does he take warning and reform? Not he! He wings his flight still further south, in search of other luxuries. We hear of him gorging himself in the rice swamps; filling himself with rice almost to bursting; he can hardly fly for corpulency. Last stage of his career, we hear of him spitted by dozens, and served up on the table of the gourmand, the most vaunted of southern dainties, the *rice-bird* of the Carolinas.

Such is the story of the once musical and admired, but finally sensual and persecuted Boblink. It contains a moral, worthy the attention of all little birds and little boys; warning them to keep to those refined and intellectual pursuits which raised him to so high a pitch of popularity during the early part of his career; but to eschew all tendency to that gross and dissipated indulgence, which brought this mistaken little bird to an untimely end.

Which is all at present, from the well-wisher of little boys and little birds,   GEOFFREY CRAYON.

RECOLLECTIONS OF THE ALHAMBRA

BY THE AUTHOR OF THE SKETCH–BOOK

DURING a summer's residence in the old Moorish palace of the Alhambra, of which I have already given numerous anecdotes to the public, I used to pass much of my time in the beautiful Hall of the Abencerrages, beside the fountain celebrated in the tragic story of that devoted race. Here it was that thirty-six cavaliers of that heroic line were treacherously sacrificed to appease the jealousy or allay the fears of a tyrant. The fountain which now throws up its sparkling jet, and sheds a dewy freshness around, ran red with the noblest blood of Granada, and a deep stain on the marble pavement is still pointed out, by the cicerones of the pile, as a sanguinary record of the massacre. I have regarded it with the same determined faith with which I have regarded the traditional stains of Rizzio's blood on the floor of the chamber of the unfortunate Mary, at Holyrood. I thank no one for endeavoring to enlighten my credulity on such points of popular belief. It is like breaking up the shrine of the pilgrim; it is robbing a poor traveler of half the reward of his toils; for, strip traveling of its historical illusions, and what a mere fag you make of it!

For my part, I gave myself up, during my sojourn in the Alhambra, to all the romantic and fabulous traditions connected with the pile. I lived in the midst of an Arabian tale, and shut my eyes, as much as possible, to everything that called me back to every-day life; and if there is any country in Europe where one can do so, it is in poor, wild, legendary, proud-spirited, romantic Spain; where the old magnificent barbaric spirit still contends against the utilitarianism of modern civilization.

In the silent and deserted halls of the Alhambra, surrounded with the insignia of regal sway, and the still vivid, though dilapidated traces of Oriental voluptuousness, I was in the stronghold of Moorish story, and everything spoke and breathed of the glorious days of Granada when under the dominion of the crescent. When I sat in the Hall of the Abencerrages, I suffered my mind to conjure up all that I had read of that illustrious line. In the proudest days of Moslem domination, the Abencerrages were the soul of everything noble and chivalrous. The veterans of the family, who sat in the royal council, were the foremost to devise those heroic enterprises which carried dismay into the territories of the Christians; and what the sages of the family devised the young men of the name were the foremost to execute. In all services of hazard, in all adventurous forays and hairbreadth hazards, the Abencerrages were sure to win the brightest laurels. In those noble recreations, too, which bear so close an affinity to war; in the tilt and tourney, the riding at the ring, and the daring bull-fight; still the Abencerrages carried off the palm. None could equal them for the splendor of their array, the gallantry of their devices; for their noble bearing, and glorious horsemanship. Their open-handed munificence made them the idols of the populace, while their lofty magnanimity, and perfect faith, gained them golden opinions from the generous and high-minded. Never were they known to decry the merits of a rival, or to betray the confidings of a friend; and the "word of an Abencerrage" was a guarantee that never admitted of a doubt.

And then their devotion to the fair! Never did Moorish beauty consider the fame of her charms established until she had an Abencerrage for a lover; and never did an Abencerrage prove recreant to his vows. Lovely Granada! City of delights! Who ever bore the favors of thy dames more proudly on their casques, or championed them more gallantly in the chivalrous tilts of the Vivarambla? Or who ever made thy moonlit balconies, thy gardens of myrtles and roses, of oranges, citrons, and pomegranates, respond to more tender serenades?

I speak with enthusiasm on this theme; for it is connected with the recollection of one of the sweetest evenings and sweetest scenes that ever I enjoyed in Spain. One of the greatest pleasures of the Spaniards is to sit in the beautiful summer evenings and listen to traditional ballads, and tales about the wars of the Moors and Christians, and the "buenas andanzas" and "grandes hechos," the "good fortunes" and "great exploits" of the hardy warriors of yore. It is worthy of remark, also, that many of these songs, or romances, as they are called, celebrate the prowess and magnanimity in war, and the tenderness and fidelity in love, of the Moorish cavaliers, once their most formidable and hated foes. But centuries have elapsed to extinguish the bigotry of the zealot; and the once detested warriors of Granada are now held up by Spanish poets as the mirrors of chivalric virtue.

Such was the amusement of the evening in question. A number of us were seated in the Hall of the Abencerrages, listening to one of the most gifted and fascinating beings that I had ever met with in my wanderings. She was young and beautiful; and light and ethereal; full of fire, and spirit, and pure enthusiasm. She wore the fanciful Andalusian dress; touched the guitar with speaking eloquence; improvised with wonderful facility; and, as she became excited by her theme, or by the rapt attention of her auditors, would pour forth, in the richest and most melodious strains, a succession of couplets, full of striking description, or stirring narration, and composed, as I was assured, at the moment. Most of these were suggested by the place, and related to the ancient glories of Granada and the prowess of her chivalry. The Abencerrages were her favorite heroes; she felt a woman's admiration of their gallant courtesy and high-souled honor; and it was touching and inspiring to hear the praises of that generous but devoted race chanted in this fated hall of their calamity by the lips of Spanish beauty.

Among the subjects of which she treated was a tale of Moslem honor and old-fashioned Spanish courtesy, which made a strong impression on me. She disclaimed all merit of invention, however, and said she had merely dilated into verse a popular tradition; and, indeed, I have since found the main facts inserted at the end of Conde's History of the Domination of the Arabs, and the story itself embodied in the form of an episode in the Diana of Montemayor. From these sources I have drawn it forth, and endeavored to shape it according to my recollection of the version of the beautiful minstrel; but, alas! what can supply the want of that voice, that look, that form, that action, which gave magical effect to her chant, and held every one rapt in breathless admiration! Should this mere travesty of her inspired numbers ever meet her eye, in her stately abode at Granada, may it meet with that indulgence which belongs to her benignant nature. Happy should I be if it could awaken in her bosom one kind recollection of the lonely stranger and sojourner, for whose gratification she did not think it beneath her to exert those fascinating powers which were the delight of brilliant circles; and who will ever recall with enthusiasm the happy evening passed in listening to her strains, in the moonlit halls of the Alhambra.   GEOFFREY CRAYON.

THE ABENCERRAGE

A SPANISH TALE

ON the summit of a craggy hill, a spur of the mountains of Ronda, stands the castle of Allora, now a mere ruin, infested by bats and owlets, but in old times one of the strong border holds of the Christians, to keep watch upon the frontiers of the warlike kingdom of Granada, and to hold the

Moors in check.   It was a post always confided to some well-
tried commander; and, at the time of which we treat, was
held by Rodrigo de Narvaez, a veteran, famed, both among
Moors and Christians, not only for his hardy feats of arms,
but also for that magnanimous courtesy which should ever
be entwined with the sterner virtues of the soldier.

The castle of Allora was a mere part of his command; he
was alcayde or military governor of Antiquera, but he passed
most of his time at this frontier post, because its situation on
the borders gave more frequent opportunity for those adventurous exploits which were the delight of the Spanish chivalry.
His garrison consisted of fifty chosen cavaliers, all well
mounted and well appointed: with these he kept vigilant
watch upon the Moslems; patroling the roads, and paths,
and defiles of the mountains, so that nothing could escape
his eye; and now and then signalizing himself by some dashing foray into the very vega of Granada.

On a fair and beautiful night in summer, when the freshness of the evening breeze had tempered the heat of day, the
worthy alcayde sallied forth, with nine of his cavaliers, to
patrol the neighborhood, and seek adventures.   They rode
quietly and cautiously, lest they should be overheard by
Moorish scout or traveler; and kept along ravines and hollow ways, lest they should be betrayed by the glittering of
the full moon upon their armor.   Coming to where the road
divided, the alcayde directed five of his cavaliers to take one
of the branches, while he, with the remaining four, would
take the other.   Should either party be in danger, the blast
of a horn was to be the signal to bring their comrades to their
aid.

The party of five had not proceeded far when, in passing
through a defile, overhung with trees, they heard the voice
of a man singing.   They immediately concealed themselves
in a grove, on the brow of a declivity, up which the stranger
would have to ascend.   The moonlight, which left the grove
in deep shadow, lighted up the whole person of the wayfarer,
as he advanced, and enabled them to distinguish his dress

and appearance with perfect accuracy. He was a Moorish cavalier, and his noble demeanor, graceful carriage, and splendid attire, showed him to be of lofty rank. He was superbly mounted, on a dapple-gray steed of powerful frame and generous spirit, and magnificently caparisoned. His dress was a marlota, or tunic, and an albernoz of crimson damask, fringed with gold. His Tunisian turban, of many folds, was of silk and cotton, striped, and bordered with golden fringe. At his girdle hung a scimiter of Damascus steel, with loops and tassels of silk and gold. On his left arm he bore an ample target, and his right hand grasped a long double-pointed lance. Thus equipped, he sat negligently on his steed, as one who dreamed of no danger, gazing on the moon, and singing, with a sweet and manly voice, a Moorish love ditty.

Just opposite the place where the Spanish cavaliers were concealed was a small fountain in the rock, beside the road, to which the horse turned to drink; the rider threw the reins on his neck, and continued his song.

The Spanish cavaliers conferred together; they were all so pleased with the gallant and gentle appearance of the Moor that they resolved not to harm, but to capture him, which, in his negligent mood, promised to be an easy task; rushing, therefore, from their concealment, they thought to surround and seize him. Never were men more mistaken. To gather up his reins, wheel round his steed, brace his buckler, and couch his lance, was the work of an instant; and there he sat, fixed like a castle in his saddle, beside the fountain.

The Christian cavaliers checked their steeds and reconnoitered him warily, loth to come to an encounter which must end in his destruction.

The Moor now held a parley: "If you be true knights," said he, "and seek for honorable fame, come on, singly, and I am ready to meet each in succession; but if you be mere lurkers of the road, intent on spoil, come all at once, and do your worst!"

The cavaliers communed for a moment apart, when one, advancing singly, exclaimed: "Although no law of chivalry obliges us to risk the loss of a prize, when clearly in our power, yet we willingly grant, as a courtesy, what we might refuse as a right. Valiant Moor! defend thyself!"

So saying, he wheeled, took proper distance, couched his lance, and putting spurs to his horse, made at the stranger. The latter met him in mid career, transpierced him with his lance, and threw him headlong from his saddle. A second and a third succeeded, but were unhorsed with equal facility, and thrown to the earth, severely wounded. The remaining two, seeing their comrades thus roughly treated, forgot all compact of courtesy, and charged both at once upon the Moor. He parried the thrust of one, but was wounded by the other in the thigh, and, in the shock and confusion, dropped his lance. Thus disarmed, and closely pressed, he pretended to fly, and was hotly pursued. Having drawn the two cavaliers some distance from the spot, he suddenly wheeled short about, with one of those dexterous movements for which the Moorish horsemen are renowned; passed swiftly between them, swung himself down from his saddle, so as to catch up his lance, then, lightly replacing himself, turned to renew the combat.

Seeing him thus fresh for the encounter, as if just issued from his tent, one of the cavaliers put his lips to his horn and blew a blast that soon brought the alcayde and his four companions to the spot.

The valiant Narvaez, seeing three of his cavaliers extended on the earth, and two others hotly engaged with the Moor, was struck with admiration, and coveted a contest with so accomplished a warrior. Interfering in the fight, he called upon his followers to desist, and addressing the Moor, with courteous words, invited him to a more equal combat. The latter readily accepted the challenge. For some time their contest was fierce and doubtful, and the alcayde had need of all his skill and strength to ward off the blows of his antagonist. The Moor, however, was exhausted by previous fighting, and by loss of blood. He no longer sat his horse firmly, nor managed him with his wonted skill. Collecting all his strength for a last assault, he rose in his stirrups, and made a violent thrust with his lance; the alcayde received it upon his shield, and at the same time wounded the Moor in the right arm; then closing, in the shock, he grasped him in his arms, dragged him from his saddle, and fell with him to the earth: when, putting his knee upon his breast, and his dagger to his throat, "Cavalier," exclaimed he, "render thyself my prisoner, for thy life is in my hands!"

"Kill me, rather," replied the Moor, "for death would be less grievous than loss of liberty."

The alcayde, however, with the clemency of the truly brave, assisted the Moor to rise, ministered to his wounds with his own hands, and had him conveyed with great care to the castle of Allora. His wounds were slight, and in a few days were nearly cured; but the deepest wound had been inflicted on his spirit. He was constantly buried in a profound melancholy.

The alcayde, who had conceived a great regard for him, treated him more as a friend than a captive, and tried in every way to cheer him, but in vain; he was always sad and moody, and, when on the battlements of the castle, would keep his eyes turned to the south, with a fixed and wistful gaze.

"How is this?" exclaimed the alcayde, reproachfully, "that you, who were so hardy and fearless in the field, should lose all spirit in prison? If any secret grief preys on your heart, confide it to me, as to a friend, and I promise you, on the faith of a cavalier, that you shall have no cause to repent the disclosure."

The Moorish knight kissed the hand of the alcayde. "Noble cavalier," said he, "that I am cast down in spirit is not from my wounds, which are slight, nor from my captivity, for your kindness has robbed it of all gloom; nor from my defeat, for to be conquered by so accomplished and renowned a cavalier is no disgrace. But to explain to you the

cause of my grief it is necessary to give you some particulars
of my story; and this I am moved to do by the great sympathy you have manifested toward me, and the magnanimity
that shines through all your actions.

"Know, then, that my name is Abendaraez, and that I
am of the noble but unfortunate line of the Abencerrages of
Granada. You have doubtless heard of the destruction that
fell upon our race. Charged with treasonable designs, of
which they were entirely innocent, many of them were beheaded, the rest banished; so that not an Abencerrage was
permitted to remain in Granada, excepting my father and
my uncle, whose innocence was proved, even to the satisfaction of their persecutors. It was decreed, however, that,
should they have children, the sons should be educated at a
distance from Granada, and the daughters should be married
out of the kingdom.

"Conformably to this decree, I was sent, while yet an
infant, to be reared in the fortress of Cartama, the worthy
alcayde of which was an ancient friend of my father. He
had no children, and received me into his family as his own
child, treating me with the kindness and affection of a father;
and I grew up in the belief that he really was such. A few
years afterward, his wife gave birth to a daughter, but his
tenderness toward me continued undiminished. I thus grew
up with Xarisa, for so the infant daughter of the alcayde
was called, as her own brother, and thought the growing
passion which I felt for her was mere fraternal affection. I
beheld her charms unfolding, as it were, leaf by leaf, like
the morning rose, each moment disclosing fresh beauty and
sweetness.

"At this period, I overheard a conversation between the
alcayde and his confidential domestic, and found myself to
be the subject. 'It is time,' said he, 'to apprise him of his
parentage, that he may adopt a career in life. I have de-
ferred the communication as long as possible, through reluctance to inform him that he is of a proscribed and an unlucky
race.'

"This intelligence would have overwhelmed me at an earlier period, but the intimation that Xarisa was not my sister operated like magic, and in an instant transformed my brotherly affection into ardent love.

"I sought Xarisa, to impart to her the secret I had learned. I found her in the garden, in a bower of jessamines, arranging her beautiful hair by the mirror of a crystal fountain. The radiance of her beauty dazzled me. I ran to her with open arms, and she received me with a sister's embraces. When we had seated ourselves beside the fountain she began to upbraid me for leaving her so long alone.

"In reply, I informed her of the conversation I had overheard. The recital shocked and distressed her. 'Alas!' cried she, 'then is our happiness at an end!'

" 'How!' exclaimed I; 'wilt thou cease to love me, because I am not thy brother?'

" 'Not so,' replied she; 'but do you not know that when it is once known we are not brother and sister, we can no longer be permitted to be thus always together?'

"In fact, from that moment our intercourse took a new character. We met often at the fountain among the jessamines, but Xarisa no longer advanced with open arms to meet me. She became reserved and silent, and would blush and cast down her eyes when I seated myself beside her. My heart became a prey to the thousand doubts and fears that ever attend upon true love. I was restless and uneasy, and looked back with regret to the unreserved intercourse that had existed between us, when we supposed ourselves brother and sister; yet I would not have had the relationship true for the world.

"While matters were in this state between us, an order came from the king of Granada for the alcayde to take command of the fortress of Coyn, which lies directly on the Christian frontier. He prepared to remove, with all his family, but signified that I should remain at Cartama. I exclaimed against the separation, and declared that I could not be parted from Xarisa. 'That is the very cause,' said he, 'why I leave thee behind. It is time, Abendaraez, that thou shouldst know the secret of thy birth; that thou art no son of mine, neither is Xarisa thy sister.' 'I know it all,' exclaimed I, 'and I love her with tenfold the affection of a brother. You have brought us up together; you have made us necessary to each other's happiness; our hearts have entwined themselves with our growth; do not now tear them asunder. Fill up the measure of your kindness; be indeed a father to me,

giving me Xarisa for my wife.'

"The brow of the alcayde darkened as I spoke. 'Have I then been deceived?' said he. 'Have those nurtured in my very bosom been conspiring against me? Is this your return for my paternal tenderness?—to beguile the affections of my child, and teach her to deceive her father? It was cause enough to refuse thee the hand of my daughter, that thou wert of a proscribed race, who can never approach the walls of Granada; this, however, I might have passed over; but never will I give my daughter to a man who has endeavored to win her from me by deception.'

"All my attempts to vindicate myself and Xarisa were unavailing. I retired in anguish from his presence, and seeking Xarisa, told her of this blow, which was worse than death to me. 'Xarisa,' said I, 'we part forever! I shall never see thee more! Thy father will guard thee rigidly. Thy beauty and his wealth will soon attract some happier rival, and I shall be forgotten!'

"Xarisa reproached me with my want of faith, and promised me eternal constancy. I still doubted and desponded, until, moved by my anguish and despair, she agreed to a secret union. Our espousals made, we parted, with a promise on her part to send me word from Coyn should her father absent himself from the fortress. The very day after our secret nuptials, I beheld the whole train of the alcayde depart from Cartama, nor would he admit me to his presence, or permit me to bid farewell to Xarisa. I remained at Cartama, somewhat pacified in spirit by this secret bond of union; but everything around me fed my passion, and re-

minded me of Xarisa. I saw the windows at which I had
so often beheld her. I wandered through the apartment she
had inhabited; the chamber in which she had slept. I visited
the bower of jessamines, and lingered beside the fountain in
which she had delighted. Everything recalled her to my
imagination, and filled my heart with tender melancholy.

"At length, a confidential servant brought me word that
her father was to depart that day for Granada, on a short
absence, inviting me to hasten to Coyn, describing a secret
portal at which I should apply, and the signal by which I
would obtain admittance.

"If ever you have loved, most valiant alcayde, you may
judge of the transport of my bosom. That very night I arrayed myself in my most gallant attire, to pay due honor to
my bride; and arming myself against any casual attack,
issued forth privately from Cartama. You know the rest,
and by what sad fortune of war I found myself, instead of a
happy bridegroom, in the nuptial bower of Coyn, vanquished,
wounded, and a prisoner, within the walls of Allora. The
term of absence of the father of Xarisa is nearly expired.
Within three days he will return to Coyn, and our meeting
will no longer be possible. Judge, then, whether I grieve
without cause, and whether I may not well be excused for
showing impatience under confinement."

Don Rodrigo de Narvaez was greatly moved by this recital; for, though more used to rugged war than scenes of
amorous softness, he was of a kind and generous nature.

"Abendaraez," said he, "I did not seek thy confidence to
gratify an idle curiosity. It grieves me much that the good
fortune which delivered thee into my hands should have
marred so fair an enterprise. Give me thy faith, as a true
knight, to return prisoner to my castle, within three days,
and I will grant thee permission to accomplish thy nuptials."

The Abencerrage would have thrown himself at his feet
to pour out protestations of eternal gratitude, but the alcayde
prevented him. Calling in his cavaliers, he took the Aben-

cerrage by the right hand, in their presence, exclaiming solemnly, "You promise, on the faith of a cavalier, to return to my castle of Allora within three days, and render yourself my prisoner?" And the Abencerrage said, "I promise."

Then said the alcayde, "Go! and may good fortune attend you. If you require any safeguard, I and my cavaliers are ready to be your companions."

The Abencerrage kissed the hand of the alcayde, in grateful acknowledgment. "Give me," said he, "my own armor, and my steed, and I require no guard. It is not likely that I shall again meet with so valorous a foe."

The shades of night had fallen when the tramp of the dapple-gray steed sounded over the drawbridge, and immediately afterward the light clatter of hoofs along the road bespoke the fleetness with which the youthful lover hastened to his bride. It was deep night when the Moor arrived at the castle of Coyn. He silently and cautiously walked his panting steed under its dark walls, and having nearly passed round them, came to the portal denoted by Xarisa. He paused and looked round to see that he was not observed, and then knocked three times with the butt of his lance. In a little while the portal was timidly unclosed by the duenna of Xarisa. "Alas! senor," said she, "what has detained you thus long? Every night have I watched for you; and my lady is sick at heart with doubt and anxiety."

The Abencerrage hung his lance, and shield, and scimiter against the wall, and then followed the duenna, with silent steps, up a winding staircase, to the apartment of Xarisa. Vain would be the attempt to describe the raptures of that meeting. Time flew too swiftly, and the Abencerrage had nearly forgotten, until too late, his promise to return a prisoner to the alcayde of Allora. The recollection of it came to him with a pang, and suddenly awoke him from his dream of bliss. Xarisa saw his altered looks, and heard with alarm his stifled sighs; but her countenance brightened when she heard the cause. "Let not thy spirit be cast down," said she, throwing her white arms around him. "I have the keys of my father's treasures; send ransom more than enough to satisfy the Christian, and remain with me."

"No," said Abendaraez, "I have given my word to return in person, and, like a true knight, must fulfill my promise. After that, fortune must do with me as it pleases."

"Then," said Xarisa, "I will accompany thee. Never shall you return a prisoner, and I remain at liberty."

The Abencerrage' was transported with joy at this new proof of devotion in his beautiful bride. All preparations were speedily made for their departure. Xarisa mounted behind the Moor on his powerful steed; they left the castle walls before daybreak, nor did they pause until they arrived at the gate of the castle of Allora, which was flung wide to receive them.

Alighting in the court, the Abencerrage supported the steps of his trembling bride, who remained closely veiled, into the presence of Rodrigo de Narvaez. "Behold, valiant alcayde!" said he, "the way in which an Abencerrage keeps his word. I promised to return to thee a prisoner, but I deliver two captives into your power. Behold Xarisa, and judge whether I grieved without reason over the loss of such a treasure. Receive us as your own, for I confide my life and her honor to your hands."

The alcayde was lost in admiration of the beauty of the lady and the noble spirit of the Moor. "I know not," said he, "which of you surpasses the other; but I know that my castle is graced and honored by your presence. Enter into it, and consider it your own, while you deign to reside with me."

For several days the lovers remained at Allora, happy in each other's love and in the friendship of the brave alcayde. The latter wrote a letter, full of courtesy, to the Moorish king of Granada, relating the whole event, extolling the valor and good faith of the Abencerrage, and craving for him the royal countenance.

The king was moved by the story, and was pleased with an opportunity of showing attention to the wishes of a gal-

lant and chivalrous enemy; for though he had often suffered
from the prowess of Don Rodrigo de Narvaez, he admired
the heroic character he had gained throughout the land.
Calling the alcayde of Coyn into his presence, he gave him
the letter to read. The alcayde turned pale, and trembled
with rage, on the perusal. "Restrain thine anger," said the
king; "there is nothing that the alcayde of Allora could ask
that I would not grant if in my power. Go thou to Allora;
pardon thy children; take them to thy home. I receive this
Abencerrage into my favor, and it will be my delight to heap
benefits upon you all."

The kindling ire of the alcayde was suddenly appeased.
He hastened to Allora, and folded his children to his bosom,
who would have fallen at his feet. The gallant Rodrigo de
Narvaez gave liberty to his prisoner without ransom, demanding merely a promise of his friendship. He accompanied the youthful couple and their father to Coyn, where
their nuptials were celebrated with great rejoicings. When
the festivities were over, Don Rodrigo de Narvaez returned
to his fortress of Allora.

After his departure, the alcayde of Coyn addressed his
children: "To your hands," said he, "I confide the disposition of my wealth. One of the first things I charge you is
not to forget the ransom you owe to the alcayde of Allora.
His magnanimity you can never repay, but you can prevent
it from wronging him of his just dues. Give him, moreover,
your entire friendship, for he merits it fully, though of a
different faith."

The Abencerrage thanked him for his generous proposition, which so truly accorded with his own wishes. He took
a large sum of gold, and inclosed it in a rich coffer; and, on
his own part, sent six beautiful horses, superbly caparisoned;
with six shields and lances, mounted and embossed with
gold. The beautiful Xarisa, at the same time, wrote a
letter to the alcayde, filled with expressions of gratitude
and friendship, and sent him a box of fragrant cypress-
wood, containing linen of the finest quality for his person.

The valiant alcayde disposed of the present in a character-istic manner. The horses and armor he shared among the cavaliers who had accompanied him on the night of the skirmish. The box of cypress-wood and its contents he re-tained for the sake of the beautiful Xarisa; and sent her, by the hands of the messenger, the sum of gold paid as a ran-som, entreating her to receive it as a wedding present. This courtesy and magnanimity raised the character of the Al-cayde Rodrigo de Narvaez still higher in the estimation of the Moors, who extolled him as a perfect mirror of chivalric virtue; and from that time forward there was a continual exchange of good offices between them.

THE ENCHANTED ISLAND

BY THE AUTHOR OF THE SKETCH-BOOK

"Break, Phantsie, from thy cave of cloud,
 And wave thy purple wings,
Now all thy figures are allowed,
 And various shapes of things.
Create of airy forms a stream;
 It must have blood and naught of phlegm;
And though it be a walking dream,
 Yet let it like an odor rise
  To all the senses here,
 And fall like sleep upon their eyes,
  Or music on their ear."—BEN JONSON

"THERE are more things in heaven and earth than are dreamed of in our philosophy," and among these may be placed that marvel and mystery of the seas, the island of St. Brandan. Every schoolboy can enumerate and call by name the Canaries, the Fortunate Islands of the ancients; which, according to some ingenious speculative minds, are mere wrecks and remnants of the vast island of Atlantis, men-tioned by Plato as having been swallowed up by the ocean. Whoever has read the history of those isles, will remember the wonders told of another island, still more beautiful, seen occasionally from their shores, stretching away in the clear bright west, with long shadowy promontories, and high, sun-gilt peaks. Numerous expeditions, both in ancient and modern days, have launched forth from the Canaries in quest of that island; but, on their approach, mountain and promontory have gradually faded away, until nothing has remained but the blue sky above and the deep blue water below. Hence it was termed by the geographers of old Aprositus or the Inaccessible; while modern navigators have called its very existence in question, pronouncing it a mere optical illusion, like the Fata Morgana of the Straits of Messina; or classing it with those unsubstantial regions known to mariners as Cape Flyaway and the Coast of Cloud Land.

Let not, however, the doubts of the worldly-wise skeptics of modern days rob us of all the glorious realms owned by happy credulity in days of yore. Be assured, O reader of easy faith!—thou for whom I delight to labor—be assured, that such an island does actually exist, and has, from time to time, been revealed to the gaze, and trodden by the feet, of favored mortals. Nay, though doubted by historians and philosophers, its existence is fully attested by the poets, who, being an inspired race, and gifted with a kind of second sight, can see into the mysteries of nature hidden from the eyes of ordinary mortals. To this gifted race it has ever been a region of fancy and romance, teeming with all kinds of wonders. Here once bloomed, and perhaps still blooms, the famous garden of the Hesperides, with its golden fruit. Here, too, was the enchanted garden of Armida, in which that sorceress held the Christian paladin, Rinaldo, in delicious but inglorious thralldom; as is set forth in the immortal lay of Tasso. It was on this island also that Sycorax, the witch, held sway, when the good Prospero, and his infant daughter Miranda were wafted to its shores. The isle was then

"—— full of noises,
Sounds, and sweet airs, that give delight, and hurt not."

Who does not know the tale, as told in the magic page of Shakespeare?

In fact, the island appears to have been, at different times, under the sway of different powers, genii of earth, and air, and ocean; who made it their shadowy abode; or rather, it is the retiring place of old worn-out deities and dynasties, that once ruled the poetic world, but are now nearly shorn of all their attributes. Here Neptune and Amphitrite hold a diminished court, like sovereigns in exile. Their ocean-chariot lies bottom upward, in a cave of the island, almost a perfect wreck, while their pursy Tritons and haggard Nereids bask listlessly like seals about the rocks. Sometimes they assume a shadow of their ancient pomp, and glide in state about the glassy sea; while the crew of some tall Indiaman, that lies becalmed with flapping sails, hear with astonishment the mellow note of the Triton's shell swelling upon the ear, as the invisible pageant sweeps by. Sometimes the quondam monarch of the ocean is permitted to make himself visible to mortal eyes, visiting the ships that cross the line, to exact a tribute from newcomers; the only remnant of his ancient rule, and that, alas! performed with tattered state and tarnished splendor.

On the shores of this wondrous island the mighty kraken heaves his bulk and wallows many a rood; here, too, the sea-serpent lies coiled up, during the intervals of his much-contested revelations to the eyes of true believers; and here, it is said, even the "Flying Dutchman" finds a port, and casts his anchor, and furls his shadowy sail, and takes a short repose from his eternal wanderings.

Here all the treasures lost in the deep are safely garnered. The caverns of the shores are piled with golden ingots, boxes of pearls, rich bales of oriental silks; and their deep recesses sparkle with diamonds, or flame with carbuncles. Here, in deep bays and harbors, lies many a spell-bound ship, long given up as lost by the ruined merchant. Here, too, its crew, long bewailed as swallowed up in ocean, lie sleeping in mossy grottoes, from age to age, or wander about enchanted shores and groves, in pleasing oblivion of all things.

Such are some of the marvels related of this island, and which may serve to throw some light on the following legend, of unquestionable truth, which I recommend to the entire belief of the reader.

THE ADELANTADO OF THE SEVEN CITIES

A LEGEND OF ST. BRANDAN

IN the early part of the fifteenth century, when Prince Henry of Portugal, of worthy memory, was pushing the career of discovery along the western coast of Africa, and the world was resounding with reports of golden regions on the mainland, and new-found islands in the ocean, there arrived at Lisbon an old bewildered pilot of the seas, who had been driven by tempests, he knew not whither, and who raved about an island far in the deep, on which he had landed, and which he had found peopled with Christians, and adorned with noble cities.

The inhabitants, he said, gathered round, and regarded him with surprise, having never before been visited by a ship. They told him they were descendants of a band of Christians who fled from Spain when that country was conquered by the Moslems. They were curious about the state of their fatherland, and grieved to hear that the Moslems still held possession of the kingdom of Granada. They would have taken the old navigator to church, to convince him of their orthodoxy; but, either through lack of devotion, or lack of faith in their words, he declined their invitation, and preferred to return on board of his ship. He was properly punished. A furious storm arose, drove him from his anchorage, hurried him out to sea, and he saw no more of the unknown island.

This strange story caused great marvel in Lisbon and elsewhere. Those versed in history remembered to have read, in an ancient chronicle, that, at the time of the conquest of Spain, in the eighth century, when the blessed cross was cast down and the crescent erected in its place, and when Christian churches were turned into Moslem mosques, seven bishops, at the head of seven bands of pious exiles, had fled from the peninsula, and embarked in quest of some ocean island, or distant land, where they might found seven Christian cities, and enjoy their faith unmolested.

The fate of these pious saints-errant had hitherto remained a mystery, and their story had faded from memory; the report of the old tempest-tossed pilot, however, revived this long-forgotten theme; and it was determined by the pious and enthusiastic that the island thus accidentally discovered was the identical place of refuge, whither the wandering bishops had been guided by a protecting Providence, and where they had folded their flocks.

This most excitable of worlds has always some darling object of chimerical enterprise. The "Island of the Seven Cities" now awakened as much interest and longing among zealous Christians as has the renowned city of Timbuctoo among adventurous travelers, or the Northeast Passage among hardy navigators; and it was a frequent prayer of the devout that these scattered and lost portions of the Christian family might be discovered, and reunited to the great body of Christendom.

No one, however, entered into the matter with half the zeal of Don Fernando de Ulmo, a young cavalier of high standing in the Portuguese court, and of most sanguine and romantic temperament. He had recently come to his estate, and had run the round of all kinds of pleasures and excitements, when this new theme of popular talk and wonder presented itself. The Island of the Seven Cities became now the constant subject of his thoughts by day and his dreams by night; it even rivaled his passion for a beautiful girl, one of the greatest belles of Lisbon, to whom he was betrothed. At length his imagination became so inflamed on the subject that he determined to fit out an expedition, at his own expense, and set sail in quest of this sainted island. It could not be a cruise of any great extent; for, according to the calculations of the tempest-tossed pilot, it must be somewhere in the latitude of the Canaries; which at that time, when the new world was as yet undiscovered, formed the frontier of ocean enterprise. Don Fernando applied to the crown for countenance and protection. As he was a favorite at court, the usual patronage was readily extended to him; that is to say, he received a commission from the king, Don Ioam II., constituting him adelantado, or military governor, of any country he might discover, with the single proviso that he should bear all the expenses of the discovery and pay a tenth of the profits to the crown.

Don Fernando now set to work in the true spirit of a projector. He sold acre after acre of solid land, and invested the proceeds in ships, guns, ammunition and sea-stores. Even his old family mansion in Lisbon was mortgaged without scruple, for he looked forward to a palace in one of the Seven Cities of which he was to be adelantado. This was the age of nautical romance, when the thoughts of all speculative dreamers were turned to the ocean. The scheme of Don Fernando, therefore, drew adventurers of every kind. The merchant promised himself new marts of opulent traffic; the soldier hoped to sack and plunder some one or other of those Seven Cities; even the fat monk shook off the sleep and sloth of the cloister to join in a crusade which promised such increase to the possessions of the church.

One person alone regarded the whole project with sovereign contempt and growling hostility. This was Don Ramiro Alvarez, the father of the beautiful Serafina, to whom Don Fernando was betrothed. He was one of those perverse, matter-of-fact old men who are prone to oppose everything speculative and romantic. He had no faith in the Island of the Seven Cities; regarded the projected cruise as a crackbrained freak; looked with angry eye and internal heart-

burning on the conduct of his intended son-in-law, chaffering
away solid lands for lands in the moon, and scoffingly dubbed
him Adelantado of Lubberland. In fact, he had never really
relished the intended match, to which his consent had been
slowly extorted by the tears and entreaties of his daughter.
It is true he could have no reasonable objections to the
youth, for Don Fernando was the very flower of Portuguese
chivalry. No one could excel him at the tilting match, or
the riding at the ring; none was more bold and dexterous
in the bull-fight; none composed more gallant madrigals in
praise of his lady's charms, or sang them with sweeter tones
to the accompaniment of her guitar; nor could any one
handle the castanets and dance the bolero with more captivating grace. All these admirable qualities and endowments, however, though they had been sufficient to win the
heart of Serafina, were nothing in the eyes of her unreasonable father. Oh, Cupid, god of Love! why will fathers
always be so unreasonable!

The engagement to Serafina had threatened at first to
throw an obstacle in the way of the expedition of Don Fernando, and for a long time perplexed him in the extreme.
He was passionately attached to the young lady; but he was
also passionately bent on this romantic enterprise. How he
should reconcile the two passionate inclinations? A simple
and obvious arrangement at length presented itself; marry
Serafina, enjoy a portion of the honeymoon at once, and
defer the rest until his return from the discovery of the Seven
Cities!

He hastened to make known this most excellent arrangement to Don Ramiro, when the long-smothered wrath of the
old cavalier burst forth in a storm about his ears. He reproached him with being the dupe of wandering vagabonds
and wild schemers, and of squandering all his real possessions in pursuit of empty bubbles. Don Fernando was too
sanguine a projector, and too young a man, to listen tamely
to such language. He acted with what is technically called
"becoming spirit." A high quarrel ensued; Don Ramiro

pronounced him a madman, and forbade all further intercourse with his daughter until he should give proof of returning sanity by abandoning this mad-cap enterprise; while
Don Fernando flung out of the house, more bent than ever
on the expedition, from the idea of triumphing over the
incredulity of the gray-beard when he should return successful.

Don Ramiro repaired to his daughter's chamber the
moment the youth had departed. He represented to her the
sanguine, unsteady character of her lover and the chimerical
nature of his schemes; showed her the propriety of suspending all intercourse with him until he should recover from his
present hallucination; folded her to his bosom with parental
fondness, kissed the tear that stole down her cheek, and, as
he left the chamber, gently locked the door; for although he
was a fond father, and had a high opinion of the submissive
temper of his child, he had a still higher opinion of the con-
servative virtues of lock and key. Whether the damsel had
been in any wise shaken in her faith as to the schemes of her
lover, and the existence of the Island of the Seven Cities, by
the sage representations of her father, tradition does not say;
but it is certain that she became a firm believer the moment
she heard him turn the key in the lock.

Notwithstanding the interdict of Don Ramiro, therefore,
and his shrewd precautions, the intercourse of the lovers
continued, although clandestinely. Don Fernando toiled all
day, hurrying forward his nautical enterprise, while at night
he would repair, beneath the grated balcony of his mistress,
to carry on at equal pace the no less interesting enterprise of
the heart. At length the preparations for the expedition
were completed. Two gallant caravels lay anchored in the
Tagus, ready to sail with the morning dawn; while late at
night, by the pale light of a waning moon, Don Fernando
sought the stately mansion of Alvarez to take a last farewell
of Serafina. The customary signal of a few low touches of
a guitar brought her to the balcony. She was sad at heart
and full of gloomy forebodings; but her lover strove to im-

part to her his own buoyant hope and youthful confidence.
"A few short months," said he, "and I shall return in triumph. Thy father will then blush at his incredulity, and
will once more welcome me to his house, when I cross its
threshold a wealthy suitor and adelantado of the Seven
Cities."

The beautiful Serafina shook her head mournfully. It
was not on those points that she felt doubt or dismay. She
believed most implicitly in the Island of the Seven Cities,
and trusted devoutly in the success of the enterprise; but she
had heard of the inconstancy of the seas, and the inconstancy of those who roam them. Now, let the truth be
spoken, if Don Fernando had any fault in the world it
was that he was a little too inflammable; that is to say, a
little too subject to take fire from the sparkle of every bright
eye; he had been somewhat of a rover among the sex on
shore, what might he not be on sea? Might he not meet
with other loves in foreign ports? Might he not behold
some peerless beauty, in one or other of those seven cities,
who might efface the image of Serafina from his thoughts?

At length she ventured to hint her doubts; but Don
Fernando spurned at the very idea. Never could his heart
be false to Serafina! Never could another be captivating in
his eye!—never—never! Repeatedly did he bend his knee,
and smite his breast, and call upon the silver moon to witness the sincerity of his vows. But might not Serafina, herself, be forgetful of her plighted faith? Might not some
wealthier rival present, while he was tossing on the sea, and,
backed by the authority of her father, win the treasure of
her hand?

Alas, how little did he know Serafina's heart! The more
her father should oppose, the more would she be fixed in her
faith. Though years should pass before his return, he would
find her true to her vows. Even should the salt seas swallow him up (and her eyes streamed with salt tears at the
very thought), never would she be the wife of another—
never—never! She raised her beautiful white arms between

the iron bars of the balcony, and invoked the moon as a testimonial of her faith.

Thus, according to immemorial usage, the lovers parted, with many a vow of eternal constancy. But will they keep those vows? Perish the doubt! Have they not called the constant moon to witness?

With the morning dawn the caravels dropped down the Tagus and put to sea. They steered for the Canaries, in those days the regions of nautical romance. Scarcely had they reached those latitudes when a violent tempest arose. Don Fernando soon lost sight of the accompanying caravel, and was driven out of all reckoning by the fury of the storm. For several weary days and nights he was tossed to and fro, at the mercy of the elements, expecting each moment to be swallowed up. At length, one day toward evening, the storm subsided; the clouds cleared up, as though a veil had suddenly been withdrawn from the face of heaven, and the setting sun shone gloriously upon a fair and mountainous island, that seemed close at hand. The tempest-tossed mariners rubbed their eyes and gazed almost incredulously upon this land, that had emerged so suddenly from the murky gloom; yet there it lay, spread out in lovely landscapes; enlivened by villages, and towers, and spires, while the late stormy sea rolled in peaceful billows to its shores. About a league from the sea, on the banks of a river, stood a noble city, with lofty walls and towers, and a protecting castle. Don Fernando anchored off the mouth of the river, which appeared to form a spacious harbor. In a little while a barge was seen issuing from the river. It was evidently a barge of ceremony, for it was richly though quaintly carved and gilt, and decorated with a silken awning and fluttering streamers, while a banner, bearing the sacred emblem of the cross, floated to the breeze. The barge advanced slowly, impelled by sixteen oars painted of a bright crimson. The oarsmen were uncouth or rather antique in their garb, and kept stroke to the regular cadence of an old Spanish ditty. Beneath the awning sat a cavalier, in a rich though old-fashioned doublet, with an enormous sombrero and feather.

When the barge reached the caravel the cavalier stepped on board. He was tall and gaunt, with a long, Spanish visage and lack-luster eyes, and an air of lofty and somewhat pompous gravity. His mustaches were curled up to his ears, his beard was forked and precise; he wore gauntlets that reached to his elbows, and a Toledo blade that strutted out behind, while, in front, its huge basket-hilt might have served for a porringer.

Thrusting out a long spindle leg, and taking off his sombrero with a grave and stately sweep, he saluted Don Fernando by name, and welcomed him, in old Castilian language and in the style of old Castilian courtesy.

Don Fernando was startled at hearing himself accosted by name, by an utter stranger, in a strange land. As soon as he could recover from his surprise, he inquired what land it was at which he had arrived.

"The Island of the Seven Cities!"

Could this be true? Had he indeed been thus tempest-driven upon the very land of which he was in quest? It was even so. The other caravel, from which he had been separated in the storm, had made a neighboring port of the island, and announced the tidings of this expedition, which came to restore the country to the great community of Christendom. The whole island, he was told, was given up to rejoicings on the happy event; and they only awaited his arrival to acknowledge allegiance to the crown of Portugal and hail him as adelantado of the Seven Cities. A grand fete was to be solemnized that very night in the palace of the alcayde or governor of the city; who, on beholding the most opportune arrival of the caravel, had dispatched his grand chamberlain, in his barge of state, to conduct the future adelantado to the ceremony.

Don Fernando could scarcely believe but that this was all a dream. He fixed a scrutinizing gaze upon the grand chamberlain, who, having delivered his message, stood in buckram dignity, drawn up to his full stature, curling his whiskers, stroking his beard, and looking down upon him with inexpressible loftiness through his lack-luster eyes. There was no doubting the word of so grave and ceremonious a hidalgo.

Don Fernando now arrayed himself in gala attire. He would have launched his boat, and gone on shore with his own men, but he was informed the barge of state was expressly provided for his accommodation, and, after the fete, would bring him back to his ship; in which, on the following day, he might enter the harbor in befitting style. He accordingly stepped into the barge and took his seat beneath the awning. The grand chamberlain seated himself on the cushion opposite. The rowers bent to their oars and renewed their mournful old ditty, and the gorgeous, but unwieldy barge moved slowly and solemnly through the water.

The night closed in before they entered the river. They swept along, past rock and promontory, each guarded by its tower. The sentinels at every post challenged them as they passed by.

"Who goes there?"

"The adelantado of the Seven Cities."

"He is welcome. Pass on."

On entering the harbor, they rowed close along an armed galley of the most ancient form. Soldiers with crossbows were stationed on the deck.

"Who goes there?" was again demanded.

"The adelantado of the Seven Cities."

"He is welcome. Pass on."

They landed at a broad flight of stone steps, leading up, between two massive towers, to the water-gate of the city, at which they knocked for admission. A sentinel, in an ancient steel casque, looked over the wall. "Who is there?"

"The adelantado of the Seven Cities."

The gate swung slowly open, grating upon its rusty hinges. They entered between two rows of iron-clad warriors, in battered armor, with crossbows, battle-axes, and

...ient maces, and with faces as old-fashioned and rusty ...eir armor. They saluted Don Fernando in military styl but with perfect silence, as he passed between their rank The city was illuminated, but in such manner as to give more shadowy and solemn effect to its old-time architectur There were bonfires in the principal streets, with groups abou them in such old-fashioned garbs that they looked like th fantastic figures that roam the streets in carnival time. Eve the stately dames who gazed from the balconies, which the had hung with antique tapestry, looked more like effigie dressed up for a quaint mummery than like ladies in the: fashionable attire. Everything, in short, bore the stamp o former ages, as if the world had suddenly rolled back a fev centuries. Nor was this to be wonderd at. Had not th Island of the Seven Cities been for several hundred year cut off from all communication with the rest of the world and was it not natural that the inhabitants should retain man of the modes and customs brought here by their ancestors

One thing certainly they had conserved; the old-fashione Spanish gravity and stateliness. Though this was a time o public rejoicing, and though Don Fernando was the objec of their gratulations, everything was conducted with th most solemn ceremony, and wherever he appeared, instea of acclamations, he was received with profound silence, an the most formal reverences and swayings of their sombreros

Arrived at the palace of the alcayde, the usual ceremonia was repeated. The chamberlain knocked for admission.

"Who is there?" demanded the porter.

"The adelantado of the Seven Cities."

"He is welcome. Pass on."

The grand portal was thrown open. The chamberlain led the way up a vast but heavily molded marble staircase and so through one of those interminable suites of apart ments that are the pride of Spanish palaces. All were fur nished in a style of obsolete magnificence. As they passe through the chambers, the title of Don Fernando was for warded on by servants stationed at every door, and every

where produced the most profound reverences and courtes_s.
At length they reached a magnificent saloon, blazing w_.
tapers, in which the alcayde and the principal dignitaries o.
the city were waiting to receive their illustrious guest. The
grand chamberlain presented Don Fernando in due form,
and falling back among the other officers of the household,
stood as usual curling his whiskers and stroking his forked
beard.

Don Fernando was received by the alcayde and the other
dignitaries with the same stately and formal courtesy that
he had everywhere remarked. In fact, there was so much
form and ceremonial that it seemed difficult to get at anything social or substantial. Nothing but bows and compliments and old-fashioned courtesies. The alcayde and his
courtiers resembled, in face and form, those quaint worthies
to be seen in the pictures of old illuminated manuscripts;
while the cavaliers and dames who thronged the saloon
might have been taken for the antique figures of Gobelin
tapestry suddenly vivified and put in motion.

The banquet, which had been kept back until the arrival
of Don Fernando, was now announced; and such a feast!
such unknown dishes and obsolete dainties; with the pea-
cock, that bird of state and ceremony, served up in full
plumage, in a golden dish, at the head of the table. And
then, as Don Fernando cast his eyes over the glittering
board, what a vista of odd heads and headdresses, of formal
bearded dignitaries, and stately dames, with castellated locks
and towering plumes!

As fate would have it, on the other side of Don Fernando
was seated the daughter of the alcayde. She was arrayed,
it is true, in a dress that might have been worn before the
flood; but then, she had a melting black Andalusian eye
that was perfectly irresistible. Her voice, too, her manner,
her movements, all smacked of Andalusia, and showed how
female fascination may be transmitted from age to age, and
clime to clime, without ever losing its power, or going out of
fashion. Those who know the witchery of the sex, in that

amorous region of old Spain, may judge what must
have been the fascination to which Don Fernando was exposed, when seated beside one of the most captivating of its
descendants. He was, as has already been hinted, of an
inflammable temperament; with a heart ready to get in a
light blaze at every instant. And then he had been so
wearied by pompous, tedious old cavaliers, with their formal
bows and speeches; is it to be wondered at that he turned
with delight to the alcayde's daughter, all smiles, and
dimples, and melting looks, and melting accents? Besides,
for I wish to give him every excuse in my power, he was in
a particularly excitable mood from the novelty of the scene
before him, and his head was almost turned with this sudden
and complete realization of all his hopes and fancies; and
then, in the flurry of the moment, he had taken frequent
draughts at the wine-cup, presented him at every instant by
officious pages, and all the world knows the effect of such
draughts in giving potency to female charms. In a word,
there is no concealing the matter, the banquet was not half
over before Don Fernando was making love, outright, to the
alcayde's daughter. It was his old habitude, contracted
long before his matrimonial engagement. The young lady
hung her head coyly; her eye rested upon a ruby heart, sparkling in a ring on the hand of Don Fernando, a parting gage
of love from Serafina. A blush crimsoned her very temples.
She darted a glance of doubt at the ring, and then at Don
Fernando. He read her doubt, and in the giddy intoxication
of the moment drew off the pledge of his affianced bride,
and slipped it on the finger of the alcayde's daughter.

At this moment the banquet broke up. The chamberlain,
with his lofty demeanor and his lack-luster eyes, stood before
him, and announced that the barge was waiting to conduct
him back to the caravel. Don Fernando took a formal leave
of the alcayde and his dignitaries, and a tender farewell of
the alcayde's daughter, with a promise to throw himself at
her feet on the following day. He was rowed back to his
vessel in the same slow and stately manner, to the cadence

of the same mournful old ditty.   He retired to his cabin, his brain whirling with all that he had seen, and his heart now and then giving him a twinge as he recollected his temporary infidelity to the beautiful Serafina.   He flung himself on his bed, and soon fell into a feverish sleep.   His dreams were wild and incoherent.   How long he slept he knew not, but when he awoke he found himself in a strange cabin, with persons around him of whom he had no knowledge.   He rubbed his eyes to ascertain whether he were really awake. In reply to his inquiries, he was informed that he was on board of a Portuguese ship, bound to Lisbon; having been taken senseless from a wreck drifting about the ocean.

Don Fernando was confounded and perplexed.   He retraced everything distinctly that had happened to him in the Island of the Seven Cities, and until he had retired to rest on board of the caravel.   Had his vessel been driven from her anchors and wrecked during his sleep?   The people about him could give him no information on the subject.   He talked to them of the Island of the Seven Cities, and of all that had befallen him there.   They regarded his words as the ravings of delirium, and in their honest solicitude administered such rough remedies that he was fain to drop the subject and observe a cautious taciturnity.

At length they arrived in the Tagus, and anchored before the famous city of Lisbon.   Don Fernando sprang joyfully on shore, and hastened to his ancestral mansion.   To his surprise, it was inhabited by strangers; and when he asked about his family, no one could give him any information concerning them.

He now sought the mansion of Don Ramiro, for the temporary flame kindled by the bright eyes of the alcayde's daughter had long since burned itself out, and his genuine passion for Serafina had revived with all its fervor.   He approached the balcony, beneath which he had so often serenaded her.   Did his eyes deceive him?   No!   There was Serafina herself at the balcony.   An exclamation of rapture burst from him as he raised his arms toward her.   She cast upon him a look of indignation, and, hastily retiring, closed the casement. Could she have heard of his flirtation with the alcayde's daughter? He would soon dispel every doubt of his constancy. The door was open. He rushed upstairs, and, entering the room, threw himself at her feet. She shrank back with affright, and took refuge in the arms of a youthful cavalier.

"What mean you, sir," cried the latter, "by this intrusion?"

"What right have you," replied Don Fernando, "to ask the question?"

"The right of an affianced suitor!"

Don Fernando started and turned pale. "Oh, Serafina! Serafina!" cried he, in a tone of agony, "is this thy plighted constancy?"

"Serafina?—what mean you by Serafina? If it be this young lady you intend, her name is Maria."

"Is not this Serafina Alvarez, and is not that her portrait?" cried Don Fernando, pointing to a picture of his mistress.

"Holy Virgin!" cried the young lady; "he is talking of my great-grandmother!"

An explanation ensued, if that could be called an explanation which plunged the unfortunate Fernando into tenfold perplexity. If he might believe his eyes, he saw before him his beloved Serafina; if he might believe his ears, it was merely her hereditary form and features, perpetuated in the person of her great-granddaughter.

His brain began to spin. He sought the office of the Minister of Marine, and made a report of his expedition, and of the Island of the Seven Cities, which he had so fortunately discovered. Nobody knew anything of such an expedition or such an island. He declared that he had undertaken the enterprise under a formal contract with the crown and had received a regular commission, constituting him adelantado. This must be matter of record, and he insisted loudly that the books of the department should be consulted.

The wordy strife at length attracted the attention of an old, gray-headed clerk, who sat perched on a high stool, at a high desk, with iron-rimmed spectacles on the top of a thin, pinched nose, copying records into an enormous folio. He had wintered and summered in the department for a great part of a century, until he had almost grown to be a piece of the desk at which he sat; his memory was a mere index of official facts and documents, and his brain was little better than red tape and parchment. After peering down for a time from his lofty perch, and ascertaining the matter in controversy, he put his pen behind his ear and descended. He remembered to have heard something from his predecessor about an expedition of the kind in question, but then it had sailed during the reign of Don Ioam II., and he had been dead at least a hundred years. To put the matter beyond dispute, however, the archives of the Torve do Tombo, that sepulcher of old Portuguese documents, were diligently searched, and a record was found of a contract between the crown and one Fernando de Ulmo, for the discovery of the Island of the Seven Cities, and of a commission secured to him as adelantado of the country he might discover.

"There," cried Don Fernando, triumphantly, "there you have proof, before your own eyes, of what I have said. I am the Fernando de Ulmo specified in that record. I have discovered the Island of the Seven Cities, and am entitled to be adelantado, according to contract."

The story of Don Fernando had certainly what is pronounced the best of historical foundation, documentary evidence; but when a man, in the bloom of youth, talked of events that had taken place above a century previously as having happened to himself, it is no wonder that he was set down for a madman.

The old clerk looked at him from above and below his spectacles, shrugged his shoulders, stroked his chin, reascended his lofty stool, took the pen from behind his ears, and resumed his daily and eternal task, copying records into the fiftieth volume of a series of gigantic folios. The other

*** S

clerks winked at each other shrewdly, and dispersed to their several places, and poor Don Fernando, thus left to himself, flung out of the office, almost driven wild by these repeated perplexities.

In the confusion of his mind, he instinctively repaired to the mansion of Alvarez, but it was barred against him. To break the delusion under which the youth apparently labored, and to convince him that the Serafina about whom he raved was really dead, he was conducted to her tomb. There she lay, a stately matron, cut out in alabaster; and there lay her husband beside her; a portly cavalier, in armor; and there knelt, on each side, the effigies of a numerous progeny, proving that she had been a fruitful vine. Even the very monument gave proof of the lapse of time, for the hands of her husband, which were folded as if in prayer, had lost their fingers, and the face of the once lovely Serafina was noseless.

Don Fernando felt a transient glow of indignation at beholding this monumental proof of the inconstancy of his mistress; but who could expect a mistress to remain constant during a whole century of absence? And what right had he to rail about constancy, after what had passed between him and the alcayde's daughter? The unfortunate cavalier performed one pious act of tender devotion; he had the alabaster nose of Serafina restored by a skillful statuary, and then tore himself from the tomb.

He could now no longer doubt the fact that, somehow or other, he had skipped over a whole century during the night he had spent at the Island of the Seven Cities; and he was now as complete a stranger in his native city as if he had never been there. A thousand times did he wish himself back to that wonderful island, with its antiquated banquet halls, where he had been so courteously received; and now that the once young and beautiful Serafina was nothing but a great-grandmother in marble, with generations of descendants, a thousand times would he recall the melting black eyes of the alcayde's daughter, who doubtless, like himself, was

still flourishing in fresh juvenility, and breathe a secret wish
that he were seated by her side.

He would at once have set on foot another expedition at
his own expense, to cruise in search of the sainted island, but
his means were exhausted. He endeavored to rouse others
to the enterprise, setting forth the certainty of profitable results, of which his own experience furnished such unquestionable proof. Alas! no one would give faith to his tale;
but looked upon it as the feverish dream of a shipwrecked
man. He persisted in his efforts; holding forth in all places
and all companies, until he became an object of jest and jeer
to the light-minded, who mistook his earnest enthusiasm for
a proof of insanity; and the very children in the streets ban-
tered him with the title of "The Adelantado of the Seven
Cities."

Finding all his efforts in vain in his native city of Lisbon,
he took shipping for the Canaries, as being nearer the latitude of his former cruise, and inhabited by people given to
nautical adventure. Here he found ready listeners to his
story; for the old pilots and mariners of those parts were
notorious island-hunters and devout believers in all the wonders of the seas. Indeed, one and all treated his adventure
as a common occurrence, and turning to each other, with a
sagacious nod of the head, observed, "He has been at the
Island of St. Brandan."

They then went on to inform him of that great marvel
and enigma of the ocean; of its repeated appearance to the
inhabitants of their islands; and of the many but ineffectual
expeditions that had been made in search of it. They took
him to a promontory of the island of Palma, from whence
the shadowy St. Brandan had oftenest been described, and
they pointed out the very tract in the west where its mountains had been seen.

Don Fernando listened with rapt attention. He had no
longer a doubt that this mysterious and fugacious island
must be the same with that of the Seven Cities; and that
there must be some supernatural influence connected with it

that had operated upon himself, and made the events of a night occupy the space of a century.

He endeavored, but in vain, to rouse the islanders to another attempt at discovery; they had given up the phantom island as indeed inaccessible. Fernando, however, was not to be discouraged. The idea wore itself deeper and deeper in his mind, until it became the engrossing subject of his thoughts and object of his being. Every morning he would repair to the promontory of Palma, and sit there throughout the livelong day, in hopes of seeing the fairy mountains of St. Brandan peering about the horizon; every evening he returned to his home a disappointed man, but ready to resume his post on the following morning.

His assiduity was all in vain. He grew gray in his ineffectual attempt; and was at length found dead at his post. His grave is still shown in the island of Palma, and a cross is erected on the spot where he used to sit and look out upon the sea, in hopes of the reappearance of the enchanted island.

NATIONAL NOMENCLATURE

TO THE EDITOR OF THE KNICKERBOCKER

Sir—I am somewhat of the same way of thinking, in regard to names, with that profound philosopher, Mr. Shandy, the elder, who maintained that some inspired high thoughts and heroic aims, while others entailed irretrievable meanness and vulgarity; insomuch that a man might sink under the insignificance of his name, and be absolutely "Nicodemused into nothing." I have ever, therefore, thought it a great hardship for a man to be obliged to struggle through life with some ridiculous or ignoble *Christian* name, as it is too often falsely called, inflicted on him in infancy, when he could not choose for himself; and would give him free liberty to change it for one more to his taste, when he had arrived at years of discretion.

I have the same notion with respect to local names. Some at once prepossess us in favor of a place; others repel us, by unlucky associations of the mind; and I have known scenes worthy of being the very haunt of poetry and romance, yet doomed to irretrievable vulgarity by some ill-chosen name, which not even the magic numbers of a Halleck or a Bryant could elevate into poetical acceptation.

This is an evil unfortunately too prevalent throughout our country. Nature has stamped the land with features of sublimity and beauty; but some of our noblest mountains and loveliest streams are in danger of remaining forever unhonored and unsung, from bearing appellations totally abhorrent to the Muse. In the first place, our country is deluged with names taken from places in the old world, and applied to places having no possible affinity or resemblance to their namesakes. This betokens a forlorn poverty of invention, and a second-hand spirit, content to cover its nakedness with borrowed or cast-off clothes of Europe.

Then we have a shallow affectation of scholarship: the whole catalogue of ancient worthies is shaken out from the back of Lempriere's Classical Dictionary, and a wide region of wild country sprinkled over with the names of the heroes, poets, and sages of antiquity, jumbled into the most whimsical juxtaposition. Then we have our political godfathers; topographical engineers, perhaps, or persons employed by government to survey and lay out townships. These, forsooth, glorify the patrons that give them bread; so we have the names of the great official men of the day scattered over the land as if they were the real "salt of the earth," with which it was to be seasoned. Well for us is it, when these official great men happen to have names of fair acceptation; but woe unto us should a Tubbs or a Potts be in power; we are sure, in a little while, to find Tubbsvilles and Pottsylvanias springing up in every direction.

Under these melancholy dispensations of taste and loyalty,

therefore, Mr. Editor, it is with a feeling of dawning hope
that I have lately perceived the attention of persons of intelligence beginning to be awakened on this subject. I trust,
if the matter should once be taken up, it will not be readily
abandoned. We are yet young enough, as a country, to
remedy and reform much of what has been done, and to
release many of our rising towns and cities, and our noble
streams, from names calculated to vulgarize the land.

I have, on former occasion, suggested the expediency of
searching out the original Indian names of places, and where-
ever they are striking and euphonious, and those by which
they have been superseded are glaringly objectionable, to restore them. They would have the merit of originality, and
of belonging to the country; and they would remain as relics
of the native lords of the soil, when every other vestige had
disappeared. Many of these names may easily be regained
by reference to old title deeds, and to the archives of states
and counties. In my own case, by examining the records of
the county clerk's office, I have discovered the Indian names
of various places and objects in the neighborhood, and have
found them infinitely superior to the trite, poverty-stricken
names which had been given by the settlers. A beautiful
pastoral stream, for instance, which winds for many a mile
through one of the loveliest little valleys in the State, has long
been known by the commonplace name of the "Saw-mill
River." In the old Indian grants it is designated as the
Neperan. Another, a perfectly wizard stream, which winds
through the wildest recesses of Sleepy Hollow, bears the hum-
drum name of Mill Creek: in the Indian grants it sustains
the euphonious title of the Pocantico.

Similar researches have released Long Island from many
of those paltry and vulgar names which fringed its beautiful
shores; their Cow Bays, and Cow Necks, and Oyster Ponds,
and Mosquito Coves, which spread a spell of vulgarity over
the whole island, and kept persons of taste and fancy at a
distance.

It would be an object worthy the attention of the histori-

cal societies, which are springing up in various parts of the
Union, to have maps executed of their respective States or
neighborhoods, in which all the Indian local names should,
as far as possible, be restored. In fact, it appears to me that
the nomenclature of the country is almost of sufficient importance for the foundation of a distinct society; or rather,
a corresponding association of persons of taste and judgment
of all parts of the Union. Such an association, if properly
constituted and composed, comprising especially all the literary talent of the country, though it might not have legisla-
tive power in its enactments, yet would have the all-pervading power of the press; and the changes in nomenclature
which it might dictate, being at once adopted by elegant
writers in prose and poetry, and interwoven with the literature of the country, would ultimately pass into popular currency.

Should such a reforming association arise, I beg to recommend to its attention all those mongrel names that have
the adjective *New* prefixed to them, and pray they may be
one and all kicked out of the country. I am for none of
these second-hand appellations that stamp us a second-hand
people, and that are to perpetuate us a new country to the
end of time. Odds my life! Mr. Editor, I hope and trust
we are to live to be an old nation, as well as our neighbors,
and have no idea that our cities, when they shall have attained to venerable antiquity, shall still be dubbed *New* York,
and *New* London, and *new* this and *new* that, like the Pont
Neuf (the New Bridge) at Paris, which is the oldest bridge
in that capital, or like the Vicar of Wakefield's horse, which
continued to be called "the colt" until he died of old age.

Speaking of New York reminds me of some observations
which I met with some time since, in one of the public papers,
about the name of our State and city. The writer proposes
to substitute for the present names those of the STATE OF
ONTARIO, and the CITY OF MANHATTAN. I concur in his
suggestion most heartily. Though born and brought up in
the city of New York, and though I love every stick and

stone about it, yet I do not, nor ever did, relish its name. I like neither its sound nor its significance. As to its *significance*, the very adjective *new* gives to our great commercial metropolis a second-hand character, as if referring to some older, more dignified, and important place, of which it was a mere copy; though in fact, if I am rightly informed, the whole name commemorates a grant by Charles II. to his brother, the Duke of York, made in the spirit of royal munificence, of a tract of country which did not belong to him. As to the *sound*, what can you make of it, either in poetry or prose? New York! Why, sir, if it were to share the fate Troy itself; to suffer a ten years' siege, and be sacked and plundered; no modern Homer would ever be able to elevate the name to epic dignity.

Now, sir, ONTARIO would be a name worthy of the Empire State. It bears with it the majesty of that internal sea which washes our northwestern shore. Or, if any objection should be made, from its not being completely embraced within our boundaries, there is the MOHEGAN, one of the Indian names for that glorious river, the Hudson, which would furnish an excellent State appellation. So also New York might be called Manhatta, as it is named in some of the early records, and Manhattan used as the adjective. Manhattan, however, stands well as a substantive, and "Manhattanese," which I observe Mr. Cooper has adopted in some of his writings, would be a very good appellation for a citizen of the commercial metropolis.

A word or two more, Mr. Editor, and I have done. We want a NATIONAL NAME. We want it poetically, and we want it politically. With the poetical necessity of the case I shall not trouble myself. I leave it to our poets to tell how they manage to steer that collocation of words, "The United States of North America," down the swelling tide of song, and to float the whole raft out upon the sea of heroic poesy. I am now speaking of the mere purposes of common life. How is a citizen of this republic to designate himself? As an American? There are two Americas, each subdivided

into various empires, rapidly rising in importance. As a
citizen of the United States? It is a clumsy, lumbering title,
yet still it is not distinctive; for we have now the United
States of Central America; and heaven knows how many
"United States" may spring up under the Proteus changes
of Spanish America.

This may appear matter of small concernment; but any
one that has traveled in foreign countries must be conscious
of the embarrassment and circumlocution sometimes occasioned by the want of a perfectly distinct and explicit national appellation. In France, when I have announced myself as an American, I have been supposed to belong to one
of the French colonies; in Spain, to be from Mexico, or Peru,
or some other Spanish-American country. Repeatedly have
I found myself involved in a long geographical and political
definition of my national identity.

Now, sir, meaning no disrespect to any of our coheirs of
this great quarter of the world, I am for none of this copar-
ceny in a name that is to mingle us up with the riff-raff colonies and offsets of every nation of Europe. The title of
American may serve to tell the quarter of the world to which
I belong, the same as a Frenchman or an Englishman may
call himself a European; but I want my own peculiar national name to rally under. I want an appellation that shall
tell at once, and in a way not to be mistaken, that I belong
to this very portion of America, geographical and political,
to which it is my pride and happiness to belong; that I am
of the Anglo-Saxon race which founded this Anglo-Saxon
empire in the wilderness; and that I have no part or parcel
with any other race or empire, Spanish, French, or Portuguese, in either of the Americas. Such an appellation, sir,
would have magic in it. It would bind every part of the
confederacy together as with a keystone; it would be a pass-
port to the citizen of our republic throughout the world.

We have it in our power to furnish ourselves with such a
national appellation from one of the grand and eternal features of our country; from that noble chain of mountains

which formed its backbone, and ran through the "old confederacy," when it first declared our national independence.
I allude to the Appalachian or Alleghany mountains. We
might do this without any very inconvenient change in our
present titles. We might still use the phrase, "The United
States," substituting Appalachia, or Alleghania (I should
prefer the latter), in place of America. The title of Appalachian, or Alleghanian, would still announce us as Americans, but would specify us as citizens of the Great Republic.
Even our old national cipher of U. S. A. might remain un-
altered, designating the United States of Alleghania.

These are crude ideas, Mr. Editor, hastily thrown out to
elicit the ideas of others, and to call attention to a subject of
more national importance than may at first be supposed.

Very respectfully yours,

GEOFFREY CRAYON.

DESULTORY THOUGHTS ON CRITICISM

"Let a man write never so well, there are nowadays a sort of persons
they call critics, that, egad, have no more wit in them than so many
hobby-horses; but they'll laugh at you, sir, and find fault, and censure
things, that, egad, I'm sure they are notable to do themselves; a sort of
envious persons, that emulate the glories of persons of parts, and think
to build their fame by calumniation of persons, that, egad, to my
knowledge, of all persons in the world, are in nature the persons that
do as much despise all that, as—a— In fine, I'll say no more of 'em!"
—REHEARSAL

ALL the world knows the story of the tempest-tossed voy-
ager, who, coming upon a strange coast, and seeing a man
hanging in chains, hailed it with joy as the sign of a civilized country. In like manner we may hail, as a proof of the
rapid advancement of civilization and refinement in this country, the increasing number of delinquent authors daily gib-
beted for the edification of the public.

In this respect, as in every other, we are "going ahead" with accelerated velocity, and promising to outstrip the superannuated countries of Europe. It is really astonishing to see the number of tribunals incessantly springing up for the trial of literary offenses. Independent of the high courts of Oyer and Terminer, the great quarterly reviews, we have innumerable minor tribunals, monthly and weekly, down to the Pie-poudre courts in the daily papers; insomuch that no culprit stands so little chance of escaping castigation as an unlucky author guilty of an unsuccessful attempt to please the public.

Seriously speaking, however, it is questionable whether our national literature is sufficiently advanced to bear this excess of criticism; and whether it would not thrive better if allowed to spring up, for some time longer, in the freshness and vigor of native vegetation. When the worthy Judge Coulter, of Virginia, opened court for the first time in one of the upper counties, he was for enforcing all the rules and regulations that had grown into use in the old, long-settled counties. "This is all very well," said a shrewd old farmer; "but let me tell you, Judge Coulter, you set your coulter too deep for a new soil."

For my part, I doubt whether either writer or reader is benefited by what is commonly called criticism. The former is rendered cautious and distrustful; he fears to give way to those kindling emotions and brave sallies of thought which bear him up to excellence; the latter is made fastidious and cynical; or, rather, he surrenders his own independent taste and judgment, and learns to like and dislike at second hand.

Let us, for a moment, consider the nature of this thing called criticism, which exerts such a sway over the literary world. The pronoun *we*, used by critics, has a most imposing and delusive sound. The reader pictures to himself a conclave of learned men, deliberating gravely and scrupulously on the merits of the book in question; examining it page by page, comparing and balancing their opinions, and when they have united in a conscientious verdict publishing it for the benefit of the world: whereas the criticism is generally the crude and hasty production of an individual, scribbling to while away an idle hour, to oblige a bookseller, or to defray current expenses. How often is it the passing notion of the hour, affected by accidental circumstances; by indisposition, by peevishness, by vapors or indigestion; by personal prejudice, or party feeling. Sometimes a work is sacrificed, because the reviewer wishes a satirical article; sometimes because he wants a humorous one; and sometimes because the author reviewed has become offensively celebrated and offers high game to the literary marksman.

How often would the critic himself, if a conscientious man, reverse his opinion, had he time to revise it in a more sunny moment; but the press is waiting, the printer's devil is at his elbow; the article is wanted to make the requisite variety for the number of the review, or the author has pressing occasion for the sum he is to receive for the article; so it is sent off, all blotted and blurred, with a shrug of the shoulders, and the consolatory ejaculation: "Pshaw! curse it! it's nothing but a review!"

The critic, too, who dictates thus oracularly to the world, is perhaps some dingy, ill-favored, ill-mannered varlet, who, were he to speak by word of mouth, would be disregarded, if not scoffed at; but such is the magic of types; such the mystic operation of anonymous writing; such the potential effect of the pronoun *we*, that his crude decisions, fulminated through the press, become circulated far and wide, control the opinions of the world, and give or destroy reputation.

Many readers have grown timorous in their judgments since the all-pervading currency of criticism. They fear to express a revised, frank opinion about any new work, and to relish it honestly and heartily, lest it should be condemned in the next review, and they stand convicted of bad taste. Hence they hedge their opinions, like a gambler his bets, and leave an opening to retract, and retreat, and qualify, and neutralize every unguarded expression of delight, until their very praise declines into a faintness that is damning.

Were every one, on the contrary, to judge for himself, and speak his mind frankly and fearlessly, we should have more true criticism in the world than at present. Whenever a person is pleased with a work he may be assured that it has good qualities. An author who pleases a variety of readers must possess substantial powers of pleasing; or, in other words, intrinsic merits; for otherwise we acknowledge an effect and deny the cause. The reader, therefore, should not suffer himself to be readily shaken from the conviction of his own feelings by the sweeping censures of pseudo critics. The author he has admired may be chargeable with a thousand faults; but it is nevertheless beauties and excellences that have excited his admiration; and he should recollect that taste and judgment are as much evinced in the perception of beauties among defects as in a detection of defects among beauties. For my part, I honor the blessed and blessing spirit that is quick to discover and extol all that is pleasing and meritorious. Give me the honest bee that extracts honey from the humblest weed, but save me from the ingenuity of the spider, which traces its venom, even in the midst of a flower-garden.

If the mere fact of being chargeable with faults and imperfections is to condemn an author, who is to escape? The greatest writers of antiquity have, in this way, been obnoxious to criticism. Aristotle himself has been accused of ignorance; Aristophanes of impiety and buffoonery; Virgil of plagiarism, and a want of invention; Horace of obscurity; Cicero has been said to want vigor and connection, and Demosthenes to be deficient in nature, and in purity of language. Yet these have all survived the censures of the critic, and flourished on to a glorious immortality. Every now and then the world is startled by some new doctrines in matters of taste, some leveling attacks on established creeds, some sweeping denunciations of whole generations, or schools of writers, as they are called, who had seemed to be embalmed and canonized in public opinion. Such has been the case, for instance, with Pope, and Dryden, and Addison,

who for a time have almost been shaken from their pedes-
tals, and treated as false idols.

It is singular, also, to see the fickleness of the world with
respect to its favorites. Enthusiasm exhausts itself, and pre-
pares the way for dislike. The public is always for positive
sentiments, and new sensations. When wearied of admiring, it delights to censure; thus coining a double set of enjoyments out of the same subject. Scott and Byron are scarce
cold in their graves, and already we find criticism beginning
to call in question those powers which held the world in
magic thralldom. Even in our own country, one of its greatest geniuses has had some rough passages with the censors
of the press; and instantly criticism begins to unsay all that
it has repeatedly said in his praise; and the public are almost
led to believe that the pen which has so often delighted them
is absolutely destitute of the power to delight!

If, then, such reverses in opinion as to matters of taste
can be so readily brought about, when may an author feel
himself secure? Where is the anchoring-ground of popularity, when he may thus be driven from his moorings, and
foundered even in harbor? The reader, too, when is he to
consider himself safe in admiring, when he sees long-estab-
lished altars overthrown and his household deities dashed to
the ground!

There is one consolatory reflection. Every abuse carries
with it its own remedy or palliation. Thus the excess of
crude and hasty criticism which has of late prevailed throughout the literary world, and threatened to overrun our country,
begins to produce its own antidote. Where there is a multi-
plicity of contradictory paths, a man must make his choice;
in so doing, he has to exercise his judgment, and that is
one great step to mental independence. He begins to doubt
all, where all differ, and but one can be in the right. He is
driven to trust to his own discernment, and his natural feelings; and here he is most likely to be safe. The author, too,
finding that what is condemned at one tribunal is applauded
at another, though perplexed for a time, gives way at length

to the spontaneous impulse of his genius and the dictates of his taste, and writes in the way most natural to himself. It is thus that criticism, which by its severity may have held the little world of writers in check, may, by its very excess, disarm itself of its terrors, and the hardihood of talent become restored.   G. C.

SPANISH ROMANCE

TO THE EDITOR OF THE KNICKERBOCKER

SIR—I have already given you a legend or two drawn from ancient Spanish sources, and may occasionally give you a few more. I love these old Spanish themes, especially when they have a dash of the Morisco in them, and treat of the times when the Moslems maintained a foothold in the peninsula. They have a high, spicy, Oriental flavor, not to be found in any other themes that are merely European. In fact, Spain is a country that stands alone in the midst of Europe; severed in habits, manners, and modes of thinking, from all its continental neighbors. It is a romantic country; but its romance has none of the sentimentality of modern European romance; it is chiefly derived from the brilliant regions of the East, and from the high-minded school of Saracenic chivalry.

The Arab invasion and conquest brought a higher civilization and a nobler style of thinking into Gothic Spain. The Arabs were a quick-witted, sagacious, proud-spirited, and poetical people, and were imbued with Oriental science and literature. Wherever they established a seat of power, it became a rallying place for the learned and ingenious; and they softened and refined the people whom they conquered. By degrees, occupancy seemed to give them a hereditary right to their foothold in the land; they ceased to be looked upon as invaders, and were regarded as rival neighbors.

The peninsula, broken up into a variety of states, both Christian and Moslem, became for centuries a great campaigning
ground, where the art of war seemed to be the principal business of man, and was carried to the highest pitch of romantic chivalry. The original ground of hostility, a difference
of faith, gradually lost its rancor. Neighboring states, of
opposite creeds, were occasionally linked together in alli-
ances, offensive and defensive; so that the cross and crescent
were to be seen side by side fighting against some common
enemy. In times of peace, too, the noble youth of either
faith resorted to the same cities, Christian or Moslem, to
school themselves in military science. Even in the temporary truces of sanguinary wars, the warriors who had recently striven together in the deadly conflicts of the field
laid aside their animosity, met at tournaments, jousts, and
other military festivities, and exchanged the courtesies of
gentle and generous spirits. Thus the opposite races became
frequently mingled together in peaceful intercourse, or if any
rivalry took place, it was in those high courtesies and nobler
acts which bespeak the accomplished cavalier. Warriors of
opposite creeds became ambitious of transcending each other
in magnanimity as well as valor. Indeed, the chivalric
virtues were refined upon to a degree sometimes fastidious
and constrained; but at other times, inexpressibly noble and
affecting. The annals of the times teem with illustrious instances of high-wrought courtesy, romantic generosity, lofty
disinterestedness, and punctilious honor, that warm the very
soul to read them. These have furnished themes for national
plays and poems, or have been celebrated in those all-pervading ballads which are as the life-breath of the people, and
thus have continued to exercise an influence on the national
character which centuries of vicissitude and decline have
not been able to destroy; so that, with all their faults, and
they are many, the Spaniards, even at the present day, are
on many points the most high-minded and proud-spirited
people of Europe. It is true, the romance of feeling derived
from the sources I have mentioned has, like all other ro-

mance, its affectations and extremes. It renders the Spaniard at times pompous and grandiloquent; prone to carry the
"pundonor," or point of honor, beyond the bounds of sober
sense and sound morality; disposed, in the midst of poverty,
to affect the "grande caballero," and to look down with sovereign disdain upon "arts mechanical," and all the gainful
pursuits of plebeian life; but this very inflation of spirit,
while it fills his brain with vapors, lifts him above a thousand meannesses; and though it often keeps him in indigence,
ever protects him from vulgarity.

In the present day, when popular literature is running
into the low levels of life and luxuriating on the vices and
follies of mankind, and when the universal pursuit of gain is
trampling down the early growth of poetic feeling and is
wearing out the verdure of the soul, I question whether
it would not be of service for the reader occasionally to
turn to these records of prouder times and loftier modes of
thinking, and to steep himself to the very lips in old Spanish
romance.

For my own part, I have a shelf or two of venerable, parch-
ment-bound tomes, picked up here and there about the peninsula, and filled with chronicles, plays, and ballads, about
Moors and Christians, which I keep by me as mental tonics,
in the same way that a provident housewife has her cupboard of cordials. Whenever I find my mind brought below
par by the commonplace of every-day life, or jarred by the
sordid collisions of the world, or put out of tune by the shrewd
selfishness of modern utilitarianism, I resort to these venerable tomes, as did the worthy hero of La Mancha to his
books of chivalry, and refresh and tone up my spirit by a
deep draught of their contents. They have some such effect
upon me as Falstaff ascribes to a good Sherris sack, "warm-
ing the blood and filling the brain with fiery and delectable
shapes."

I here subjoin, Mr. Editor, a small specimen of the
cordials I have mentioned, just drawn from my Spanish cupboard, which I recommend to your palate. If

you find it to your taste, you may pass it on to your readers.

Your correspondent and well-wisher,

GEOFFREY CRAYON.

LEGEND OF DON MUNIO SANCHO DE HINOJOSA

BY THE AUTHOR OF THE SKETCH–BOOK

IN the cloisters of the ancient Benedictine convent of San Domingo, at Silos, in Castile, are the mouldering yet magnificent monuments of the once powerful and chivalrous family of Hinojosa. Among these reclines the marble figure of a knight in complete armor, with the hands pressed together, as if in prayer. On one side of his tomb is sculptured in relief a band of Christian cavaliers, capturing a cavalcade of male and female Moors; on the other side, the same cavaliers are represented kneeling before an altar. The tomb, like most of the neighboring monuments, is almost in ruins, and the sculpture is nearly unintelligible, excepting to the keen eye of the antiquary. The story connected with the sepulcher, however, is still preserved in the old Spanish chronicles, and is to the following purport.

IN old times, several hundred years ago, there was a noble Castilian cavalier named Don Munio Sancho de Hinojosa, lord of a border castle, which had stood the brunt of many a Moorish foray. He had seventy horsemen as his household troops, all of the ancient Castilian proof; stark warriors, hard riders, and men of iron; with these he scoured the Moorish lands, and made his name terrible throughout the borders. His castle hall was covered with banners, and scimiters, and Moslem helms, the trophies of his prowess. Don Munio was, moreover, a keen huntsman; and rejoiced in hounds of all kinds, steeds for the chase, and hawks for the towering sport of falconry. When not engaged in warfare, his delight was to beat up the neighboring forests; and scarcely ever did he ride forth without hound and horn, a boar-spear in his hand, or a hawk upon his fist, and an attendant train of huntsmen.

His wife, Donna Maria Palacin, was of a gentle and timid nature, little fitted to be the spouse of so hardy and adventurous a knight; and many a tear did the poor lady shed when he sallied forth upon his daring enterprises, and many a prayer did she offer up for his safety.

As this doughty cavalier was one day hunting, he stationed himself in a thicket, on the borders of a green glade of the forest, and dispersed his followers to rouse the game and drive it toward his stand. He had not been here long, when a cavalcade of Moors, of both sexes, came prankling over the forest lawn. They were unarmed, and magnificently dressed in robes of tissue and embroidery, rich shawls of India, bracelets and anklets of gold, and jewels that sparkled in the sun.

At the head of this gay cavalcade rode a youthful cavalier, superior to the rest in dignity and loftiness of demeanor, and in splendor of attire; beside him was a damsel, whose veil, blown aside by the breeze, displayed a face of surpassing beauty, and eyes cast down in maiden modesty, yet beaming with tenderness and joy.

Don Munio thanked his stars for sending him such a prize, and exulted at the thought of bearing home to his wife the glittering spoils of these infidels. Putting his hunting-horn to his lips, he gave a blast that rung through the forest. His huntsmen came running from all quarters, and the astonished Moors were surrounded and made captives.

The beautiful Moor wrung her hands in despair, and her female attendants uttered the most piercing cries. The young Moorish cavalier alone retained self-possession. He inquired the name of the Christian knight who commanded this troop of horsemen. When told that it was Don Munio Sancho de Hinojosa his countenance lighted up. Approaching that cavalier, and kissing his hand, "Don Munio Sancho," said he, "I have heard of your fame as a true and valiant knight, terrible in arms, but schooled in the noble virtues of chivalry. Such do I trust to find you. In me you behold Abadil, son of a Moorish alcayde. I am on the way to celebrate my nuptials with this lady; chance has thrown us in your power, but I confide in your magnanimity. Take all our treasure and jewels; demand what ransom you think proper for our persons, but suffer us not to be insulted or dishonored."

When the good knight heard this appeal, and beheld the beauty of the youthful pair, his heart was touched with tenderness and courtesy. "God forbid," said he, "that I should disturb such happy nuptials. My prisoners in troth shall ye be, for fifteen days, and immured within my castle, where I claim, as conqueror, the right of celebrating your espousals."

So saying, he dispatched one of his fleetest horsemen in advance, to notify Donna Maria Palacin of the coming of this bridal party; while he and his huntsmen escorted the cavalcade, not as captors, but as a guard of honor. As they drew near to the castle, the banners were hung out, and the trumpets sounded from the battlements; and on their nearer approach, the drawbridge was lowered, and Donna Maria came forth to meet them, attended by her ladies and knights, her pages and her minstrels. She took the young bride, Allifra, in her arms, kissed her with the tenderness of a sister, and conducted her into the castle. In the meantime, Don Munio sent forth missives in every direction, and had viands and dainties of all kinds collected from the country round; and the wedding of the Moorish lovers was celebrated with all possible state and festivity. For fifteen days the castle was given up to joy and revelry. There were tiltings and jousts at the ring, and bull-fights, and banquets, and dances to the sound of minstrelsy. When the fifteen days were at an end, he made the bride and bridegroom magnifi cent presents, and conducted them and their attendants safely beyond the borders. Such, in old times, were the courtesy and generosity of a Spanish cavalier.

Several years after this event, the king of Castile sum

moned his nobles to assist him in a campaign against the Moors. Don Munio Sancho was among the first to answer to the call, with seventy horsemen, all stanch and well-tried warriors. His wife, Donna Maria, hung about his neck. "Alas, my lord!" exclaimed she, "how often wilt thou tempt thy fate, and when will thy thirst for glory be appeased!"

"One battle more," replied Don Munio, "one battle more for the honor of Castile, and I here make a vow, that when this is over I will lay by my sword and repair with my cava-liers in pilgrimage to the sepulcher of Our Lord at Jerusa-lem." The cavaliers all joined with him in the vow, and Donna Maria felt in some degree soothed in spirit: still, she saw with a heavy heart the departure of her husband, and watched his banner with wistful eyes until it disappeared among the trees of the forest.

The king of Castile led his army to the plains of Al-manara, where they encountered the Moorish host, near to Ucles. The battle was long and bloody; the Christians re-peatedly wavered, and were as often rallied by the energy of their commanders. Don Munio was covered with wounds, but refused to leave the field. The Christians at length gave way, and the king was hardly pressed and in danger of being captured.

Don Munio called upon his cavaliers to follow him to the rescue. "Now is the time," cried he, "to prove your loyalty. Fall to, like brave men! We fight for the true faith, and if we lose our lives here we gain a better life hereafter."

Rushing with his men between the king and his pursuers, they checked the latter in their career, and gave time for their monarch to escape; but they fell victims to their loy-alty. They all fought to the last gasp. Don Munio was singled out by a powerful Moorish knight, but having been wounded in the right arm he fought to disadvantage and was slain. The battle being over, the Moor paused to possess himself of the spoils of this redoubtable Christian warrior. When he unlaced the helmet, however, and beheld the coun-tenance of Don Munio, he gave a great cry and smote his

breast. "Woe is me!" cried he; "I have slain my bene-
factor! The flower of knightly virtue! the most magnanimous of cavaliers!"

WHILE the battle had been raging on the plain of Salmanara, Donna Maria Palacin remained in her castle, a prey
to the keenest anxiety. Her eyes were ever fixed on the road
that led from the country of the Moors, and often she asked
the watchman of the tower, "What seest thou?"

One evening, at the shadowy hour of twilight, the warden
sounded his horn. "I see," cried he, "a numerous train
winding up the valley. There are mingled Moors and Christians. The banner of my lord is in the advance. Joyful
tidings!" exclaimed the old seneschal: "my lord returns in
triumph and brings captives!" Then the castle courts rang
with shouts of joy; and the standard was displayed, and the
trumpets were sounded, and the drawbridge was lowered,
and Donna Maria went forth with her ladies and her
knights, and her pages, and her minstrels, to welcome her
lord from the wars. But as the train drew nigh, she beheld
a sumptuous bier, covered with black velvet, and on it lay a
warrior, as if taking his repose; he lay in his armor, with
his helmet on his head, and his sword in his hand, as one
who had never been conquered, and around the bier were
the escutcheons of the house of Hinojosa.

A number of Moorish cavaliers attended the bier with
emblems of mourning, and with dejected countenances; and
their leader cast himself at the feet of Donna Maria, and hid
his face in his hands. She beheld in him the gallant Abadil,
whom she had once welcomed with his bride to her castle,
but who now came with the body of her lord, whom he had
unknowingly slain in battle!

THE sepulcher erected in the cloisters of the Convent
of San Domingo was achieved at the expense of the Moor
Abadil, as a feeble testimony of his grief for the death of the
good knight Don Munio, and his reverence for his memory.

The tender and faithful Donna Maria soon followed her lord
to the tomb. On one of the stones of a small arch, beside his
sepulcher, is the following simple inscription: *"Hic jacet
Maria Palacin, uxor Munonis Sancij De Finojosa"*:
Here lies Maria Palacin, wife of Munio Sancho de Hinojosa.

The legend of Don Munio Sancho does not conclude with
his death. On the same day on which the battle took place
on the plain of Salmanara, a chaplain of the Holy Temple at
Jerusalem, while standing at the outer gate, beheld a train
of Christian cavaliers advancing, as if in pilgrimage. The
chaplain was a native of Spain, and as the pilgrims approached, he knew the foremost to be Don Munio Sancho de
Hinojosa, with whom he had been well acquainted in former
times. Hastening to the patriarch, he told him of the honorable rank of the pilgrims at the gate. The patriarch, therefore, went forth with a grand procession of priests and monks,
and received the pilgrims with all due honor. There were
seventy cavaliers, beside their leader, all stark and lofty
warriors. They carried their helmets in their hands, and
their faces were deadly pale. They greeted no one, nor
looked either to the right or to the left, but entered the
chapel, and kneeling before the sepulcher of Our Saviour
performed their orisons in silence. When they had concluded, they rose as if to depart, and the patriarch and his
attendants advanced to speak to them, but they were no
more to be seen. Every one marveled what could be the
meaning of this prodigy. The patriarch carefully noted
down the day, and sent to Castile to learn tidings of Don
Munio Sancho de Hinojosa. He received for reply that on
the very day specified, that worthy knight, with seventy of
his followers, had been slain in battle. These, therefore,
must have been the blessed spirits of those Christian warriors
come to fulfill their vow of a pilgrimage to the Holy Sepulcher
at Jerusalem. Such was Castilian faith, in the olden time,
which kept its word even beyond the grave.

If any one should doubt of the miraculous apparition of
these phantom knights, let him consult the "History of the

Kings of Castile and Leon," by the learned and pious Fray Prudencio de Sandoval, bishop of Pamplona, where he will find it recorded in the History of the King Don Alonzo VI., on the hundred and second page. It is too precious a legend to be lightly abandoned to the doubter.

COMMUNIPAW

TO THE EDITOR OF THE KNICKERBOCKER

SIR—I observe, with pleasure, that you are performing from time to time a pious duty, imposed upon you, I may say, by the name you have adopted as your titular standard, in following in the footsteps of the venerable Knickerbocker, and gleaning every fact concerning the early times of the Manhattoes which may have escaped his hand. I trust, therefore, a few particulars, legendary and statistical, concerning a place which figures conspicuously in the early pages of his history, will not be unacceptable. I allude, sir, to the ancient and renowned village of Communipaw, which, according to the veracious Diedrich, and to equally veracious tradition, was the first spot where our ever-to-be-lamented Dutch progenitors planted their standard and cast the seeds of empire, and from whence subsequently sailed the memorable expedition under Oloffe the Dreamer, which landed on the opposite island of Manna-hata, and founded the present city of New York, the city of dreams and speculations.

Communipaw, therefore, may truly be called the parent of New York; yet it is an astonishing fact that, though immediately opposite to the great city it has produced, from whence its red roofs and tin weather-cocks can actually be descried peering above the surrounding apple orchards, it should be almost as rarely visited and as little known by the inhabitants of the metropolis as if it had been locked up among the Rocky Mountains. Sir, I think there is something

unnatural in this, especially in these times of ramble and research, when our citizens are antiquity-hunting in every part
of the world. Curiosity, like charity, should begin at home;
and I would enjoin it on our worthy burghers, especially
those of the real Knickerbocker breed, before they send their
sons abroad to wonder and grow wise among the remains
of Greece and Rome, to let them make a tour of ancient
Pavonia, from Weehawk even to the Kills, and meditate,
with filial reverence, on the moss-grown mansions of Communipaw.

Sir, I regard this much-neglected village as one of the
most remarkable places in the country. The intelligent
traveler, as he looks down upon it from the Bergen Heights,
modestly nestled among its cabbage-gardens, while the great
flaunting city it has begotten is stretching far and wide on
the opposite side of the bay, the intelligent traveler, I say,
will be filled with astonishment; not, sir, at the village of
Communipaw, which in truth is a very small village, but at
the almost incredible fact that so small a village should have
produced so great a city. It looks to him, indeed, like some
squat little dame, with a tall grenadier of a son strutting by
her side; or some simple-hearted hen that has unwittingly
hatched out a long-legged turkey.

But this is not all for which Communipaw is remarkable.
Sir, it is interesting on another account. It is to the ancient
province of the New Netherlands and the classic era of the
Dutch dynasty what Herculaneum and Pompeii are to
ancient Rome and the glorious days of the empire. Here
everything remains in statu quo, as it was in the days of
Oloffe the Dreamer, Walter the Doubter, and the other
worthies of the golden age; the same broad-brimmed hats
and broad-bottomed breeches; the same knee-buckles and
shoe-buckles; the same close-quilled caps and linsey-woolsey
short gowns and petticoats; the same implements and utensils
and forms and fashions; in a word, Communipaw at the
present day is a picture of what New Amsterdam was before
the conquest. The "intelligent traveler" aforesaid, as he

treads its streets, is struck with the primitive character of everything around him. Instead of Grecian temples for dwelling-houses, with a great column of pine boards in the way of every window, he beholds high peaked roofs, gable ends to the street, with weather-cocks at top, and windows of all sorts and sizes; large ones for the grown-up members of the family, and little ones for the little folk. Instead of cold marble porches, with close-locked doors and brass knockers, he sees the doors hospitably open; the worthy burgher smoking his pipe on the old-fashioned stoop in front, with his "vrouw" knitting beside him; and the cat and her kittens at their feet sleeping in the sunshine.

Astonished at the obsolete and "old world" air of everything around him, the intelligent traveler demands how all this has come to pass. Herculaneum and Pompeii remain, it is true, unaffected by the varying fashions of centuries; but they were buried by a volcano and preserved in ashes. What charmed spell has kept this wonderful little place unchanged, though in sight of the most changeful city in the universe? Has it, too, been buried under its cabbage-gardens and only dug out in modern days for the wonder and edification of the world? The reply involves a point of history worthy of notice and record, and reflecting immortal honor on Communipaw.

At the time when New Amsterdam was invaded and conquered by British foes, as has been related in the history of the venerable Diedrich, a great dispersion took place among the Dutch inhabitants. Many, like the illustrious Peter Stuyvesant, buried themselves in rural retreats in the Bowerie; others, like Wolfert Acker, took refuge in various remote parts of the Hudson; but there was one stanch, unconquerable band that determined to keep together and preserve themselves, like seed corn, for the future fructification and perpetuity of the Knickerbocker race. These were headed by one Garret Van Horne, a gigantic Dutchman, the Pelayo of the New Netherlands. Under his guidance, they retreated across the bay and buried themselves among the marshes of ancient Pavonia, as did the followers of Pelayo among the mountains of Asturias, when Spain was overrun by its Arabian invaders.

The gallant Van Horne set up his standard at Communipaw, and invited all those to rally under it who were true Nederlanders at heart, and determined to resist all foreign intermixture or encroachment. A strict non-intercourse was observed with the captured city; not a boat ever crossed to it from Communipaw, and the English language was rigorously tabooed throughout the village and its dependencies. Every man was sworn to wear his hat, cut his coat, build his house, and harness his horses, exactly as his father had done before him; and to permit nothing but the Dutch language to be spoken in his household.

As a citadel of the place and a stronghold for the preservation and defense of everything Dutch, the gallant Van Horne erected a lordly mansion, with a chimney perched at every corner, which thence derived the aristocratical name of "The House of the Four Chimneys." Hither he transferred many of the precious relics of New Amsterdam; the great round-crowned hat that once covered the capacious head of Walter the Doubter, and the identical shoe with which Peter the Headstrong kicked his pusillanimous councilors downstairs. St. Nicholas, it is said, took this loyal house under his especial protection; and a Dutch soothsayer predicted, that as long as it should stand Communipaw would be safe from the intrusion either of Briton or Yankee.

In this house would the gallant Van Horne and his compeers hold frequent councils of war as to the possibility of re-conquering the province from the British; and here would they sit for hours, nay, days, together smoking their pipes and keeping watch upon the growing city of New York; groaning in spirit whenever they saw a new house erected or ship launched, and persuading themselves that Admiral Van Tromp would one day or other arrive to sweep out the invaders with the broom which he carried at his masthead.

Years rolled by, but Van Tromp never arrived. The

British strengthened themselves in the land, and the captured city flourished under their domination. Still the worthies of Communipaw would not despair; something or other, they were sure, would turn up to restore the power of the Hogen Mogens, the Lords States-General; so they kept smoking and smoking, and watching and watching, and turning the same few thoughts over and over in a perpetual circle, which is commonly called deliberating. In the meantime, being hemmed up within a narrow compass, between the broad bay and the Bergen Hills, they grew poorer and poorer, until they had scarce the wherewithal to maintain their pipes in fuel during their endless deliberations.

And now must I relate a circumstance which will call for a little exertion of faith on the part of the reader; but I can only say that if he doubts it he had better not utter his doubts in Communipaw, as it is among the religious beliefs of the place. It is, in fact, nothing more nor less than a miracle, worked by the blessed St. Nicholas for the relief and sustenance of this loyal community.

It so happened, in this time of extremity, that in the course of cleaning the House of the Four Chimneys, by an ignorant housewife who knew nothing of the historic value of the relics it contained, the old hat of Walter the Doubter and the executive shoe of Peter the Headstrong were thrown out of doors as rubbish. But mark the consequence. The good St. Nicholas kept watch over these precious relics, and wrought out of them a wonderful providence.

The hat of Walter the Doubter falling on a stercoraceous heap of compost, in the rear of the house, began forthwith to vegetate. Its broad brim spread forth grandly and exfoliated, and its round crown swelled and crimped and consolidated until the whole became a prodigious cabbage, rivaling in magnitude the capacious head of the Doubter. In a word, it was the origin of that renowned species of cabbage known, by all Dutch epicures, by the name of the Governor's Head, and which is to this day the glory of Communipaw.

On the other hand, the shoe of Peter Stuyvesant, being thrown into the river in front of the house, gradually hardened and concreted, and became covered with barnacles, and at length turned into a gigantic oyster; being the progenitor of that illustrious species known throughout the gastronomical world by the name of the Governor's Foot.

These miracles were the salvation of Communipaw. The sages of the place immediately saw in them the hand of St. Nicholas and understood their mystic signification. They set to work with all diligence to cultivate and multiply these great blessings; and so abundantly did the gubernatorial hat and shoe fructify and increase, that in a little time great patches of cabbages were to be seen extending from the village of Communipaw quite to the Bergen Hills; while the whole bottom of the bay in front became a vast bed of oysters. Ever since that time this excellent community has been divided into two great classes: those who cultivate the land and those who cultivate the water. The former have devoted themselves to the nurture and edification of cabbages, rearing them in all their varieties, while the latter have formed parks and plantations, under water, to which juvenile oysters are transplanted from foreign parts to finish their education.

As these great sources of profit multiplied upon their hands, the worthy inhabitants of Communipaw began to long for a market at which to dispose of their superabundance. This gradually produced once more an intercourse with New York; but it was always carried on by the old people and the negroes; never would they permit the young folks of either sex to visit the city, lest they should get tainted with foreign manners and bring home foreign fashions. Even to this day, if you see an old burgher in the market, with hat and garb of antique Dutch fashion, you may be sure he is one of the old unconquered race of the "bitter blood," who maintain their stronghold at Communipaw.

In modern days, the hereditary bitterness against the

English has lost much of its asperity, or rather has become merged in a new source of jealousy and apprehension; I allude to the incessant and widespreading irruptions from New England. Word has been continually brought back to Communipaw, by those of the community who return from their trading voyages in cabbages and oysters, of the alarming power which the Yankees are gaining in the ancient city of New Amsterdam; elbowing the genuine Knickerbockers out of all civic posts of honor and profit; bargaining them out of their hereditary homesteads; pulling down the venerable houses, with crow-step gables, which have stood since the time of the Dutch rule, and erecting, instead, granite stores and marble banks; in a word, evincing a deadly determination to obliterate every vestige of the good old Dutch times.

In consequence of the jealousy thus awakened, the worthy traders from Communipaw confine their dealings, as much as possible, to the genuine Dutch families. If they furnish the Yankees at all, it is with inferior articles. Never can the latter procure a real "Governor's Head," or "Governor's Foot," though they have offered extravagant prices for the same, to grace their table on the annual festival of the New England Society.

But what has carried this hostility to the Yankees to the highest pitch, was an attempt made by that all-pervading race to get possession of Communipaw itself. Yes, sir; during the late mania for land speculation a daring company of Yankee projectors landed before the village; stopped the honest burghers on the public highway and endeavored to bargain them out of their hereditary acres; displayed lithographic maps, in which their cabbage-gardens were laid out into town lots; their oyster parks into docks and quays; and even the House of the Four Chimneys metamorphosed into a bank, which was to enrich the whole neighborhood with paper money.

Fortunately the gallant Van Hornes came to the rescue, just as some of the worthy burghers were on the point of capitulating. The Yankees were put to the rout, with signal confusion, and have never since dared to show their faces in the place. The good people continue to cultivate their cabbages and rear their oysters; they know nothing of banks, nor joint-stock companies, but treasure up their money in stocking-feet, at the bottom of the family chest, or bury it in iron pots, as did their fathers and grandfathers before them.

As to the House of the Four Chimneys, it still remains in the great and tall family of the Van Hornes. Here are to be seen ancient Dutch corner cupboards, chests of drawers, and massive clothes-presses, quaintly carved, and carefully waxed and polished; together with divers thick, black-letter volumes, with brass clasps, printed of yore in Leyden and Amsterdam, and handed down from generation to generation in the family, but never read. They are preserved in the archives, among sundry old parchment deeds, in Dutch and English, bearing the seals of the early governors of the province.

In this house the primitive Dutch holidays of Paas and Pinxter are faithfully kept up; and New Year celebrated with cookies and cherry-bounce; nor is the festival of the blessed St. Nicholas forgotten, when all the children are sure to hang up their stockings, and to have them filled according to their deserts; though, it is said, the good saint is occasionally perplexed in his nocturnal visits which chimney to descend.

Of late, this portentous mansion has begun to give signs of dilapidation and decay. Some have attributed this to the visits made by the young people to the city, and their bringing thence various modern fashions; and to their neglect of the Dutch language, which is gradually becoming confined to the older persons in the community. The house, too, was greatly shaken by high winds, during the prevalence of the speculation mania, especially at the time of the landing of the Yankees. Seeing how mysteriously the fate of Communipaw is identified with this venerable mansion, we cannot wonder that the older and wiser heads of the community should be filled with dismay, whenever a brick is toppled down from one of the chimneys, or a weather-cock is blown off from a gable end.

The present lord of this historic pile, I am happy to say, is calculated to maintain it in all its integrity. He is of patriarchal age, and is worthy of the days of the patriarchs. He has done his utmost to increase and multiply the true race in the land. His wife has not been inferior to him in zeal, and they are surrounded by a goodly progeny of children, and grandchildren, and great-grandchildren, who promise to perpetuate the name of Van Horne until time shall be no more. So be it! Long may the horn of the Van Hornes continue to be exalted in the land! Tall as they are, may their shadows never be less! May the House of the Four Chimneys remain for ages the citadel of Communipaw, and the smoke of its chimneys continue to ascend a sweet-smelling incense in the nose of St. Nicholas!

With great respect, Mr. Editor,

Your ob't servant,

HERMANUS VANDERDONK.

CONSPIRACY OF THE COCKED HATS

TO THE EDITOR OF THE KNICKERBOCKER

SIR—I have read with great satisfaction the valuable paper of your correspondent, Mr. Hermanus Vanderdonk (who, I take it, is a descendant of the learned Adrian Vanderdonk, one of the early historians of the Nieuw Nederlandts), giving sundry particulars, legendary and statistical, touching the venerable village of Communipaw and its fate-bound citadel, the House of the Four Chimneys. It goes to prove what I have repeatedly maintained, that we live in the midst of history and mystery and romance; and that there is no spot in the world more rich in themes for the writer of historic novels, heroic melodramas, and rough-shod epics, than this same business-looking city of the Manhattoes and its environs. He who would find these elements, however, must not seek them among the modern improvements and modern people of this moneyed metropolis, but must dig for them, as for Kidd the pirate's treasures, in out-of-the-way places and among the ruins of the past.

Poetry and romance received a fatal blow at the over-throw of the ancient Dutch dynasty, and have ever since been gradually withering under the growing domination of the Yankees. They abandoned our hearths when the old Dutch tiles were superseded by marble chimney-pieces; when brass and irons made way for polished grates, and the crackling and blazing fire of nut-wood gave place to the smoke and stench of Liverpool coal; and on the downfall of the last gable-end house their requiem was tolled from the tower of the Dutch church in Nassau Street by the old bell that came from Holland. But poetry and romance still live unseen among us, or seen only by the enlightened few, who are able to contemplate this city and its environs through the medium of tradition and clothed with the associations of foregone ages.

Would you seek these elements in the country, Mr. Editor, avoid all turnpikes, railroads, and steamboats, those abominable inventions by which the usurping Yankees are strengthening themselves in the land, and subduing everything to utility and commonplace. Avoid all towns and cities of white clap-board palaces and Grecian temples, studded with "Academies," "Seminaries," and "Institutes," which glisten along our bays and rivers—these are the strongholds of Yankee usurpation; but if haply you light upon some rough, rambling road, winding between stone fences, gray with moss, and overgrown with elder, poke-berry, mullein, and sweet-brier, with here and there a low, red-roofed, whitewashed farmhouse, cowering among apple and cherry trees; an old stone church, with elms, willows, and button-woods, as old-looking as itself, and tombstones almost buried in their

own graves; and, peradventure, a small log schoolhouse at
a cross-road, where the English is still taught with a thick-
ness of the tongue, instead of a twang of the nose; should
you, I say, light upon such a neighborhood, Mr. Editor, you
may thank your stars that you have found one of the lingering haunts of poetry and romance.

Your correspondent, sir, has touched upon that sublime
and affecting feature in the history of Communipaw, the retreat of the patriotic band of Nederlanders, led by Van Horne,
whom he justly terms the Pelayo of the New Netherlands.
He has given you a picture of the manner in which they en-
sconced themselves in the House of the Four Chimneys, and
awaited with heroic patience and perseverance the day that
should see the flag of the Hogen Mogens once more floating
on the fort of New Amsterdam.

Your correspondent, sir, has but given you a glimpse over
the threshold; I will now let you into the heart of the mystery of this most mysterious and eventful village.   Yes, sir,
I will now

>   "——Unclasp a secret book;
>   And to your quick conceiving discontents
>   I'll read you matter deep and dangerous,
>   As full of peril and adventurous spirit
>   As to o'erwalk a current, roaring loud,
>   On the unsteadfast footing of a spear."

Sir, it is one of the most beautiful and interesting facts connected with the history of Communipaw that the early feeling of resistance to foreign rule, alluded to by your correspondent, is still kept up.   Yes, sir, a settled, secret, and
determined conspiracy has been going on for generations
among this indomitable people, the descendants of the refugees from New Amsterdam; the object of which is to redeem
their ancient seat of empire and to drive the losel Yankees out
of the land.

Communipaw, it is true, has the glory of originating this
conspiracy; and it was hatched and reared in the House of
the Four Chimneys; but it has spread far and wide over an-

cient Pavonia, surmounted the heights of Bergen, Hoboken,
and Weehawk, crept up along the banks of the Passaic and
the Hackensack, until it pervades the whole chivalry of the
country from Tappan Slote in the north to Piscataway in the
south, including the pugnacious village of Rahway, more
heroically denominated Spank-town.

Throughout all these regions a great "in-and-in-confed-
eracy" prevails, that is to say, a confederacy among the
Dutch families, by dint of diligent and exclusive intermarriage, to keep the race pure and to multiply. If ever, Mr.
Editor, in the course of your travels between Spank-town
and Tappan Slote, you should see a cozy, low-eaved farmhouse, teeming with sturdy, broad-built little urchins, you
may set it down as one of the breeding places of this grand
secret confederacy, stocked with the embryo deliverers of
New Amsterdam.

Another step in the progress of this patriotic conspiracy
is the establishment, in various places within the ancient
boundaries of the Nieuw Nederlandts, of secret, or rather
mysterious associations, composed of the genuine sons of the
Nederlanders, with the ostensible object of keeping up the
memory of old times and customs, but with the real object
of promoting the views of this dark and mighty plot, and
extending its ramifications throughout the land.

Sir, I am descended from a long line of genuine Nederlanders, who, though they remained in the city of New Amsterdam after the conquest, and throughout the usurpation,
have never in their hearts been able to tolerate the yoke imposed upon them. My worthy father, who was one of the
last of the cocked hats, had a little knot of cronies of his own
stamp, who used to meet in our wainscoted parlor, round a
nut-wood fire, talk over old times, when the city was ruled
by its native burgomasters, and groan over the monopoly of
all places of power and profit by the Yankees. I well recollect the effect upon this worthy little conclave, when the
Yankees first instituted their New England Society, held
their "national festival," toasted their "fatherland," and

sang their foreign songs of triumph within the very pre-
cincts of our ancient metropolis. Sir, from that day my
father held the smell of codfish and potatoes, and the sight
of pumpkin pie, in utter abomination; and whenever the annual dinner of the New England Society came round it was
a sore anniversary for his children. He got up in an ill
humor, grumbled and growled throughout the day, and not
one of us went to bed that night without having had his
jacket well trounced to the tune of "The Pilgrim Fathers."

You may judge, then, Mr. Editor, of the exaltation of all
true patriots of this stamp, when the Society of Saint Nicholas was set up among us, and intrepidly established, cheek
by jole, alongside of the society of the invaders. Never shall
I forget the effect upon my father and his little knot of brother
groaners, when tidings were brought them that the ancient
banner of the Manhattoes was actually floating from the
window of the City Hotel. Sir, they nearly jumped out of
their silver-buckled shoes for joy. They took down their
cocked hats from the pegs on which they had hanged them,
as the Israelites of yore hung their harps upon the willows,
in token of bondage, clapped them resolutely once more upon
their heads, and cocked them in the face of every Yankee
they met on the way to the banqueting-room.

The institution of this society was hailed with transport
throughout the whole extent of the New Netherlands; being
considered a secret foothold gained in New Amsterdam, and
a flattering presage of future triumph. Whenever that society holds its annual feast, a sympathetic hilarity prevails
throughout the land; ancient Pavonia sends over its con-
tributions of cabbages and oysters; the House of the Four
Chimneys is splendidly illuminated, and the traditional song
of Saint Nicholas, the mystic bond of union and conspiracy,
is chanted with closed doors in every genuine Dutch family.

I have thus, I trust, Mr. Editor, opened your eyes to
some of the grand moral, poetical and political phenomena
with which you are surrounded. You will now be able to
read the "signs of the times." You will now understand

what is meant by those "Knickerbocker Halls," and "Knickerbocker Hotels," and "Knickerbocker Lunches," that are
daily springing up in our city; and what all these "Knickerbocker Omnibuses" are driving at.   You will see in them so
many clouds before a storm; so many mysterious but sublime
intimations of the gathering vengeance of a great though oppressed people.   Above all you will now contemplate our bay
and its portentous borders with proper feelings of awe and
admiration.   Talk of the Bay of Naples and its volcanic
mountains!   Why, sir, little Communipaw, sleeping among
its cabbage gardens, "quiet as gunpowder," yet with this
tremendous conspiracy brewing in its bosom, is an object ten
times as sublime (in a moral point of view, mark me) as
Vesuvius in repose, though charged with lava and brimstone, and ready for an eruption.

Let me advert to a circumstance connected with this
theme, which cannot but be appreciated by every heart of
sensibility.   You must have remarked, Mr. Editor, on summer evenings, and on Sunday afternoons, certain grave,
primitive-looking personages walking the Battery, in close
confabulation, with their canes behind their backs, and ever
and anon turning a wistful gaze toward the Jersey shore.
These, sir, are the sons of Saint Nicholas, the genuine Nederlanders; who regard Communipaw with pious reverence, not
merely as the progenitor, but the destined regenerator, of this
great metropolis.   Yes, sir; they are looking with longing
eyes to the green marshes of ancient Pavonia, as did the
poor conquered Spaniards of yore toward the stern mountains of Asturias, wondering whether the day of deliverance
is at hand.   Many is the time, when, in my boyhood,
I have walked with my father and his confidential compeers on the Battery, and listened to their calculations and
conjectures, and observed the points of their sharp cocked
hats evermore turned toward Pavonia.   Nay, sir, I am
convinced that at this moment, if I were to take down the
cocked hat of my lamented father from the peg on which
it has hung for years, and were to carry it to the Battery,

its center point, true as the needle to the pole, would turn to Communipaw.

Mr. Editor, the great historic drama of New Amsterdam is but half acted. The reigns of Walter the Doubter, William the Testy, and Peter the Headstrong, with the rise, progress, and decline of the Dutch dynasty, are but so many parts of the main action, the triumphant catastrophe of which is yet to come. Yes, sir! the deliverance of the New Netherlands from Yankee domination will eclipse the far-famed redemption of Spain from the Moors, and the oft-sung conquest of Granada will fade before the chivalrous triumph of New Amsterdam. Would that Peter Stuyvesant could rise from his grave to witness that day!

Your humble servant,
Roloff Van Ripper.

P.S.—Just as I had concluded the foregoing epistle, I received a piece of intelligence which makes me tremble for the fate of Communipaw. I fear, Mr. Editor, the grand conspiracy is in danger of being countermined and counteracted by those all-pervading and indefatigable Yankees. Would you think it, sir! one of them has actually effected an entry in the place by covered way; or, in other words, under cover of the petticoats. Finding every other mode ineffectual, he secretly laid siege to a Dutch heiress, who owns a great cabbage-garden in her own right. Being a smooth-tongued varlet, he easily prevailed on her to elope with him, and they were privately married at Spank-town! The first notice the good people of Communipaw had of this awful event was a lithographed map of the cabbage-garden laid out in town lots and advertised for sale! On the night of the wedding, the main weathercock of the House of the Four Chimneys was carried away in a whirlwind! The greatest consternation reigns throughout the village!

A LEGEND OF COMMUNIPAW

TO THE EDITOR OF THE KNICKERBOCKER MAGAZINE

SIR—I observed in your last month's periodical a communication from a Mr. Vanderdonk, giving some information concerning Communipaw. I herewith send you, Mr. Editor, a legend connected with that place; and am much surprised it should have escaped the researches of your very authentic correspondent, as it relates to an edifice scarcely less fated than the House of the Four Chimneys. I give you the legend in its crude and simple state, as I heard it related; it is capable, however, of being dilated, inflated, and dressed up into very imposing shape and dimensions. Should any of your ingenious contributors in this line feel inclined to take it in hand, they will find ample materials, collateral and illustrative, among the papers of the late Reinier Skaats, many years since crier of the court, and keeper of the City Hall, in the city of the Manhattoes; or in the library of that important and utterly renowned functionary, Mr. Jacob Hays, long time high constable, who, in the course of his extensive researches, has amassed an amount of valuable facts, to be rivaled only by that great historical collection, "The Newgate Calendar."

Your humble servant,

BARENT VAN SCHAICK.

GUESTS FROM GIBBET ISLAND

A LEGEND OF COMMUNIPAW

WHOEVER has visited the ancient and renowned village of Communipaw may have noticed an old stone building of most ruinous and sinister appearance. The doors and win-

dow-shutters are ready to drop from their hinges; old clothes
are stuffed in the broken panes of glass, while legions of
half-starved dogs prowl about the premises and rush out
and bark at every passer-by; for your beggarly house in a
village is most apt to swarm with profligate and ill-condi-
tioned dogs. What adds to the sinister appearance of this
mansion is a tall frame in front, not a little resembling a
gallows, and which looks as if waiting to accommodate some
of the inhabitants with a well-merited airing. It is not a
gallows, however, but an ancient sign-post; for this dwelling, in the golden days of Communipaw, was one of the most
orderly and peaceful of village taverns, where all the public
affairs of Communipaw were talked and smoked over. In
fact, it was in this very building that Oloffe the Dreamer
and his companions concerted that great voyage of discovery
and colonization, in which they explored Buttermilk Channel, were nearly shipwrecked in the strait of Hell-gate, and
finally landed on the island of Manhattan, and founded the
great city of New Amsterdam.

Even after the province had been cruelly wrested from
the sway of their High Mightinesses, by the combined forces
of the British and the Yankees, this tavern continued its ancient loyalty. It is true, the head of the Prince of Orange
disappeared from the sign; a strange bird being painted over
it, with the explanatory legend of "Die Wilde Gans," or
The Wild Goose; but this all the world knew to be a sly rid-
dle of the landlord, the worthy Teunis Van Gieson, a knowing man in a small way, who laid his finger beside his nose
and winked, when any one studied the signification of his
sign, and observed that his goose was hatching, but would
join the flock whenever they flew over the water; an enigma
which was the perpetual recreation and delight of the loyal
but fat-headed burghers of Communipaw.

Under the sway of this patriotic, though discreet and
quiet publican, the tavern continued to flourish in primeval
tranquillity, and was the resort of all true-hearted Nederlanders from all parts of Pavonia; who met here quietly and

secretly, to smoke and drink the downfall of Briton and Yankee, and success to Admiral Van Tromp.

The only drawback on the comfort of the establishment was a nephew of mine host, a sister's son, Yan Yost Vanderscamp by name, and a real scamp by nature. This unlucky whipster showed an early propensity to mischief, which he gratified in a small way by playing tricks upon the frequenters of the Wild Goose; putting gunpowder in their pipes, or squibs in their pockets, and astonishing them with an explosion, while they sat nodding round the fireplace in the bar-room; and if perchance a worthy burgher from some distant part of Pavonia had lingered until dark over his potation, it was odds but that young Vanderscamp would slip a brier under his horse's tail, as he mounted, and send him clattering along the road, in neck-or-nothing style, to his infinite astonishment and discomfiture.

It may be wondered at, that mine host of the Wild Goose did not turn such a graceless varlet out of doors; but Teunis Van Gieson was an easy-tempered man, and, having no child of his own, looked upon his nephew with almost parental indulgence. His patience and good-nature were doomed to be tried by another inmate of his mansion. This was a cross-grained curmudgeon of a negro named Pluto, who was a kind of enigma in Communipaw. Where he came from nobody knew. He was found one morning, after a storm, cast like a sea-monster on the strand, in front of the Wild Goose, and lay there more dead than alive. The neighbors gathered round, and speculated on this production of the deep; whether it were fish or flesh, or a compound of both, commonly yclept a merman. The kind-hearted Teunis Van Gieson, seeing that he wore the human form, took him into his house, and warmed him into life. By degrees he showed signs of intelligence, and even uttered sounds very much like language, but which no one in Communipaw could understand. Some thought him a negro just from Guinea, who had either fallen overboard or escaped from a slave-ship. Nothing, however, could ever draw from him any account of his origin. When questioned on the subject, he merely pointed to Gibbet Island, a small rocky islet which lies in the open bay, just opposite to Communipaw, as if that were his native place, though everybody knew it had never been inhabited.

In the process of time he acquired something of the Dutch language, that is to say, he learned all its vocabulary of oaths and maledictions, with just words sufficient to string them together. "Donder en blicksem!" (thunder and lightning) was the gentlest of his ejaculations. For years he kept about the Wild Goose, more like one of those familiar spirits or household goblins that we read of than like a human being. He acknowledged allegiance to no one, but performed various domestic offices when it suited his humor; waiting occasionally on the guests; grooming the horses, cutting wood, drawing water; and all this without being ordered. Lay any command on him and the stubborn sea-urchin was sure to rebel. He was never so much at home, however, as when on the water, plying about in skiff or canoe, entirely alone, fishing, crabbing, or grabbing for oysters, and would bring home quantities for the larder of the Wild Goose, which he would throw down at the kitchen door with a growl. No wind nor weather deterred him from launching forth on his favorite element: indeed, the wilder the weather the more he seemed to enjoy it. If a storm was brewing he was sure to put off from shore, and would be seen far out in the bay, his light skiff dancing like a feather on the waves, when sea and sky were all in a turmoil, and the stoutest ships were fain to lower their sails. Sometimes, on such occasions, he would be absent for days together. How he weathered the tempest, and how and where he subsisted, no one could divine, nor did any one venture to ask, for all had an almost superstitious awe of him. Some of the Communipaw oystermen declared that they had more than once seen him suddenly disappear, canoe and all, as if they plunged beneath the waves, and after a while come up again, in quite a different part of the bay; whence they concluded that he could live under water like that notable species of wild duck, commonly

called the Hell-diver. All began to consider him in the light
of a foul-weather bird, like the Mother Carey's Chicken or
Stormy Petrel; and whenever they saw him putting far out
in his skiff, in cloudy weather, made up their minds for a
storm.

The only being for whom he seemed to have any liking
was Yan Yost Vanderscamp, and him he liked for his very
wickedness. He in a manner took the boy under his tute-
lage, prompted him to all kinds of mischief, aided him in
every wild, harum-scarum freak, until the lad became the
complete scapegrace of the village; a pest to his uncle and
to every one else. Nor were his pranks confined to the land;
he soon learned to accompany old Pluto on the water. Together these worthies would cruise about the broad bay and
all the neighboring straits and rivers; poking around in skiffs
and canoes; robbing the set-nets of the fishermen; landing
on remote coasts, and laying waste orchards and watermelon
patches; in short, carrying on a complete system of piracy
on a small scale. Piloted by Pluto, the youthful Vanderscamp soon became acquainted with all the bays, rivers,
creeks, and inlets of the watery world around him; could
navigate from the Hook to Spiting Devil on the darkest
night, and learned to set even the terrors of Hell-gate at
defiance.

At length, negro and boy suddenly disappeared, and days
and weeks elapsed, but without tidings of them. Some said
they must have run away and gone to sea; others jocosely
hinted that old Pluto, being no other than his namesake in
disguise, had spirited away the boy to the nether regions.
All, however, agreed in one thing, that the village was well
rid of them.

In the process of time, the good Teunis Van Gieson slept
with his fathers, and the tavern remained shut up, waiting
for a claimant, for the next heir was Yan Yost Vanderscamp, and he had not been heard of for years. At length,
one day, a boat was seen pulling for the shore from a long,
black, rakish-looking schooner that lay at anchor in the bay.

The boat's crew seemed worthy of the craft from which they debarked. Never had such a set of noisy, roistering, swaggering varlets landed in peaceful Communipaw. They were outlandish in garb and demeanor, and were headed by a rough, burly, bully ruffian, with fiery whiskers, a copper nose, a scar across his face, and a great Flanderish beaver slouched on one side of his head, in whom, to their dismay, the quiet inhabitants were made to recognize their early pest, Yan Yost Vanderscamp. The rear of this hopeful gang was brought up by old Pluto, who had lost an eye, grown grizzly-headed, and looked more like a devil than ever. Vander-scamp renewed his acquaintance with the old burghers, much against their will, and in a manner not at all to their taste. He slapped them familiarly on the back, gave them an iron grip of the hand, and was hail fellow well met. According to his own account he had been all the world over; had made money by bagfuls; had ships in every sea, and now meant to turn the Wild Goose into a country seat, where he and his comrades, all rich merchants from foreign parts, might enjoy themselves in the interval of their voyages.

Sure enough, in a little while there was a complete meta-morphosis of the Wild Goose. From being a quiet, peace-ful Dutch public-house it became a most riotous, uproarious private dwelling; a complete rendezvous for boisterous men of the seas, who came here to have what they called a "blow out" on dry land, and might be seen at all hours, lounging about the door, or lolling out of the windows; swearing among themselves, and cracking rough jokes on every passer-by. The house was fitted up, too, in so strange a manner: hammocks slung to the walls, instead of bedsteads; odd kinds of furniture of foreign fashion; bamboo couches, Spanish chairs; pistols, cutlasses, and blunderbusses, sus-pended on every peg; silver crucifixes on the mantel-pieces, silver candlesticks and porringers on the tables, contrasting oddly with the pewter and Delf ware of the original estab-lishment. And then the strange amusements of these sea-monsters! Pitching Spanish dollars, instead of quoits; firing blunderbusses out of the window; shooting at a mark, or at any unhappy dog, or cat, or pig, or barn-door fowl, that might happen to come within reach.

The only being who seemed to relish their rough waggery was old Pluto; and yet he led but a dog's life of it; for they practiced all kinds of manual jokes upon him; kicked him about like a football; shook him by his grizzly mop of wool, and never spoke to him without coupling a curse by way of adjective to his name, and consigning him to the infernal regions. The old fellow, however, seemed to like them the better the more they cursed him, though his utmost expression of pleasure never amounted to more than the growl of a petted bear when his ears are rubbed.

Old Pluto was the ministering spirit at the orgies of the Wild Goose; and such orgies as took place there! Such drinking, singing, whooping, swearing; with an occasional interlude of quarreling and fighting. The noisier grew the revel the more old Pluto plied the potations, until the guests would become frantic in their merriment, smashing everything to pieces and throwing the house out of the windows. Sometimes, after a drinking bout, they sallied forth and scoured the village, to the dismay of the worthy burghers, who gathered their women within doors, and would have shut up the house. Vanderscamp, however, was not to be rebuffed. He insisted on renewing acquaintance with his old neighbors, and on introducing his friends, the merchants, to their families; swore he was on the lookout for a wife, and meant, before he stopped, to find husbands for all their daughters. So, will-ye, nil-ye, sociable he was; swaggered about their best parlors, with his hat on one side of his head; sat on the good wife's nicely-waxed mahogany table, kicking his heels against the carved and polished legs; kissed and tousled the young vrouws; and, if they frowned and pouted, gave them a gold rosary, or a sparkling cross, to put them in good humor again.

Sometimes nothing would satisfy him but he must have some of his old neighbors to dinner at the Wild Goose. There was no refusing him, for he had got the complete upper-hand of the community, and the peaceful burghers all stood in awe of him. But what a time would the quiet, worthy men have, among these rake-hells, who would delight to astound them with the most extravagant gunpowder tales, embroidered with all kinds of foreign oaths; clink the can with them; pledge them in deep potations; bawl drinking songs in their ears; and occasionally fire pistols over their heads, or under the table, and then laugh in their faces and ask them how they liked the smell of gunpowder.

Thus was the little village of Communipaw for a time like the unfortunate wight possessed with devils; until Vanderscamp and his brother merchants would sail on another trading voyage, when the Wild Goose would be shut up, and everything relapse into quiet, only to be disturbed by his next visitation.

The mystery of all these proceedings gradually dawned upon the tardy intellects of Communipaw. These were the times of the notorious Captain Kidd, when the American harbors were the resorts of piratical adventurers of all kinds, who, under pretext of mercantile voyages, scoured the West Indies, made plundering descents upon the Spanish Main, visited even the remote Indian Seas, and then came to dispose of their booty, have their revels, and fit out new expeditions, in the English colonies.

Vanderscamp had served in this hopeful school, and having risen to importance among the buccaneers, had pitched upon his native village and early home, as a quiet, out-of-the-way, unsuspected place, where he and his comrades, while anchored at New York, might have their feasts, and concert their plans, without molestation.

At length the attention of the British government was called to these piratical enterprises that were becoming so frequent and outrageous. Vigorous measures were taken to check and punish them. Several of the most noted freebooters were caught and executed, and three of Vanderscamp's chosen comrades, the most riotous swash-bucklers of the

Wild Goose, were hanged in chains on Gibbet Island, in full sight of their favorite resort. As to Vanderscamp himself, he and his man Pluto again disappeared, and it was hoped by the people of Communipaw that he had fallen in some foreign brawl, or been swung on some foreign gallows.

For a time, therefore, the tranquillity of the village was restored; the worthy Dutchmen once more smoked their pipes in peace, eying, with peculiar complacency, their old pests and terrors, the pirates, dangling and drying in the sun on Gibbet Island.

This perfect calm was doomed at length to be ruffled. The fiery persecution of the pirates gradually subsided. Justice was satisfied with the examples that had been made, and there was no more talk of Kidd and the other heroes of like kidney. On a calm summer evening, a boat, somewhat heavily laden, was seen pulling into Communipaw. What was the surprise and disquiet of the inhabitants to see Yan Yost Vanderscamp seated at the helm and his man Pluto tugging at the oars! Vanderscamp, however, was apparently an altered man. He brought home with him a wife who seemed to be a shrew and to have the upper-hand of him. He no longer was the swaggering, bully ruffian, but affected the regular merchant, and talked of retiring from business and settling down quietly to pass the rest of his days in his native place.

The Wild Goose mansion was again opened, but with diminished splendor and no riot. It is true, Vanderscamp had frequent nautical visitors, and the sound of revelry was occasionally overheard in his house; but everything seemed to be done under the rose; and old Pluto was the only servant that officiated at these orgies. The visitors, indeed, were by no means of the turbulent stamp of their predecessors; but quiet, mysterious traders, full of nods, and winks, and hieroglyphic signs, with whom, to use their cant phrase, "everything was smug." Their ships came to anchor at night in the lower bay; and, on a private signal, Vanderscamp would launch his boat, and, accompanied solely by his

man Pluto, would make them mysterious visits.   Sometimes
boats pulled in at night, in front of the Wild Goose, and
various articles of merchandise were landed in the dark, and
spirited away nobody knew whither.   One of the more curious of the inhabitants kept watch, and caught a glimpse of
the features of some of these night visitors, by the casual
glance of a lantern, and declared that he recognized more
than one of the freebooting frequenters of the Wild Goose,
in former times; from whence he concluded that Vanderscamp was at his old game, and that this mysterious merchandise was nothing more nor less than piratical plunder.
The more charitable opinion, however, was that Vanderscamp and his comrades, having been driven from their old
line of business, by the "oppressions of government," had
resorted to smuggling to make both ends meet.

   Be that as it may: I come now to the extraordinary fact
which is the butt-end of this story.   It happened late one
night that Yan Yost Vanderscamp was returning across the
broad bay, in his light skiff, rowed by his man Pluto.   He
had been carousing on board of a vessel, newly arrived, and
was somewhat obfuscated in intellect by the liquor he had
imbibed.   It was a still, sultry night; a heavy mass of lurid
clouds was rising in the west, with the low muttering of
distant thunder.   Vanderscamp called on Pluto to pull lustily, that they might get home before the gathering storm.
The old negro made no reply, but shaped his course so as to
skirt the rocky shores of Gibbet Island. A faint creaking
overhead caused Vanderscamp to cast up his eyes, when, to
his horror, he beheld the bodies of his three pot companions
and brothers in iniquity dangling in the moonlight, their rags
fluttering, and their chains creaking, as they were slowly
swung backward and forward by the rising breeze.

   "What do you mean, you blockhead!" cried Vanderscamp, "by pulling so close to the island?"

   "I thought you'd be glad to see your old friends once
more," growled the negro; "you were never afraid of a living man, what do you fear from the dead?"

"Who's afraid?" hiccuped Vanderscamp, partly heated
by liquor, partly nettled by the jeer of the negro; "who's
afraid! Hang me, but I would be glad to see them once
more, alive or dead, at the Wild Goose. Come, my lads in
the wind!" continued he, taking a draught and flourishing
the bottle above his head, "here's fair weather to you in the
other world; and if you should be walking the rounds to-
night, odds fish! but I'll be happy if you will drop in to
supper."

A dismal creaking was the only reply. The wind blew
loud and shrill, and as it whistled round the gallows, and
among the bones, sounded as if there were laughing and
gibbering in the air. Old Pluto chuckled to himself and now
pulled for home. The storm burst over the voyagers while
they were yet far from shore. The rain fell in torrents, the
thunder crashed and pealed, and the lightning kept up an
incessant blaze. It was stark midnight before they landed
at Communipaw.

Dripping and shivering, Vanderscamp crawled homeward.
He was completely sobered by the storm; the water soaked
from without having diluted and cooled the liquor within.
Arrived at the Wild Goose, he knocked timidly and dubi-
ously at the door, for he dreaded the reception he was to
experience from his wife. He had reason to do so. She
met him at the threshold in a precious ill humor.

"Is this a time," said she, "to keep people out of their
beds, and to bring home company to turn the house upside
down?"

"Company?" said Vanderscamp, meekly; "I have brought
no company with me, wife."

"No, indeed! they have got here before you, but by your
invitation; and blessed-looking company they are, truly!"

Vanderscamp's knees smote together. "For the love of
heaven, where are they, wife?"

"Where?—why, in the blue-room, upstairs, making themselves as much at home as if the house were their own."

Vanderscamp made a desperate effort, scrambled up to

the room and threw open the door.   Sure enough, there at a
table, on which burned a light as blue as brimstone, sat the
three guests from Gibbet Island, with halters round their
necks, and bobbing their cups together, as if they were hob-
or-nobbing, and trolling the old Dutch freebooter's glee, since
translated into English:

> "For three merry lads be we,
> And three merry lads be we;
> I on the land, and thou on the sand,
> And Jack on the gallows-tree."

Vanderscamp saw and heard no more.   Starting back
with horror, he missed his footing on the landing place, and
fell from the top of the stairs to the bottom.   He was taken
up speechless, and, either from the fall or the fright, was
buried in the yard of the little Dutch church at Bergen on
the following Sunday.

From that day forward the fate of the Wild Goose was
sealed.   It was pronounced a *haunted house*, and avoided
accordingly.   No one inhabited it but Vanderscamp's shrew
of a widow and old Pluto, and they were considered but little
better than its hobgoblin visitors.   Pluto grew more and
more haggard and morose, and looked more like an imp of
darkness than a human being.   He spoke to no one, but
went about muttering to himself; or, as some hinted, talking
with the devil, who, though unseen, was ever at his elbow.
Now and then he was seen pulling about the bay alone, in
his skiff, in dark weather, or at the approach of nightfall;
nobody could tell why, unless on an errand to invite more
guests from the gallows.   Indeed it was affirmed that the
Wild Goose still continued to be a house of entertainment
for such guests, and that on stormy nights the blue chamber was occasionally illuminated, and sounds of diabolical
merriment were overheard, mingling with the howling of
the tempest.   Some treated these as idle stories, until on one
such night, it was about the time of the equinox, there was
a horrible uproar in the Wild Goose that could not be mistaken.   It was not so much the sound of revelry, however,

as strife, with two or three piercing shrieks, that pervaded every part of the village. Nevertheless, no one thought of hastening to the spot. On the contrary, the honest burghers of Communipaw drew their nightcaps over their ears, and buried their heads under the bedclothes, at the thoughts of Vanderscamp and his gallows companions.

The next morning, some of the bolder and more curious undertook to reconnoiter. All was quiet and lifeless at the Wild Goose. The door yawned wide open, and had evidently been open all night, for the storm had beaten into the house. Gathering more courage from the silence and apparent desertion, they gradually ventured over the threshold. The house had indeed the air of having been possessed by devils. Everything was topsy-turvy; trunks had been broken open, and chests of drawers and corner cupboards turned inside out, as in a time of general sack and pillage; but the most woful sight was the widow of Yan Yost Vanderscamp, extended a corpse on the floor of the blue chamber, with the marks of a deadly gripe on the wind-pipe.

All now was conjecture and dismay at Communipaw; and the disappearance of old Pluto, who was nowhere to be found, gave rise to all kinds of wild surmises. Some suggested that the negro had betrayed the house to some of Vanderscamp's buccaneering associates, and that they had decamped, together with the booty; others surmised that the negro was nothing more nor less than a devil incarnate, who had now accomplished his ends and made off with his dues.

Events, however, vindicated the negro from this last imputation. His skiff was picked up, drifting about the bay, bottom upward, as if wrecked in a tempest; and his body was found shortly afterward, by some Communipaw fishermen, stranded among the rocks of Gibbet Island, near the foot of the pirates' gallows. The fishermen shook their heads, and observed that old Pluto had ventured once too often to invite guests from Gibbet Island.

THE BERMUDAS

A SHAKESPEARIAN RESEARCH: BY THE AUTHOR OF THE SKETCH-BOOK

"Who did not think, till within these foure yeares, but that these islands had been rather a habitation for Divells, than fit for men to dwell in? Who did not hate the name, when hee was on land, and shun the place when he was on the seas? But behold the misprision and conceits of the world! For true and large experience hath now told us, it is one of the sweetest paradises that be upon earth."

—A PLAINE DESCRIPT. OF THE BARMUDAS: 1613.

IN the course of a voyage home from England, our ship had been struggling, for two or three weeks, with perverse head-winds and a stormy sea. It was in the month of May, yet the weather had at times a wintry sharpness, and it was apprehended that we were in the neighborhood of floating islands of ice, which at that season of the year drift out of the Gulf of St. Lawrence, and sometimes occasion the wreck of noble ships.

Wearied out by the continued opposition of the elements, our captain at length bore away to the south, in hopes of catching the expiring breath of the trade-winds, and making what is called the southern passage. A few days wrought, as it were, a magical "sea change" in everything around us. We seemed to emerge into a different world. The late dark and angry sea, lashed up into roaring and swashing surges, became calm and sunny; the rude winds died away; and gradually a light breeze sprang up directly aft, filling out every sail, and wafting us smoothly along on an even keel. The air softened into a bland and delightful temperature. Dolphins began to play about us; the nautilus came floating by, like a fairy ship, with its mimic sail and rainbow tints; and flying-fish, from time to time, made their short excursive flights, and occasionally fell upon the deck. The cloaks and overcoats in which we had hitherto wrapped ourselves, and moped about the vessel, were thrown aside; for a summer warmth had succeeded to the late wintry chills. Sails were stretched as awnings over the quarter-deck to protect us from the midday sun. Under these we lounged away the day, in luxurious indolence, musing, with half-shut eyes, upon the quiet ocean. The night was scarcely less beautiful than the day. The rising moon sent a quivering column of silver along the undulating surface of the deep, and, gradually climbing the heaven, lighted up our towering topsails and swelling mainsails, and spread a pale, mysterious light around. As our ship made her whispering way through this dreamy world of waters, every boisterous sound on board was charmed to silence; and the low whistle or drowsy song of a sailor from the forecastle, or the tinkling of a guitar, and the soft warbling of a female voice from the quarter-deck, seemed to derive a witching melody from the scene and hour. I was reminded of Oberon's exquisite description of music and moonlight on the ocean:

> "——Thou rememberest
> Since once I sat upon a promontory,
> And heard a mermaid on a dolphin's back
> Uttering such dulcet and harmonious breath
> That the rude sea grew civil at her song?
> And certain stars shot madly from their spheres
> To hear the sea-maid's music."

Indeed, I was in the very mood to conjure up all the imaginary beings with which poetry has peopled old ocean, and almost ready to fancy I heard the distant song of the mermaid, or the mellow shell of the triton, and to picture to myself Neptune and Amphitrite with all their pageant sweeping along the dim horizon.

A day or two of such fanciful voyaging brought us in sight of the Bermudas, which first looked like mere summer clouds, peering above the quiet ocean. All day we glided along in sight of them, with just wind enough to fill our sails; and never did land appear more lovely. They were

clad in emerald verdure, beneath the serenest of skies; not
an angry wave broke upon their quiet shores, and small
fishing craft, riding on the crystal waves, seemed as if hung
in air.   It was such a scene that Fletcher pictured to himself, when he extolled the halcyon lot of the fisherman:

> "Ah! would thou knewest how much it better were
>   To bide among the simple fisher-swains:
> No shrieking owl, no night-crow lodgeth here,
>   Nor is our simple pleasure mixed with pains.
> Our sports begin with the beginning year;
> In calms, to pull the leaping fish to land,
> In roughs, to sing and dance along the yellow sand."

In contemplating these beautiful islands, and the peaceful
sea around them, I could hardly realize that these were the
"still vext Bermoothes" of Shakespeare, once the dread of
mariners, and infamous in the narratives of the early discoverers, for the dangers and disasters which beset them.
Such, however, was the case, and the islands derived additional interest in my eyes, from fancying that I could trace
in their early history, and in the superstitious notions connected with them, some of the elements of Shakespeare's
wild and beautiful drama of the "Tempest." I shall take the
liberty of citing a few historical facts, in support of this idea,
which may claim some additional attention from the American reader, as being connected with the first settlement of
Virginia.

At the time when Shakespeare was in the fullness of his
talent, and seizing upon everything that could furnish ali-
ment to his imagination, the colonization of Virginia was a
favorite object of enterprise among people of condition in
England, and several of the courtiers of the court of Queen
Elizabeth were personally engaged in it.   In the year 1609
a noble armament of nine ships and five hundred men sailed
for the relief of the colony.   It was commanded by Sir George
Somers, as admiral, a gallant and generous gentleman, above
sixty years of age, and possessed of an ample fortune, yet
still bent upon hardy enterprise, and ambitious of signalizing
himself in the service of his country.

On board of his flagship, the "Sea Vulture," sailed also
Sir Thomas Gates, lieutenant-general of the colony. The
voyage was long and boisterous. On the twenty-fifth of
July, the admiral's ship was separated from the rest, in a
hurricane. For several days she was driven about at the
mercy of the elements, and so strained and racked that her
seams yawned open and her hold was half filled with water.
The storm subsided, but left her a mere foundering wreck.
The crew stood in the hold to their waists in water, vainly
endeavoring to bail her with kettles, buckets, and other
vessels. The leaks rapidly gained on them, while their
strength was as rapidly declining. They lost all hope of
keeping the ship afloat until they should reach the American
coast; and, wearied with fruitless toil, determined in their
despair to give up all further attempt, shut down the
hatches, and abandon themselves to Providence. Some, who
had spirituous liquors, or "comfortable waters," as the old
record quaintly terms them, brought them forth and shared
them with their comrades, and they all drank a sad farewell
to one another, as men who were soon to part company in
this world.

In this moment of extremity, the worthy admiral, who
kept sleepless watch from the high stern of the vessel, gave
the thrilling cry of "land!" All rushed on deck in a frenzy
of joy, and nothing now was to be seen or heard on board,
but the transports of men who felt as if rescued from the
grave. It is true the land in sight would not, in ordinary
circumstances, have inspired much self-gratulation. It could
be nothing else but the group of islands called after their
discoverer, one Juan Bermudas, a Spaniard, but stigmatized
among the mariners of those days as "the islands of devils!"
"For the islands of the Barmudas," says the old narrative
of this voyage, "as every man knoweth that hath heard
or read of them, were never inhabited by any Christian or
heathen people, but were ever esteemed and reputed a most
prodigious and inchanted place, affording nothing but gusts,
stormes and foul weather, which made every navigator and

mariner to avoide them, as Scylla and Charybdis, or as they would shun the Divell himself.''*

Sir George Somers and his tempest-tossed comrades, however, hailed them with rapture, as if they had been a terrestrial paradise. Every sail was spread, and every exertion made to urge the foundering ship to land. Before long she struck upon a rock. Fortunately, the late stormy winds had subsided and there was no surf. A swelling wave lifted her from off the rock and bore her to another; and thus she was borne on from rock to rock, until she remained wedged between two, as firmly as if set upon the stocks. The boats were immediately lowered, and, though the shore was above a mile distant, the whole crew were landed in safety.

Every one had now his task assigned him. Some made all haste to unload the ship before she should go to pieces; some constructed wigwams of palmetto leaves, and others ranged the island in quest of wood and water. To their surprise and joy, they found it far different from the desolate and frightful place they had been taught, by seamen's stories, to expect. It was well-wooded and fertile; there were birds of various kinds, and herds of swine roaming about, the progeny of a number that had swam ashore, in former years, from a Spanish wreck. The island abounded with turtle, and great quantities of their eggs were to be found among the rocks. The bays and inlets were full of fish; so tame, that if any one stepped into the water they would throng around him. Sir George Somers, in a little while, caught enough with hook and line to furnish a meal to his whole ship's company. Some of them were so large that two were as much as a man could carry. Crawfish, also, were taken in abundance. The air was soft and salubrious, and the sky beautifully serene. Waller, in his ''Summer Islands,'' has given us a faithful picture of the climate:

"For the kind spring (which but salutes us here),
Inhabits these, and courts them all the year:

* A Plaine Description of the Barmudas.

> Ripe fruits and blossoms on the same trees live;
> At once they promise, and at once they give:
> So sweet the air, so moderate the clime,
> None sickly lives, or dies before his time.
> Heaven sure has kept this spot of earth uncursed,
> To show how all things were created first."

We may imagine the feelings of the shipwrecked mariners, on finding themselves cast by stormy seas upon so happy a coast; where abundance was to be had without labor; where what in other climes constituted the costly luxuries of the rich were within every man's reach; and where life promised to be a mere holiday. Many of the common sailors, especially, declared they desired no better lot than to pass the rest of their lives on this favored island.

The commanders, however, were not so ready to console themselves with mere physical comforts, for the severance from the enjoyment of cultivated life and all the objects of honorable ambition. Despairing of the arrival of any chance ship on these shunned and dreaded islands, they fitted out the long boat, making a deck of the ship's hatches, and having manned her with eight picked men, dispatched her, under the command of an able and hardy mariner, named Raven, to proceed to Virginia, and procure shipping to be sent to their relief.

While waiting in anxious idleness for the arrival of the looked-for aid, dissensions arose between Sir George Somers and Sir Thomas Gates, originating, very probably, in jealousy of the lead which the nautical experience and professional station of the admiral gave him in the present emergency. Each commander, of course, had his adherents: these dissensions ripened into a complete schism; and this handful of shipwrecked men, thus thrown together, on an uninhabited island, separated into two parties, and lived asunder in bitter feud, as men rendered fickle by prosperity, instead of being brought into brotherhood by a common calamity.

Weeks and months elapsed without bringing the looked-for aid from Virginia, though that colony was within but a few days' sail. Fears were now entertained that the long-boat had been either swallowed up in the sea or wrecked on some savage coast; one or other of which most probably was the case, as nothing was ever heard of Raven and his comrades.

Each party now set to work to build a vessel for itself out of the cedar with which the island abounded. The wreck of the "Sea Vulture" furnished rigging and various other articles; but they had no iron for bolts and other fastenings; and for want of pitch and tar, they payed the seams of their vessels with lime and turtle's oil, which soon dried and became as hard as stone.

On the tenth of May, 1610, they set sail, having been about nine months on the island. They reached Virginia without further accident, but found the colony in great distress for provisions. The account they gave of the abundance that reigned in the Bermudas, and especially of the herds of swine that roamed the island, determined Lord Delaware, the governor of Virginia, to send thither for supplies. Sir George Somers, with his wonted promptness and generosity, offered to undertake what was still considered a dangerous voyage. Accordingly, on the nineteenth of June, he set sail in his own cedar vessel of thirty tons, accompanied by another small vessel, commanded by Captain Argall.

The gallant Somers was doomed again to be tempest-tossed. His companion vessel was soon driven back to port, but he kept the sea; and, as usual, remained at his post on deck in all weathers. His voyage was long and boisterous, and the fatigues and exposures which he underwent were too much for a frame impaired by age and by previous hardships. He arrived at the Bermudas completely exhausted and broken down.

His nephew, Captain Mathew Somers, attended him in his illness with affectionate assiduity. Finding his end approaching, the veteran called his men together and exhorted them to be true to the interests of Virginia; to procure provisions with all possible dispatch and hasten back to the relief of the colony.

With this dying charge, he gave up the ghost, leaving his nephew and crew overwhelmed with grief and consternation. Their first thought was to pay honor to his remains. Opening the body, they took out the heart and entrails, and buried them, erecting a cross over the grave. They then embalmed the body and set sail with it for England; thus, while paying empty honors to their deceased commander, neglecting his earnest wish and dying injunction that they should return with relief to Virginia.

The little bark arrived safely at Whitechurch, in Dorsetshire, with its melancholy freight. The body of the worthy Somers was interred with the military honors due to a brave soldier, and many volleys were fired over his grave. The Bermudas have since received the name of the Somer Islands, as a tribute to his memory.

The accounts given by Captain Mathew Somers and his crew of the delightful climate, and the great beauty, fertility, and abundance of these islands, excited the zeal of enthusiasts and the cupidity of speculators, and a plan was set on foot to colonize them. The Virginia company sold their right to the islands to one hundred and twenty of their own members, who erected themselves into a distinct corporation, under the name of the "Somer Island Society"; and Mr. Richard More was sent out, in 1612, as governor, with sixty men, to found a colony: and this leads me to the second branch of this research.

THE THREE KINGS OF BERMUDA

AND THEIR TREASURE OF AMBERGRIS

At the time that Sir George Somers was preparing to launch his cedar-built bark, and sail for Virginia, there were three culprits among his men who had been guilty of capital

offenses. One of them was shot; the others, named Chris-
topher Carter and Edward Waters, escaped. Waters, indeed, made a very narrow escape, for he had actually been
tied to a tree to be executed, but cut the rope with a knife
which he had concealed about his person, and fled to the
woods, where he was joined by Carter. These two worthies
kept themselves concealed in the secret parts of the island,
until the departure of the two vessels. When Sir George
Somers revisited the island, in quest of supplies for the Virginia colony, these culprits hovered about the landing-place,
and succeeded in persuading another seaman, named Edward
Chard, to join them, giving him the most seductive pictures
of the ease and abundance in which they reveled.

When the bark that bore Sir George's body to England
had faded from the watery horizon, these three vagabonds
walked forth in their majesty and might, the lords and sole
inhabitants of these islands. For a time their little commonwealth went on prosperously and happily. They built a
house, sowed corn, and the seeds of various fruits; and having plenty of hogs, wild fowl, and fish of all kinds, with
turtle in abundance, carried on their tripartite sovereignty
with great harmony and much feasting. All kingdoms,
however, are doomed to revolution, convulsion, or decay;
and so it fared with the empire of the three kings of Bermuda, albeit they were monarchs without subjects. In an
evil hour, in their search after turtle among the fissures of
the rocks, they came upon a great treasure of ambergris,
which had been cast on shore by the ocean. Besides a number of pieces of smaller dimensions, there was one great
mass, the largest that had ever been known, weighing eighty
pounds, and which of itself, according to the market value
of ambergris in those days, was worth about nine or ten
thousand pounds!

From that moment the happiness and harmony of the
three kings of Bermuda were gone forever. While poor
devils, with nothing to share but the common blessings of
the island, which administered to present enjoyment, but

had nothing of convertible value, they were loving and
united: but here was actual wealth, which would make
them rich men, whenever they could transport it to a
market.

Adieu the delights of the island! They now became flat
and insipid. Each pictured to himself the consequence he
might now aspire to, in civilized life, could he once get there
with this mass of ambergris. No longer a poor Jack Tar,
frolicking in the low taverns of Wapping, he might roll
through London in his coach, and perchance arrive, like
Whittington, at the dignity of Lord Mayor.

With riches came envy and covetousness. Each was now
for assuming the supreme power, and getting the monopoly
of the ambergris. A civil war at length broke out: Chard
and Waters defied each other to mortal combat, and the
kingdom of the Bermudas was on the point of being deluged
with royal blood. Fortunately, Carter took no part in the
bloody feud. Ambition might have made him view it with
secret exultation; for if either or both of his brother poten-
tates were slain in the conflict he would be a gainer in purse
and ambergris. But he dreaded to be left alone in this uninhabited island, and to find himself the monarch of a solitude;
so he secretly purloined and hid the weapons of the belligerent rivals, who, having no means of carrying on the war,
gradually cooled down into a sullen armistice.

The arrival of Governor More, with an overpowering
force of sixty men, put an end to the empire. He took possession of the kingdom, in the name of the Somer Island
Company, and forthwith proceeded to make a settlement.
The three kings tacitly relinquished their sway, but stood up
stoutly for their treasure. It was determined, however, that
they had been fitted out at the expense, and employed in the
service, of the Virginia Company; that they had found the
ambergris while in the service of that company, and on that
company's land; that the ambergris, therefore, belonged to
that company, or, rather, to the Somer Island Company, in
consequence of their recent purchase of the island, and all

their appurtenances. Having thus legally established their right, and being moreover able to back it by might, the company laid the lion's paw upon the spoil; and nothing more remains on historic record of the Three Kings of Bermuda and their treasure of ambergris.

THE reader will now determine whether I am more extravagant than most of the commentators on Shakespeare, in my surmise that the story of Sir George Somers' shipwreck, and the subsequent occurrences that took place on the uninhabited island, may have furnished the bard with some of the elements of his drama of the "Tempest." The tidings of the shipwreck, and of the incidents connected with it, reached England not long before the production of this drama, and made a great sensation there. A narrative of the whole matter, from which most of the foregoing particulars are extracted, was published at the time in London, in a pamphlet form, and could not fail to be eagerly perused by Shakespeare, and to make a vivid impression on his fancy. His expression, in the "Tempest," of "the still vext Bermoothes," accords exactly with the storm-beaten character of those islands. The enchantments, too, with which he has clothed the island of Prospero, may they not be traced to the wild and superstitious notions entertained about the Bermudas? I have already cited two passages from a pamphlet published at the time, showing that they were esteemed "a most *prodigious* and *inchanted* place," and the "habitation of divells"; and another pamphlet, published shortly afterward, observes: "And whereas it is reported that this land of the Barmudas, with the islands about (which are many, at least a hundred), are inchanted and kept with evil and wicked spirits, it is a most idle and false report." *

The description, too, given in the same pamphlets of the real beauty and fertility of the Bermudas, and of their serene and happy climate, so opposite to the dangerous and inhos-

---

* Newes from the Barmudas: 1612.

pitable character with which they had been stigmatized, accords with the eulogium of Sebastian on the island of Prospero :

"Though this island seem to be desert, uninhabitable, and almost inaccessible, it must needs be of subtle, tender, and delicate temperance. The air breathes upon us here most sweetly. Here is everything advantageous to life. How lush and lusty the grass looks! how green!"

I think too, in the exulting consciousness of ease, security and abundance felt by the late tempest-tossed mariners, while reveling in the plenteousness of the island, and their inclination to remain there, released from the labors, the cares, and the artificial restraints of civilized life, I can see something of the golden commonwealth of honest Gonzalo :

> "Had I plantation of this isle, my lord,
> And were the king of it, what would I do?
> I' the commonwealth I would by contraries
> Execute all things: for no kind of traffic
> Would I admit; no name of magistrate;
> Letters should not be known; riches, poverty,
> And use of service, none; contract, succession
> Bourn, bound of land, tilth, vineyard, none:
> No use of metal, corn, or wine, or oil:
> No occupation; all men idle, all.
>
> .   .   .   .   .   .
>
> All things in common, nature should produce,
> Without sweat or endeavor: Treason, felony,
> Sword, pike, knife, gun, or need of any engine,
> Would I not have; but nature should bring forth,
> Of its own kind, all foizon, all abundance,
> To feed my innocent people."

But above all, in the three fugitive vagabonds who remained in possession of the island of Bermuda, on the departure of their comrades, and in their squabbles about supremacy, on the finding of their treasure, I see typified Sebastian, Trinculo, and their worthy companion Caliban :

"Trinculo, the king and all our company being drowned, we will inherit here."

"Monster, I will kill this man; his daughter and I will be king and queen (save our graces!) and Trinculo and thyself shall be viceroys."

I do not mean to hold up the incidents and characters in
the narrative and in the play as parallel, or as being strikingly similar: neither would I insinuate that the narrative
suggested the play; I would only suppose that Shakespeare,
being occupied about that time on the drama of the "Tempest," the main story of which, I believe, is of Italian origin,
had many of the fanciful ideas of it suggested to his mind
by the shipwreck of Sir George Somers on the "still vext
Bermoothes," and by the popular superstitions connected
with these islands, and suddenly put in circulation by that
event.

PELAYO AND THE MERCHANT'S DAUGHTER

BY THE AUTHOR OF THE SKETCH-BOOK

IT is the common lamentation of Spanish historiographers
that, for an obscure and melancholy space of time immediately succeeding the conquest of their country by the Moslems, its history is a mere wilderness of dubious facts, groundless fables, and rash exaggerations. Learned men, in cells
and cloisters, have worn out their lives in vainly endeavoring
to connect incongruous events, and to account for startling
improbabilities, recorded of this period. The worthy Jesuit,
Padre Abarca, declares that, for more than forty years during which he had been employed in theological controversies,
he had never found any so obscure and inexplicable as those
which rise out of this portion of Spanish history, and that the
only fruit of an indefatigable, prolix, and even prodigious
study of the subject, was a melancholy and mortifying state
of indecision.*

During this apocryphal period flourished PELAYO, the deliverer of Spain, whose name, like that of William Wallace,
will ever be linked with the glory of his country, but linked,

---

* Padre Pedro Abarca. Anales de Aragon, Anti Regno, § 2.

in like manner, by a bond in which fact and fiction are inextricably interwoven.

The quaint old chronicle of the Moor Rasis, which, though wild and fanciful in the extreme, is frequently drawn upon for early facts by Spanish historians, professes to give the birth, parentage, and whole course of fortune of Pelayo, without the least doubt or hesitation. It makes him a son of the Duke of Cantabria, and descended, both by father and mother's side, from the Gothic kings of Spain. I shall pass over the romantic story of his childhood, and shall content myself with a scene of his youth, which was spent in a castle among the Pyrenees, under the eye of his widowed and noble-minded mother, who caused him to be instructed in everything befitting a cavalier of gentle birth. While the sons of the nobility were reveling amid the pleasures of a licentious court, and sunk in that vicious and effeminate indulgence which led to the perdition of unhappy Spain, the youthful Pelayo, in his rugged mountain school, was steeled to all kinds of hardy exercise. A great part of his time was spent in hunting the bears, the wild boars and the wolves with which the Pyrenees abounded; and so purely and chastely was he brought up by his good lady mother that, if the ancient chronicle from which I draw my facts may be relied on, he had attained his one-and-twentieth year without having once sighed for woman!

Nor were his hardy contests confined to the wild beasts of the forest. Occasionally he had to contend with adversaries of a more formidable character. The skirts and defiles of these border mountains were often infested by marauders from the Gallic plains of Gascony. The Gascons, says an old chronicler, were a people who used smooth words when expedient, but force when they had power, and were ready to lay their hands on everything they met. Though poor, they were proud; for there was not one who did not pride himself on being a hijodalgo, or the son of somebody.

At the head of a band of these needy hijodalgos of Gascony was one Arnaud, a broken-down cavalier. He and four of his followers were well armed and mounted; the rest were a set of scamper-grounds on foot, furnished with darts and javelins. They were the terror of the border; here to-day and gone to-morrow; sometimes in one pass, sometimes in another. They would make sudden inroads into Spain, scour the roads, plunder the country, and were over the mountains and far away before a force could be collected to pursue them.

Now it happened one day that a wealthy burgher of Bordeaux, who was a merchant trading with Biscay, set out on a journey for that province. As he intended to sojourn there for a season he took with him his wife, who was a goodly dame, and his daughter, a gentle damsel, of marriageable age, and exceeding fair to look upon. He was attended by a trusty clerk from his comptoir, and a man servant; while another servant led a hackney, laden with bags of money, with which he intended to purchase merchandise.

When the Gascons heard of this wealthy merchant and his convoy passing through the mountains, they thanked their stars, for they considered all peaceful men of traffic as lawful spoil, sent by Providence for the benefit of hidalgos like themselves, of valor and gentle blood, who lived by the sword. Placing themselves in ambush, in a lonely defile by which the travelers had to pass, they silently awaited their coming. In a little while they beheld them approaching. The merchant was a fair, portly man, in a buff surcoat and velvet cap. His looks bespoke the good cheer of his native city, and he was mounted on a stately, well-fed steed, while his wife and daughter paced gently on palfreys by his side.

The travelers had advanced some distance in the defile when the bandoleros rushed forth and assailed them. The merchant, though but little used to the exercise of arms, and unwieldy in his form, yet made valiant defense, having his wife and daughter and money-bags at hazard. He was wounded in two places and overpowered; one of his servants was slain, the other took to flight.

The freebooters then began to ransack for spoil, but were disappointed at not finding the wealth they had expected. Putting their swords to the breast of the trembling merchant, they demanded where he had concealed his treasure, and learned from him of the hackney that was following, laden with money. Overjoyed at this intelligence, they bound their captives to trees and awaited the arrival of the golden spoil.

On this same day, Pelayo was out with his huntsmen among the mountains, and had taken his stand on a rock, at a narrow pass, to await the sallying forth of a wild boar. Close by him was a page, conducting a horse, and at the saddle-bow hung his armor, for he was always prepared for fight among these border mountains. While thus posted, the servant of the merchant came flying from the robbers. On beholding Pelayo, he fell on his knees and implored his life, for he supposed him to be one of the band. It was some time before he could be relieved from his terror and made to tell his story. When Pelayo heard of the robbers, he concluded they were the crew of Gascon hidalgos upon the scamper. Taking his armor from the page, he put on his helmet, slung his buckler round his neck, took lance in hand, and, mounting his steed, compelled the trembling servant to guide him to the scene of action. At the same time he ordered the page to seek his huntsmen, and summon them to his assistance.

When the robbers saw Pelayo advancing through the forest, with a single attendant on foot, and beheld his rich armor sparkling in the sun, they thought a new prize had fallen into their hands, and Arnaud and two of his companions, mounting their horses, advanced to meet him. As they approached, Pelayo stationed himself in a narrow pass between two rocks, where he could only be assailed in front, and bracing his buckler, and lowering his lance, awaited their coming.

"Who and what are ye," cried he, "and what seek ye in this land?"

"We are huntsmen," replied Arnaud, "and lo! our game runs into our toils!"

"By my faith," replied Pelayo, "thou wilt find the game more readily roused than taken; have at thee for a villain!"

So saying, he put spurs to his horse and ran full speed upon him. The Gascon, not expecting so sudden an attack from a single horseman, was taken by surprise. He hastily couched his lance, but it merely glanced on the shield of Pelayo, who sent his own through the middle of his breast, and threw him out of his saddle to the earth. One of the other robbers made at Pelayo, and wounded him slightly in the side, but received a blow from the sword of the latter which cleft his skullcap and sank into his brain. His companion, seeing him fall, put spurs to his steed and galloped off through the forest.

Beholding several other robbers on foot coming up, Pelayo returned to his station between the rocks, where he was assailed by them all at once. He received two of their darts on his buckler, a javelin razed his cuirass, and glancing down wounded his horse. Pelayo then rushed forth, and struck one of the robbers dead; the others, beholding several huntsmen advancing, took to flight, but were pursued and several of them taken.

The good merchant of Bordeaux and his family beheld this scene with trembling amazement, for never had they looked upon such feats of arms. They considered Don Pelayo as a leader of some rival band of robbers; and when the bonds were loosed by which they were tied to the trees they fell at his feet and implored mercy. The females were soonest undeceived, especially the daughter; for the damsel was struck with the noble countenance and gentle demeanor of Pelayo, and said to herself: "Surely nothing evil can dwell in so goodly and gracious a form."

Pelayo now sounded his horn, which echoed from rock to rock, and was answered by shouts and horns from various parts of the mountains. The merchant's heart misgave him at these signals, and especially when he beheld more than forty men gathering from glen and thicket. They were clad in hunters' dresses, and armed with boar-spears, darts, and hunting-swords, and many of them led hounds in long leashes. All this was a new and wild scene to the astonished merchant; nor were his fears abated when he saw his servant approaching with the hackney laden with money-bags; "for of a certainty," said he to himself, "this will be too tempting a spoil for these wild hunters of the mountains."

Pelayo, however, took no more notice of the gold than if it had been so much dross; at which the honest burgher marveled exceedingly. He ordered that the wounds of the merchant should be dressed and his own examined. On taking off his cuirass, his wound was found to be but slight; but his men were so exasperated at seeing his blood that they would have put the captive robbers to instant death had he not forbidden them to do them any harm.

The huntsmen now made a great fire at the foot of a tree, and bringing a boar which they had killed, cut off portions and roasted them or broiled them on the coals. Then, drawing forth loaves of bread from their wallets, they devoured. their food half raw, with the hungry relish of huntsmen and mountaineers. The merchant, his wife, and daughter, looked at all this, and wondered, for they had never beheld so savage a repast.

Pelayo then inquired of them if they did not desire to eat; they were too much in awe of him to decline, though they felt a loathing at the thought of partaking of this hunter's fare; but he ordered a linen cloth to be spread under the shade of a great oak, on the grassy margin of a clear running stream; and to their astonishment they were served, not with the flesh of the boar, but with dainty cheer, such as the merchant had scarcely hoped to find out of the walls of his native city of Bordeaux.

The good burgher was of a community renowned for gastronomic prowess: his fears having subsided, his appetite was now awakened, and he addressed himself manfully to the viands that were set before him. His daughter, however,

could not eat: her eyes were ever and anon stealing to gaze
on Pelayo, whom she regarded with gratitude for his protection and admiration for his valor; and now that he had laid
aside his helmet, and she beheld his lofty countenance, glowing with manly beauty, she thought him something more
than mortal. The heart of the gentle donzella, says the ancient chronicler, was kind and yielding; and had Pelayo
thought fit to ask the greatest boon that love and beauty
could bestow—doubtless meaning her fair hand—she could
not have had the cruelty to say him nay. Pelayo, however,
had no such thoughts: the love of woman had never yet
entered his heart; and though he regarded the damsel as the
fairest maiden he had ever beheld, her beauty caused no perturbation in his breast.

When the repast was over, Pelayo offered to conduct the
merchant and his family through the defiles of the mountains, lest they should be molested by any of the scattered
band of robbers. The bodies of the slain marauders were
buried, and the corpse of the servant was laid upon one of
the horses captured in the battle. Having formed their cavalcade, they pursued their way slowly up one of the steep
and winding passes of the Pyrenees.

Toward sunset they arrived at the dwelling of a holy hermit. It was hewn out of the living rock; there was a cross
over the door, and before it was a great spreading oak, with
a sweet spring of water at its foot. The body of the faithful
servant who had fallen in the defense of his lord was buried
close by the wall of this sacred retreat, and the hermit promised to perform masses for the repose of his soul. Then Pelayo obtained from the holy father consent that the merchant's
wife and daughter should pass the night within his cell; and
the hermit made beds of moss for them, and gave them his
benediction; but the damsel found little rest, so much were
her thoughts occupied by the youthful champion who had
rescued her from death or dishonor.

Pelayo, however, was visited by no such wandering of
the mind; but, wrapping himself in his mantle, slept soundly

by the fountain under the tree. At midnight, when everything was buried in deep repose, he was awakened from his
sleep and beheld the hermit before him, with the beams of
the moon shining upon his silver hair and beard.

"This is no time," said the latter, "to be sleeping; arise
and listen to my words, and hear of the great work for which
thou art chosen!"

Then Pelayo arose and seated himself on a rock, and the
hermit continued his discourse.

"Behold," said he, "the ruin of Spain is at hand! It will
be delivered into the hands of strangers, and will become a
prey to the spoiler. Its children will be slain or carried into
captivity; or such as may escape these evils will harbor with
the beasts of the forest or the eagles of the mountain. The
thorn and bramble will spring up where now are seen the
corn-field, the vine, and the olive; and hungry wolves will
roam in place of peaceful flocks and herds. But thou, my
son! tarry not thou to see these things, for thou canst not
prevent them. Depart on a pilgrimage to the sepulcher of
our blessed Lord in Palestine; purify thyself by prayer; enroll thyself in the order of chivalry, and prepare for the great
work of the redemption of thy country; for to thee it will be
given to raise it from the depth of its affliction."

Pelayo would have inquired further into the evils thus
foretold, but the hermit rebuked his curiosity.

"Seek not to know more," said he, "than Heaven is pleased
to reveal. Clouds and darkness cover its designs, and prophecy is never permitted to lift up but in part the veil that rests
upon the future."

The hermit ceased to speak, and Pelayo laid himself down
again to take repose, but sleep was a stranger to his eyes.

When the first rays of the rising sun shone upon the tops
of the mountains, the travelers assembled round the fountain
beneath the tree and made their morning's repast. Then,
having received the benediction of the hermit, they departed
in the freshness of the day, and descended along the hollow
defiles leading into the interior of Spain. The good mer-

chant was refreshed by sleep and by his morning's meal; and when he beheld his wife and daughter thus secure by his side, and the hackney laden with his treasure close behind him, his heart was light in his bosom, and he caroled a chansom as he went, and the woodlands echoed to his song. But Pelayo rode in silence, for he revolved in his mind the portentous words of the hermit; and the daughter of the merchant ever and anon stole looks at him full of tenderness and admiration, and deep sighs betrayed the agitation of her bosom.

At length they came to the foot of the mountains, where the forests and the rocks terminated and an open and secure country lay before the travelers. Here they halted, for their roads were widely different. When they came to part, the merchant and his wife were loud in thanks and benedictions, and the good burgher would fain have given Pelayo the largest of his sacks of gold; but the young man put it aside with a smile. "Silver and gold," said he, "need I not, but if I have deserved aught at thy hands, give me thy prayers, for the prayers of a good man are above all price."

In the meantime the daughter had spoken never a word. At length she raised her eyes, which were filled with tears, and looked timidly at Pelayo, and her bosom throbbed; and after a violent struggle between strong affection and virgin modesty, her heart relieved itself by words.

"Senor," said she, "I know that I am unworthy of the notice of so noble a cavalier; but suffer me to place this ring upon a finger of that hand which has so bravely rescued us from death; and when you regard it, you may consider it as a memorial of your own valor, and not of one who is too humble to be remembered by you."

With these words, she drew a ring from her finger and put it upon the finger of Pelayo; and having done this, she blushed and trembled at her own boldness, and stood as one abashed, with her eyes cast down upon the earth.

Pelayo was moved at the words of the simple maiden, and at the touch of her fair hand, and at her beauty, as she stood thus trembling and in tears before him; but as yet he knew nothing of woman, and his heart was free from the snares of love. "Amiga" (friend), said he, "I accept thy present, and will wear it in remembrance of thy goodness;" so saying, he kissed her on the cheek.

The damsel was cheered by these words, and hoped that she had awakened some tenderness in his bosom; but it was no such thing, says the grave old chronicler, for his heart was devoted to higher and more sacred matters; yet certain it is that he always guarded well that ring.

When they parted, Pelayo remained with his huntsmen on a cliff, watching that no evil befell them, until they were far beyond the skirts of the mountain; and the damsel often turned to look at him, until she could no longer discern him, for the distance and the tears that dimmed her eyes.

And for that he had accepted her ring, says the ancient chronicler, she considered herself wedded to him in her heart, and would never marry; nor could she be brought to look with eyes of affection upon any other man; but for the true love which she bore Pelayo she lived and died a virgin. And she composed a book which treated of love and chivalry, and the temptations of this mortal life; and one part discoursed of celestial matters, and it was called "The Contemplations of Love"; because at the time she wrote it she thought of Pelayo, and of his having accepted her jewel and called her by the gentle appellation of "Amiga." And often thinking of him in tender sadness, and of her never having beheld him more, she would take the book and would read it as if in his stead; and while she repeated the words of love which it contained, she would endeavor to fancy them uttered by Pelayo, and that he stood before her.

THE KNIGHT OF MALTA

TO THE EDITOR OF THE KNICKERBOCKER

SIR—In the course of a tour which I made in Sicily, in the days of my juvenility, I passed some little time at the ancient city of Catania, at the foot of Mount Ætna. Here I became acquainted with the Chevalier ——, an old Knight of Malta. It was not many years after the time that Napoleon had dislodged the knights from their island, and he still wore the insignia of his order. He was not, however, one of those relics of that once chivalrous body, who have been described as "a few worn-out old men, creeping about certain parts of Europe, with the Maltese cross on their breasts"; on the contrary, though advanced in life, his form was still light and vigorous; he had a pale, thin, intellectual visage, with a high forehead and a bright, visionary eye. He seemed to take a fancy to me, as I certainly did to him, and we soon became intimate. I visited him occasionally at his apartments, in the wing of an old palace looking toward Mount Ætna. He was an antiquary, a virtuoso, and a connoisseur. His rooms were decorated with mutilated statues, dug up from Grecian and Roman ruins; old vases, lachrymals, and sepulchral lamps. He had astronomical and chemical instruments, and black-letter books in various languages. I found that he had dipped a little in chimerical studies, and had a hankering after astrology and alchemy. He affected to believe in dreams and visions, and delighted in the fanciful Rosicrucian doctrines. I cannot persuade myself, however, that he really believed in all these: I rather think he loved to let his imagination carry him away into the boundless fairyland which they unfolded.

In company with the chevalier, I took several excursions on horseback about the environs of Catania, and the pictaresque skirts of Mount Ætna. One of these led through a village which had sprung up on the very tract of an ancient eruption, the houses being built of lava. At one time we passed, for some distance, along a narrow lane, between two high dead convent walls. It was a cut-throat-looking place, in a country where assassinations are frequent; and just about midway through it we observed blood upon the pavement and the walls, as if a murder had actually been committed there.

The chevalier spurred on his horse until he had extricated himself completely from this suspicious neighborhood. He then observed that it reminded him of a similar blind alley in Malta, infamous on account of the many assassinations that had taken place there; concerning one of which he related a long and tragical story that lasted until we reached Catania. It involved various circumstances of a wild and supernatural character, but which he assured me were handed down in tradition, and generally credited by the old inhabitants of Malta.

As I like to pick up strange stories, and as I was particularly struck with several parts of this, I made a minute of it, on my return to my lodgings. The memorandum was lost, with several others of my traveling papers, and the story had faded from my mind, when recently, in perusing a French memoir, I came suddenly upon it, dressed up, it is true, in a very different manner, but agreeing in the leading facts, and given upon the word of that famous adventurer, the Count Cagliostro.

I have amused myself, during a snowy day in the country, by rendering it roughly into English, for the entertainment of a youthful circle round the Christmas fire. It was well received by my auditors, who, however, are rather easily pleased. One proof of its merits is that it sent some of the youngest of them quaking to their beds, and gave them very fearful dreams. Hoping that it may have the same effect upon your ghost-hunting readers, I offer it, Mr. Editor, for insertion in your magazine. I would observe that wherever

I have modified the French version of the story it has been
in conformity to some recollection of the narrative of my
friend, the Knight of Malta.

Your obt. servt.,

GEOFFREY CRAYON.

THE GRAND PRIOR OF MINORCA

A VERITABLE GHOST STORY

"Keep my wits, heaven! They say spirits appear
To melancholy minds, and the graves open!"
—FLETCHER

ABOUT the middle of the last century, while the Knights
of Saint John of Jerusalem still maintained something of
their ancient state and sway in the Island of Malta, a tragical event took place there which is the groundwork of the
following narrative.

It may be as well to premise that, at the time we are
treating of, the order of Saint John of Jerusalem, grown
excessively wealthy, had degenerated from its originally devout and warlike character. Instead of being a hardy body
of "monk-knights," sworn soldiers of the cross, fighting the
Paynim in the Holy Land, or scouring the Mediterranean,
and scourging the Barbary coasts with their galleys, or feeding the poor and attending upon the sick at their hospitals,
they led a life of luxury and libertinism, and were to be found
in the most voluptuous courts of Europe. The order, in fact,
had become a mode of providing for the needy branches of
the Catholic aristocracy of Europe. "A commandery," we
are told, was a splendid provision for a younger brother; and
men of rank, however dissolute, provided they belonged to
the highest aristocracy, became Knights of Malta, just as
they did bishops, or colonels of regiments, or court chamber-
lains. After a brief residence at Malta, the knights passed
the rest of their time in their own countries, or only made a

visit now and then to the island. While there, having but
little military duty to perform, they beguiled their idleness
by paying attentions to the fair.

There was one circle of society, however, into which they
could not obtain currency. This was composed of a few
families of the old Maltese nobility, natives of the island.
These families, not being permitted to enroll any of their
members in the order, affected to hold no intercourse with
its chevaliers; admitting none into their exclusive coteries
but the Grand Master, whom they acknowledged as their
sovereign, and the members of the chapter which composed
his council.

To indemnify themselves for this exclusion, the chevaliers carried their gallantries into the next class of society,
composed of those who held civil, administrative, and judicial situations. The ladies of this class were called *honorate*,
or honorables, to distinguish them from the inferior orders;
and among them were many of superior grace, beauty, and
fascination.

Even in this more hospitable class, the chevaliers were
not all equally favored. Those of Germany had the decided
preference, owing to their fair and fresh complexions, and
the kindliness of their manners: next to these came the Spanish cavaliers, on account of their profound and courteous devotion, and most discreet secrecy. Singular as it may seem,
the chevaliers of France fared the worst. The Maltese ladies
dreaded their volatility, and their proneness to boast of their
amours, and shunned all entanglement with them. They
were forced, therefore, to content themselves with conquests
among females of the lower orders. They revenged themselves, after the gay French manner, by making the "honorate" the objects of all kinds of jests and mystifications; by
prying into their tender affairs with the more favored chevaliers, and making them the theme of song and epigram.

About this time, a French vessel arrived at Malta, bringing out a distinguished personage of the order of Saint John
of Jerusalem, the Commander de Foulquerre, who came to

solicit the post of commander-in-chief of the galleys. He
was descended from an old and warrior line of French nobility, his ancestors having long been seneschals of Poitou, and
claiming descent from the first counts of Angouleme.

The arrival of the commander caused a little uneasiness
among the peaceably inclined, for he bore the character, in
the island, of being fiery, arrogant, and quarrelsome. He
had already been three times at Malta, and on each visit had
signalized himself by some rash and deadly affray. As he
was now thirty-five years of age, however, it was hoped that
time might have taken off the fiery edge of his spirit, and
that he might prove more quiet and sedate than formerly.
The commander set up an establishment befitting his rank
and pretensions; for he arrogated to himself an importance
greater even than that of the Grand Master. His house immediately became the rallying place of all the young French
chevaliers. They informed him of all the slights they had
experienced or imagined, and indulged their petulant and
satirical vein at the expense of the honorate and their admirers. The chevaliers of other nations soon found the topics
and tone of conversation at the commander's irksome and
offensive, and gradually ceased to visit there. The commander remained the head of a national *clique,* who looked
up to him as their model. If he was not as boisterous and
quarrelsome as formerly, he had become haughty and overbearing. He was fond of talking over his past affairs of
punctilio and bloody duel. When walking the streets, he
was generally attended by a ruffling train of young French
cavaliers, who caught his own air of assumption and bravado.
These he would conduct to the scenes of his deadly encounters, point out the very spot where each fatal lunge had been
given, and dwell vaingloriously on every particular.

Under his tuition, the young French chevaliers began to
add bluster and arrogance to their former petulance and lev-
ity; they fired up on the most trivial occasions, particularly
with those who had been most successful with the fair; and
would put on the most intolerable drawcansir airs. The

other chevaliers conducted themselves with all possible forbearance and reserve; but they saw it would be impossible
to keep on long, in this manner, without coming to an open
rupture.

Among the Spanish cavaliers was one named Don Luis
de Lima Vasconcellos. He was distantly related to the
Grand Master; and had been enrolled at an early age
among his pages, but had been rapidly promoted by him,
until, at the age of twenty-six, he had been given the richest Spanish commandery in the order. He had, moreover,
been fortunate with the fair, with one of whom, the most
beautiful honorata of Malta, he had long maintained the
most tender correspondence.

The character, rank, and connections of Don Luis put
him on a par with the imperious Commander de Foulquerre,
and pointed him out as a leader and champion to his countrymen. The Spanish chevaliers repaired to him, therefore,
in a body; represented all the grievances they had sustained
and the evils they apprehended, and urged him to use his influence with the commander and his adherents to put a stop
to the growing abuses.

Don Luis was gratified by this mark of confidence and
esteem on the part of his countrymen, and promised to have
an interview with the Commander de Foulquerre on the subject. He resolved to conduct himself with the utmost caution and delicacy on the occasion; to represent to the commander the evil consequences which might result from the
inconsiderate conduct of the young French chevaliers, and
to entreat him to exert the great influence he so deservedly
possessed over them, to restrain their excesses. Don Luis
was aware, however, of the peril that attended any interview
of the kind with this imperious and fractious man, and apprehended, however it might commence, that it would termi-
nate in a duel. Still, it was an affair of honor, in which
Castilian dignity was concerned; besides, he had a lurking
disgust at the overbearing manners of De Foulquerre, and
perhaps had been somewhat offended by certain intrusive

attentions which he had presumed to pay to the beautiful honorata.

It was now Holy Week; a time too sacred for worldly feuds and passions, especially in a community under the dominion of a religious order; it was agreed, therefore, that the dangerous interview in question should not take place until after the Easter holydays. It is probable, from subsequent circumstances, that the Commander de Foulquerre had some information of this arrangement among the Spanish chevaliers, and was determined to be beforehand, and to mortify the pride of their champion, who was thus preparing to read him a lecture. He chose Good Friday for his purpose. On this sacred day, it is customary in Catholic countries to make a tour of all the churches, offering up prayers in each. In every Catholic church, as is well known, there is a vessel of holy water near the door. In this, every one, on entering, dips his fingers, and makes therewith the sign of the cross on his forehead and breast. An office of gallantry, among the young Spaniards, is to stand near the door, dip their hands in the holy vessel, and extend them courteously and respectfully to any lady of their acquaintance who may enter; who thus receives the sacred water at second hand, on the tips of her fingers, and proceeds to cross herself, with all due decorum. The Spaniards, who are the most jealous of lovers, are impatient when this piece of devotional gallantry is proffered to the object of their affections by any other hand: on Good Friday, therefore, when a lady makes a tour of the churches, it is the usage among them for the inamorato to follow her from church to church, so as to present her the holy water at the door of each; thus testifying his own devotion, and at the same time preventing the officious services of a rival.

On the day in question, Don Luis followed the beautiful honorata, to whom, as has already been observed, he had long been devoted. At the very first church she visited, the Commander de Foulquerre was stationed at the portal, with several of the young French chevaliers about him. Before

Don Luis could offer her the holy water, he was anticipated by the commander, who thrust himself between them, and, while he performed the gallant office to the lady, rudely turned his back upon her admirer, and trod upon his feet. The insult was enjoyed by the young Frenchmen who were present: it was too deep and grave to be forgiven by Spanish pride; and at once put an end to all Don Luis' plans of caution and forbearance. He repressed his passion for the moment, however, and waited until all the parties left the church; then, accosting the commander with an air of coolness and unconcern, he inquired after his health, and asked to what church he proposed making his second visit. "To the Magisterial Church of Saint John." Don Luis offered to conduct him thither by the shortest route. His offer was accepted, apparently without suspicion, and they proceeded together. After walking some distance, they entered a long, narrow lane, without door or window opening upon it, called the "Strada Stretta," or narrow street. It was a street in which duels were tacitly permitted, or connived at, in Malta, and were suffered to pass as accidental encounters. Everywhere else they were prohibited. This restriction had been instituted to diminish the number of duels formerly so frequent in Malta. As a further precaution to render these encounters less fatal, it was an offense, punishable with death, for any one to enter this street armed with either poniard or pistol. It was a lonely, dismal street, just wide enough for two men to stand upon their guard, and cross their swords; few persons ever traversed it unless with some sinister design; and on any preconcerted duello, the seconds posted themselves at each end, to stop all passengers, and prevent interruption.

In the present instance, the parties had scarce entered the street when Don Luis drew his sword and called upon the commander to defend himself.

De Foulquerre was evidently taken by surprise; he drew back, and attempted to expostulate; but Don Luis persisted in defying him to the combat.

After a second or two, he likewise drew his sword, but immediately lowered the point.

"Good Friday!" ejaculated he, shaking his head; "one word with you; it is full six years since I have been in a confessional: I am shocked at the state of my conscience; but within three days—that is to say, on Monday next—"

Don Luis would listen to nothing. Though naturally of a peaceable disposition, he had been stung to fury, and people of that character, when once incensed, are deaf to reason. He compelled the commander to put himself on his guard. The latter, though a man accustomed to brawl in battle, was singularly dismayed. Terror was visible in all his features. He placed himself with his back to the wall, and the weapons were crossed. The contest was brief and fatal. At the very first thrust, the sword of Don Luis passed through the body of his antagonist. The commander staggered to the wall, and leaned against it.

"On Good Friday!" ejaculated he again, with a failing voice and despairing accents. "Heaven pardon you!" added he; "take my sword to Tetefoulques, and have a hundred masses performed in the chapel of the castle, for the repose of my soul!" With these words he expired.

The fury of Don Luis was at an end. He stood aghast, gazing at the bleeding body of the commander. He called to mind the prayer of the deceased for three days' respite, to make his peace with Heaven. He had refused it; had sent him to the grave with all his sins upon his head! His conscience smote him to the core; he gathered up the sword of the commander, which he had been enjoined to take to Tetefoulques, and hurried from the fatal Strada Stretta.

The duel of course made a great noise in Malta, but had no injurious effect on the worldly fortunes of Don Luis. He made a full declaration of the whole matter before the proper authorities; the Chapter of the Order considered it one of those casual encounters of the Strada Stretta, which were mourned over, but tolerated; the public, by whom the late commander had been generally detested, declared that he had deserved his fate. It was but three days after the event that Don Luis was advanced to one of the highest dignities of the Order, being invested by the Grand Master with the priorship of the kingdom of Minorca.

From that time forward, however, the whole character and conduct of Don Luis underwent a change. He became a prey to a dark melancholy which nothing could assuage. The most austere piety, the severest penances, had no effect in allaying the horror which preyed upon his mind. He was absent for a long time from Malta; having gone, it was said, on remote pilgrimages; when he returned he was more haggard than ever. There seemed something mysterious and inexplicable in this disorder of his mind. The following is the revelation made by himself of the horrible visions, or chimeras, by which he was haunted:

"When I had made my declaration before the Chapter," said he, "and my provocations were publicly known, I had made my peace with man; but it was not so with God, nor with my confessor, nor with my own conscience. My act was doubly criminal, from the day on which it was committed and from my refusal to a delay of three days, for the victim of my resentment to receive the sacraments. His despairing ejaculation, 'Good Friday! Good Friday!' continually rang in my ears. Why did I not grant the respite! cried I to myself; was it not enough to kill the body, but must I seek to kill the soul!

"On the night of the following Friday I started suddenly from my sleep. An unaccountable horror was upon me. I looked wildly around. It seemed as if I were not in my apartment, nor in my bed, but in the fatal Strada Stretta, lying on the pavement. I again saw the commander leaning against the wall; I again heard his dying words: 'Take my sword to Tetefoulques, and have a hundred masses performed in the chapel of the castle, for the repose of my soul!'

"On the following night, I caused one of my servants to sleep in the same room with me. I saw and heard nothing, either on that night or any of the nights following, until the next Friday; when I had again the same vision, with this difference, that my valet seemed to be lying at some distance from me on the pavement of the Strada Stretta. The vision continued to be repeated on every Friday night, the commander always appearing in the same manner, and uttering the same words: 'Take my sword to Tetefoulques, and have a hundred masses performed in the chapel of the castle, for the repose of my soul!'

"On questioning my servant on the subject, he stated that on these occasions he dreamed that he was lying in a very narrow street, but he neither saw nor heard anything of the commander.

"I knew nothing of this Tetefoulques, whither the defunct was so urgent I should carry his sword. I made inquiries, therefore, concerning it among the French chevaliers. They informed me that it was an old castle, situated about four leagues from Poitiers, in the midst of a forest. It had been built in old times, several centuries since, by Foulques Taillefer (or Fulke Hackiron), a redoubtable, hard-fighting count of Angouleme, who gave it to an illegitimate son, afterward created Grand Seneschal of Poitou, which son became the progenitor of the Foulquerres of Tetefoulques, hereditary Seneschals of Poitou. They further informed me that strange stories were told of this old castle in the surrounding country, and that it contained many curious relics. Among these were the arms of Foulques Taillefer, together with all those of the warriors he had slain; and that it was an immemorial usage with the Foulquerres to have the weapons deposited there which they had wielded either in war or in single combat. This, then, was the reason of the dying injunction of the commander respecting his sword. I carried this weapon with me, wherever I went, but still I neglected to comply with his request.

"The visions still continued to harass me with undiminished horror. I repaired to Rome, where I confessed myself to the Grand Cardinal penitentiary, and informed him of the

terrors with which I was haunted.   He promised me absolution, after I should have performed certain acts of penance,
the principal of which was to execute the dying request of
the commander, by carrying his sword to Tetefoulques and
having the hundred masses performed in the chapel of the
castle for the repose of his soul.

"I set out for France as speedily as possible, and made
no delay in my journey.   On arriving at Poitiers, I found
that the tidings of the death of the commander had reached
there, but had caused no more affliction than among the
people of Malta.   Leaving my equipage in the town, I put
on the garb of a pilgrim, and, taking a guide, set out on
foot for Tetefoulques.   Indeed the roads in this part of
the country were impracticable for carriages.

"I found the castle of Tetefoulques a grand but gloomy
and dilapidated pile.   All the gates were closed, and there
reigned over the whole place an air of almost savage loneli-
ness and desertion.   I had understood that its only inhabitants were the concierge, or warder, and a kind of hermit
who had charge of the chapel.   After ringing for some
time at the gate, I at length succeeded in bringing forth the
warder, who bowed with reverence to my pilgrim's garb.   I
begged him to conduct me to the chapel, that being the end
of my pilgrimage.   We found the hermit there, chanting the
funeral service; a dismal sound to one who came to perform
a penance for the death of a member of the family.   When
he had ceased to chant, I informed him that I came to accomplish an obligation of conscience, and that I wished him
to perform a hundred masses for the repose of the soul of the
commander.   He replied that, not being in orders, he was
not authorized to perform mass, but that he would willingly
undertake to see that my debt of conscience was discharged.
I laid my offering on the altar, and would have placed the
sword of the commander there likewise.   'Hold!' said the
hermit, with a melancholy shake of the head, 'this is no
place for so deadly a weapon, that has so often been bathed
in Christian blood.   Take it to the armory; you will find

there trophies enough of like character. It is a place into which I never enter.'

"The warder here took up the theme abandoned by the peaceful man of God. He assured me that I would see in the armory the swords of all the warrior race of Foulquerres, together with those of the enemies over whom they had triumphed. This, he observed, had been a usage kept up since the time of Mellusine, and of her husband, Geoffrey a la Grand-dent, or Geoffrey with the Great-tooth.

"I followed the gossiping warder to the armory. It was a great dusty hall, hung round with Gothic-looking portraits of a stark line of warriors, each with his weapon, and the weapons of those he had slain in battle, hung beside his picture. The most conspicuous portrait was that of Foulques Taillefer (Fulke Hackiron), Count of Angouleme, and founder of the castle. He was represented at full length, armed cap-a-pie, and grasping a huge buckler, on which were emblazoned three lions passant. The figure was so striking that it seemed ready to start from the canvas; and I observed beneath this picture a trophy composed of many weapons, proofs of the numerous triumphs of this hard-fighting old cavalier. Besides the weapons connected with the portraits, there were swords of all shapes, sizes and centuries hung round the hall; with piles of armor, placed as it were in effigy.

"On each side of an immense chimney were suspended the portraits of the first seneschal of Poitou (the illegitimate son of Foulques Taillefer) and his wife Isabella de Lusignan; the progenitors of the grim race of Foulquerres that frowned around. They had the look of being perfect likenesses; and as I gazed on them, I fancied I could trace in their antiquated features some family resemblance to their unfortunate descendant whom I had slain! This was a dismal neighborhood, yet the armory was the only part of the castle that had a habitable air; so I asked the warder whether he could not make a fire, and give me something for supper there, and prepare me a bed in one corner.

" 'A fire and a supper you shall have, and that cheerfully, most worthy pilgrim,' said he; 'but as to a bed, I advise you to come and sleep in my chamber.'

" 'Why so?' inquired I; 'why shall I not sleep in this hall?'

" 'I have my reasons; I will make a bed for you close to mine.'

"I made no objections, for I recollected that it was Friday, and I dreaded the return of my vision. He brought in billets of wood, kindled a fire in the great overhanging chimney, and then went forth to prepare my supper. I drew a heavy chair before the fire, and seating myself in it gazed musingly round upon the portraits of the Foulquerres, and the antiquated armor and weapons, the mementos of many a bloody deed. As the day declined, the smoky draperies of the hall gradually became confounded with the dark ground of the paintings, and the lurid gleams from the chimney only enabled me to see visages staring at me from the gathering darkness. All this was dismal in the extreme, and somewhat appalling; perhaps it was the state of my conscience that rendered me peculiarly sensitive and prone to fearful imaginings.

"At length the warder brought in my supper. It consisted of a dish of trout and some crawfish taken in the fosse of the castle. He procured also a bottle of wine, which he informed me was wine of Poitou. I requested him to invite the hermit to join me in my repast; but the holy man sent back word that he allowed himself nothing but roots and herbs, cooked with water. I took my meal, therefore, alone, but prolonged it as much as possible, and sought to cheer my drooping spirits by the wine of Poitou, which I found very tolerable.

"When supper was over, I prepared for my evening devotions. I have always been very punctual in reciting my breviary; it is the prescribed and bounden duty of all chevaliers of the religious orders; and I can answer for it, is faithfully performed by those of Spain. I accordingly drew

forth from my pocket a small missal and a rosary, and told
the warder he need only designate to me the way to his
chamber, where I could come and rejoin him when I had
finished my prayers.

"He accordingly pointed out a winding staircase opening
from the hall. 'You will descend this staircase,' said he,
"until you come to the fourth landing-place, where you enter
a vaulted passage, terminated by an arcade, with a statue of
the blessed Jeanne of France; you cannot help finding my
room, the door of which I will leave open; it is the sixth
door from the landing-place. I advise you not to remain in
this hall after midnight. Before that hour, you will hear
the hermit ring the bell, in going the rounds of the corridors.
Do not linger here after that signal.'

"The warder retired, and I commenced my devotions. I
continued at them earnestly; pausing from time to time to
put wood upon the fire. I did not dare to look much around
me, for I felt myself becoming a prey to fearful fancies.
The pictures appeared to become animated. If I regarded
one attentively, for any length of time, it seemed to move
the eyes and lips. Above all, the portraits of the grand
seneschal and his lady, which hung on each side of the great
chimney, the progenitors of the Foulquerres of Tetefoulque,
regarded me, I thought, with angry and baleful eyes: I even
fancied they exchanged significant glances with each other.
Just then a terrible blast of wind shook all the casements,
and, rushing through the hall, made a fearful rattling and
clashing among the armor. To my startled fancy, it seemed
something supernatural.

"At length I heard the bell of the hermit and hastened
to quit the hall. Taking a solitary light, which stood on the
supper-table, I descended the winding staircase; but before I
had reached the vaulted passage leading to the statue of the
blessed Jeanne of France a blast of wind extinguished my
taper. I hastily remounted the stairs, to light it again at
the chimney; but judge of my feelings when, on arriving at
the entrance to the armory, I beheld the seneschal and his

lady, who had descended from their frames and seated themselves on each side of the fireplace!

" 'Madam, my love,' said the seneschal, with great formality and in antiquated phrase, 'what think you of the presumption of this Castilian, who comes to harbor himself and
make wassail in this our castle, after having slain our descendant, the commander, and that without granting him
time for confession?'

" 'Truly, my lord,' answered the female specter, with no
less stateliness of manner, and with great asperity of tone;
'truly, my lord, I opine that this Castilian did a grievous
wrong in this encounter; and he should never be suffered to
depart hence, without your throwing him the gauntlet.' I
paused to hear no more, but rushed again downstairs to seek
the chamber of the warder. It was impossible to find it in
the darkness and in the perturbation of my mind. After an
hour and a half of fruitless search, and mortal horror and
anxieties, I endeavored to persuade myself that the day was
about to break, and listened impatiently for the crowing of
the cock; for I thought if I could hear his cheerful note I
should be reassured; catching, in the disordered state of my
nerves, at the popular notion that ghosts never appear after
the first crowing of the cock.

"At length I rallied myself, and endeavored to shake off
the vague terrors which haunted me. I tried to persuade
myself that the two figures which I had seemed to see and
hear had existed only in my troubled imagination. I still
had the end of the candle in my hand, and determined to
make another effort to relight it and find my way to bed;
for I was ready to sink with fatigue. I accordingly sprang
up the staircase, three steps at a time, stopped at the door
of the armory, and peeped cautiously in. The two Gothic
figures were no longer in the chimney corners, but I neglected to notice whether they had reascended to their
frames. I entered, and made desperately for the fireplace,
but scarce had I advanced three strides, when Messire
Foulques Taillefer stood before me, in the center of the hall,

armed cap-a-pie and standing in guard with the point of his sword silently presented to me. I would have retreated to the staircase but the door of it was occupied by the phantom figure of an esquire who rudely flung a gauntlet in my face. Driven to fury I snatched down a sword from the wall: by chance it was that of the commander which I had placed there. I rushed upon my fantastic adversary and seemed to pierce him through and through; but at the same time I felt as if something pierced my heart, burning like a red-hot iron. My blood inundated the hall and I fell senseless.

————

"When I recovered consciousness, it was broad day, and I found myself in a small chamber attended by the warder and the hermit. The former told me that on the previous night he had awakened long after the midnight hour, and perceiving that I had not come to his chamber, he had furnished himself with a vase of holy water and set out to seek me. He found me stretched senseless on the pavement of the armory and bore me to his room. I spoke of my wound, and of the quantity of blood that I had lost. He shook his head, and knew nothing about it; and to my surprise, on examination, I found myself perfectly sound and unharmed. The wound and blood, therefore, had been all delusion. Neither the warder nor the hermit put any questions to me, but advised me to leave the castle as soon as possible. I lost no time in complying with their counsel, and felt my heart relieved from an oppressive weight as I left the gloomy and fate-bound battlements of Tetefoulques behind me.

"I arrived at Bayonne, on my way to Spain, on the following Friday. At midnight I was startled from my sleep, as I had formerly been; but it was no longer by the vision of the dying commander. It was old Foulques Taillefer who stood before me, armed cap-a-pie, and presenting the point of his sword. I made the sign of the cross, and the specter vanished, but I received the same red-hot thrust in the heart which I had felt in the armory, and I seemed to be bathed in blood. I would have called out, or have arisen from my bed and gone in quest of succor, but I could neither speak nor stir. This agony endured until the crowing of the cock, when I fell asleep again; but the next day I was ill and in a most pitiable state. I have continued to be harassed by the same vision every Friday night; no acts of penitence and devotion have been able to relieve me from it; and it is only a lingering hope in divine mercy that sustains me and enables me to support so lamentable a visitation."

THE Grand Prior of Minorca wasted gradually away under this constant remorse of conscience and this horrible incubus. He died some time after having revealed the preceding particulars of his case, evidently the victim of a diseased imagination.

The above relation has been rendered, in many parts literally, from the French memoir, in which it is given as a true story: if so, it is one of those instances in which truth is more romantic than fiction. G. C.

LEGEND OF THE ENGULFED CONVENT

BY GEOFFREY CRAYON, GENT.

AT the dark and melancholy period when Don Roderick the Goth and his chivalry were overthrown on the banks of the Guadelete, and all Spain was overrun by the Moors, great was the devastation of churches and convents throughout that pious kingdom. The miraculous fate of one of those holy piles is thus recorded in one of the authentic legends of those days.

On the summit of a hill, not very distant from the capital city of Toledo, stood an ancient convent and chapel, dedicated to the invocation of Saint Benedict, and inhabited by a sisterhood of Benedictine nuns. This holy asylum was confined to females of noble lineage. The younger sisters of the

highest families were here given in religious marriage to
their Saviour, in order that the portions of their elder sisters
might be increased, and they enabled to make suitable
matches on earth, or that the family wealth might go un-
divided to elder brothers, and the dignity of their ancient
houses be protected from decay.   The convent was renowned,
therefore, for enshrining within its walls a sisterhood of the
purest blood, the most immaculate virtue, and most resplendent beauty, of all Gothic Spain.

When the Moors overran the kingdom, there was nothing
that more excited their hostility than these virgin asylums.
The very sight of a convent spire was sufficient to set their
Moslem blood in a foment, and they sacked it with as fierce
a zeal as though the sacking of a nunnery were a sure pass-
port to Elysium.

Tidings of such outrages committed in various parts of
the kingdom reached this noble sanctuary and filled it with
dismay.   The danger came nearer and nearer; the infidel
hosts were spreading all over the country; Toledo itself was
captured; there was no flying from the convent, and no
security within its walls.

In the midst of this agitation, the alarm was given one
day that a great band of Saracens were spurring across the
plain.   In an instant the whole convent was a scene of confusion.   Some of the nuns wrung their fair hands at the
windows; others waved their veils and uttered shrieks from
the tops of the towers, vainly hoping to draw relief from a
country overrun by the foe.   The sight of these innocent
doves thus fluttering about their dove cote but increased the
zealot fury of the whiskered Moors.   They thundered at the
portal, and at every blow the ponderous gates trembled on
their hinges.

The nuns now crowded round the abbess.   They had
been accustomed to look up to her as all-powerful, and they
now implored her protection.   The mother abbess looked
with a rueful eye upon the treasures of beauty and vestal
virtue exposed to such imminent peril.   Alas! how was she

to protect them from the spoiler! She had, it is true, experienced many signal interpositions of Providence in her individual favor. Her early days had been passed amid the
temptations of a court where her virtue had been purified by
repeated trials, from none of which had she escaped but by
miracle. But were miracles never to cease? Could she hope
that the marvelous protection shown to herself would be
extended to a whole sisterhood? There was no other re-
source. The Moors were at the threshold; a few moments
more and the convent would be at their mercy. Summoning
her nuns to follow her, she hurried into the chapel; and
throwing herself on her knees before the image of the blessed
Mary, "O holy Lady!" exclaimed she, "O most pure and
immaculate of virgins! thou seest our extremity. The rav-
ager is at the gate, and there is none on earth to help us!
Look down with pity, and grant that the earth may gape
and swallow us rather than that our cloister vows should
suffer violation!"

The Moors redoubled their assault upon the portal; the
gates gave way with a tremendous crash; a savage yell of
exultation arose; when of a sudden the earth yawned; down
sank the convent, with its cloisters, its dormitories, and all
its nuns. The chapel tower was the last that sank, the bell
ringing forth a peal of triumph in the very teeth of the
infidels.

FORTY years had passed and gone since the period of this
miracle. The subjugation of Spain was complete. The
Moors lorded it over city and country; and such of the
Christian population as remained, and were permitted to
exercise their religion, did it in humble resignation to the
Moslem sway.

At this time a Christian cavalier of Cordova, hearing that
a patriotic band of his countrymen had raised the standard
of the cross in the mountains of the Asturias, resolved to
join them, and unite in breaking the yoke of bondage.
Secretly arming himself, and caparisoning his steed, he set

forth from Cordova and pursued his course by unfrequented mule-paths and along the dry channels made by winter torrents. His spirit burned with indignation, whenever, on commanding a view over a long sweeping plain, he beheld the mosque swelling in the distance, and the Arab horsemen careering about, as if the rightful lords of the soil. Many a deep-drawn sigh, and heavy groan, also, did the good cavalier utter on passing the ruins of churches and convents desolated by the conquerors.

It was on a sultry midsummer evening that this wandering cavalier, in skirting a hill thickly covered with forest, heard the faint tones of a vesper bell sounding melodiously in the air, and seeming to come from the summit of the hill. The cavalier crossed himself with wonder at this unwonted and Christian sound. He supposed it to proceed from one of those humble chapels and hermitages permitted to exist through the indulgence of the Moslem conquerors. Turning his steed up a narrow path of the forest, he sought this sanctuary, in hopes of finding a hospitable shelter for the night. As he advanced, the trees threw a deep gloom around him, and the bat flitted across his path. The bell ceased to toll, and all was silence.

Presently a choir of female voices came stealing sweetly through the forest, chanting the evening service, to the solemn accompaniment of an organ. The heart of the good cavalier melted at the sound for it recalled the happier days of his country. Urging forward his weary steed, he at length arrived at a broad grassy area, on the summit of the hill, surrounded by the forest. Here the melodious voices rose in full chorus, like the swelling of the breeze; but whence they came he could not tell. Sometimes they were before sometimes behind him; sometimes in the air, sometimes as if from within the bosom of the earth. At length they died away, and a holy stillness settled on the place.

The cavalier gazed around with bewildered eye. There was neither chapel nor convent nor humble hermitage to be seen; nothing but a moss-grown stone pinnacle, rising out of the center of the area, surmounted by a cross. The green-sward around appeared to have been sacred from the tread of man or beast, and the surrounding trees bent toward the cross, as if in adoration.

The cavalier felt a sensation of holy awe. He alighted and tethered his steed on the skirts of the forest, where he might crop the tender herbage; then approaching the cross, he knelt and poured forth his evening prayers before this relic of the Christian days of Spain. His orisons being con-cluded, he laid himself down at the foot of the pinnacle, and reclining his head against one of its stones fell into a deep sleep.

About midnight he was awakened by the tolling of a bell, and found himself lying before the gate of an ancient con-vent. A train of nuns passed by, each bearing a taper. The cavalier rose and followed them into the chapel; in the center of which was a bier, on which lay the corpse of an aged nun. The organ performed a solemn requiem; the nuns joining in chorus. When the funeral service was finished, a melodious voice chanted, "*Requiescat in pace!*"—"May she rest in peace!" The lights immediately vanished; the whole passed away as a dream; and the cavalier found himself at the foot of the cross, and beheld, by the faint rays of the rising moon, his steed quietly grazing near him.

When the day dawned, the cavalier descended the hill, and, following the course of a small brook, came to a cave, at the entrance of which was seated an ancient man, clad in hermit's garb, with rosary and cross, and a beard that de-scended to his girdle. He was one of those holy anchorites permitted by the Moors to live unmolested in dens and caves, and humble hermitages, and even to practice the rites of their religion. The cavalier checked his horse, and dis-mounting, knelt and craved a benediction. He then related all that had befallen him in the night, and besought the hermit to explain the mystery.

"What thou hast heard and seen, my son," replied the other, "is but a type and shadow of the woes of Spain."

He then related the foregoing story of the miraculous deliverance of the convent.

"Forty years," added the holy man, "have elapsed since this event, yet the bells of that sacred edifice are still heard, from time to time, sounding from under ground, together with the pealing of the organ and the chanting of the choir. The Moors avoid this neighborhood as haunted ground, and the whole place, as thou mayest perceive, has become covered with a thick and lonely forest."

The cavalier listened with wonder to the story of this engulfed convent, as related by the holy man. For three days and nights did they keep vigils beside the cross; but nothing more was to be seen of nun or convent. It is supposed that, forty years having elapsed, the natural lives of all the nuns were finished, and that the cavalier had beheld the obsequies of the last of the sisterhood. Certain it is that, from that time, bell, and organ, and choral chant have never more been heard.

The mouldering pinnacle, surmounted by the cross, still remains an object of pious pilgrimage. Some say that it anciently stood in front of the convent, but others assert that it was the spire of the sacred edifice, and that, when the main body of the building sank, this remained above ground, like the topmast of some tall ship that has been foundered. These pious believers maintain that the convent is miraculously preserved entire in the center of the mountain, where, if proper excavations were made, it would be found, with all its treasures, and monuments, and shrines, and relics, and the tombs of its virgin nuns.

Should any one doubt the truth of this marvelous interposition of the Virgin, to protect the vestal purity of her votaries, let him read the excellent work entitled "Espana Triumphante," written by Padre Fray Antonio de Sancta Maria, a bare-foot friar of the Carmelite order, and he will doubt no longer.

THE COUNT VAN HORN

DURING the minority of Louis XV., while the Duke of
Orleans was Regent of France, a young Flemish nobleman,
the Count Antoine Joseph Van Horn, made his sudden appearance in Paris, and by his character, conduct, and the
subsequent disasters in which he became involved, created a
great sensation in the high circles of the proud aristocracy.
He was about twenty-two years of age, tall, finely formed,
with a pale, romantic countenance, and eyes of remarkable
brilliancy and wildness.

He was of one of the most ancient and highly esteemed
families of European nobility, being of the line of the Princes
of Horn and Overique, sovereign Counts of Hautekerke, and
hereditary grand veneurs of the empire.

The family took its name from the little town and seign-
iory of Horn, in Brabant; and was known as early as the
eleventh century among the little dynasties of the Netherlands, and since that time by a long line of illustrious generations.   At the peace of Utrecht, when the Netherlands passed
under subjection to Austria, the house of Van Horn came
under the domination of the emperor.   At the time we treat
of, two of the branches of this ancient house were extinct;
the third and only surviving branch was represented by the
reigning prince, Maximilian Emanuel Van Horn, twenty-
four years of age, who resided in honorable and courtly style
on his hereditary domains at Baussigny, in the Netherlands,
and his brother, the Count Antoine Joseph, who is the subject of this memoir.

The ancient house of Van Horn, by the intermarriage of
its various branches with the noble families of the continent,
had become widely connected and interwoven with the high
aristocracy of Europe.   The Count Antoine, therefore, could
claim relationship to many of the proudest names in Paris.
In fact, he was grandson, by the mother's side, of the Prince

de Ligne, and even might boast of affinity to the regent (the Duke of Orleans) himself. There were circumstances, however, connected with his sudden appearance in Paris, and his previous story, that placed him in what is termed "a false position"; a word of baleful significance in the fashionable vocabulary of France.

The young count had been a captain in the service of Austria, but had been cashiered for irregular conduct, and for disrespect to Prince Louis of Baden, commander-in-chief. To check him in his wild career, and bring him to sober reflection, his brother the prince caused him to be arrested and sent to the old castle of Van Wert, in the domains of Horn. This was the same castle in which, in former times, John Van Horn, Stadtholder of Gueldres, had imprisoned his father; a circumstance which has furnished Rembrandt with the subject of an admirable painting. The governor of the castle was one Van Wert, grandson of the famous John Van Wert, the hero of many a popular song and legend. It was the intention of the prince that his brother should be held in honorable durance, for his object was to sober and improve, not to punish and afflict him. Van Wert, however, was a stern, harsh man of violent passions. He treated the youth in a manner that prisoners and offenders were treated in the strongholds of the robber counts of Germany in old times; confined him in a dungeon and inflicted on him such hardships and indignities that the irritable temperament of the young count was roused to continual fury, which ended in insanity. For six months was the unfortunate youth kept in this horrible state, without his brother the prince being informed of his melancholy condition or of the cruel treatment to which he was subjected. At length, one day, in a paroxysm of frenzy, the count knocked down two of his jailers with a beetle, escaped from the castle of Van Wert, and eluded all pursuit; and after roving about in a state of distraction, made his way to Baussigny and appeared like a specter before his brother.

The prince was shocked at his wretched, emaciated appearance and his lamentable state of mental alienation. He received him with the most compassionate tenderness; lodged him in his own room, appointed three servants to attend and watch over him day and night, and endeavored by the most soothing and affectionate assiduity to atone for the past act of rigor with which he reproached himself. When he learned, however, the manner in which his unfortunate brother had been treated in confinement, and the course of brutalities that had led to his mental malady, he was roused to indignation. His first step was to cashier Van Wert from his command. That violent man set the prince at defiance, and attempted to maintain himself in his government and his castle by instigating the peasants, for several leagues round, to revolt. His insurrection might have been formidable against the power of a petty prince; but he was put under the ban of the empire and seized as a state prisoner. The memory of his grandfather, the oft-sung John Van Wert, alone saved him from a gibbet; but he was imprisoned in the strong tower of Horn-op-Zee. There he remained until he was eighty-two years of age, savage, violent, and unconquered to the last; for we are told that he never ceased fighting and thumping as long as he could close a fist or wield a cudgel.

In the meantime a course of kind and gentle treatment and wholesome regimen, and, above all, the tender and affectionate assiduity of his brother, the prince, produced the most salutary effects upon Count Antoine. He gradually recovered his reason; but a degree of violence seemed always lurking at the bottom of his character, and he required to be treated with the greatest caution and mildness, for the least contradiction exasperated him.

In this state of mental convalescence, he began to find the supervision and restraints of brotherly affection insupportable; so he left the Netherlands furtively, and repaired to Paris, whither, in fact, it is said he was called by motives of interest, to make arrangements concerning a valuable estate, which he inherited from his relative, the Princess d'Epinay.

On his arrival in Paris, he called upon the Marquis of Crequi, and other of the high nobility with whom he was connected. He was received with great courtesy; but, as he brought no letters from his elder brother, the prince, and as various circumstances of his previous history had transpired, they did not receive him into their families nor introduce him to their ladies. Still they feted him in bachelor style, gave him gay and elegant suppers at their separate apartments, and took him to their boxes at the theaters. He was often noticed, too, at the doors of the most fashionable churches, taking his stand among the young men of fashion; and at such times his tall, elegant figure, his pale but handsome countenance, and his flashing eyes, distinguished him from among the crowd; and the ladies declared that it was almost impossible to support his ardent gaze.

The count did not afflict himself much at his limited circulation in the fastidious circles of the high aristocracy. He relished society of a wilder and less ceremonious cast; and meeting with loose companions to his taste, soon ran into all the excesses of the capital in that most licentious period. It is said that, in the course of his wild career, he had an intrigue with a lady of quality, a favorite of the regent; that he was surprised by that prince in one of his interviews; that sharp words passed between them; and that the jealousy and vengeance thus awakened ended only with his life.

About this time the famous Mississippi scheme of Law was at its height, or rather it began to threaten that disastrous catastrophe which convulsed the whole financial world. Every effort was making to keep the bubble inflated. The vagrant population of France was swept off from the streets at night, and conveyed to Havre de Grace, to be shipped to the projected colonies; even laboring people and mechanics were thus crimped and spirited away. As Count Antoine was in the habit of sallying forth at night, in disguise, in pursuit of his pleasures, he came near being carried off by a gang of crimps; it seemed, in fact, as if they had been lying in wait for him, as he had experienced very rough treatment at their hands. Complaint was made of his case by his relation, the Marquis de Crequi, who took much interest in the youth; but the marquis received mysterious intimations not to interfere in the matter, but to advise the count to quit Paris immediately: "If he lingers, he is lost!" This has been cited as a proof that vengeance was dogging at the heels of the unfortunate youth, and only watching for an opportunity to destroy him.

Such opportunity occurred but too soon. Among the loose companions with whom the count had become intimate were two who lodged in the same hotel with him. One was a youth only twenty years of age, who passed himself off as the Chevalier d'Etampes, but whose real name was Lestang, the prodigal son of a Flemish banker. The other, named Laurent de Mille, a Piedmontese, was a cashiered captain, and at the time an esquire in the service of the dissolute Princess de Carignan, who kept gambling-tables in her palace. It is probable that gambling propensities had brought these young men together, and that their losses had driven them to desperate measures; certain it is that all Paris was suddenly astounded by a murder which they were said to have committed. What made the crime more startling was, that it seemed connected with the great Mississippi scheme, at that time the fruitful source of all kinds of panics and agitations. A Jew, a stock-broker, who dealt largely in shares of the bank of Law, founded on the Mississippi scheme, was the victim. The story of his death is variously related. The darkest account states that the Jew was decoyed by these young men into an obscure tavern, under pretext of negotiating with him for bank shares to the amount of one hundred thousand crowns, which he had with him in his pocketbook. Lestang kept watch upon the stairs. The count and De Mille entered with the Jew into a chamber. In a little while there were heard cries and struggles from within. A waiter passing by the room looked in, and seeing the Jew weltering in his blood, shut the door again, double-locked it, and alarmed the house. Lestang rushed downstairs, made his way to the hotel, secured his most portable effects and fled the country. The count and De Mille endeavored to escape by the window, but were both taken and conducted to prison.

A circumstance which occurs in this part of the count's story seems to point him out as a fated man. His mother, and his brother, the Prince Van Horn, had received intelligence some time before at Baussigny, of the dissolute life that the count was leading at Paris and of his losses at play. They dispatched a gentleman of the prince's household to Paris, to pay the debts of the count and persuade him to return to Flanders; or, if he should refuse, to obtain an order from the regent for him to quit the capital. Unfortunately the gentleman did not arrive at Paris until the day after the murder.

The news of the count's arrest and imprisonment on a charge of murder caused a violent sensation among the high aristocracy. All those connected with him, who had treated him hitherto with indifference, found their dignity deeply involved in the question of his guilt or innocence. A general convocation was held at the hotel of the Marquis de Crequi, of all the relatives and allies of the house of Horn. It was an assemblage of the most proud and aristocratic personages of Paris. Inquiries were made into the circumstances of the affair. It was ascertained, beyond a doubt, that the Jew was dead, and that he had been killed by several stabs of a poniard. In escaping by the window, it was said that the count had fallen and been immediately taken; but that De Mille had fled through the streets, pursued by the populace, and had been arrested at some distance from the scene of the murder; that the count had declared himself innocent of the death of the Jew, and that he had risked his own life in endeavoring to protect him; but that De Mille, on being brought back to the tavern, confessed to a plot to murder the broker, and rob him of his pocketook, and inculpated the count in the crime.

Another version of the story was, that the Count Van Horn had deposited with the broker bank shares to the amount of eighty-eight thousand livres; that he had sought him in this tavern, which was one of his resorts, and had demanded the shares; that the Jew had denied the deposit; that a quarrel had ensued, in the course of which the Jew struck the count in the face; that the latter, transported with rage, had snatched up a knife from a table and wounded the Jew in the shoulder; and that thereupon De Mille, who was present, and who had likewise been defrauded by the broker, fell on him, and dispatched him with blows of a poniard and seized upon his pocketbook; that he had offered to divide the contents of the latter with the count, *pro rata*, of what the usurer had defrauded them; that the latter had refused the proposition with disdain, and that, at a noise of persons approaching, both had attempted to escape from the premises, but had been taken.

Regard the story in any way they might, appearances were terribly against the count, and the noble assemblage was in great consternation. What was to be done to ward off so foul a disgrace and to save their illustrious escutcheons

from this murderous stain of blood? Their first attempt
was to prevent the affair from going to trial, and their relative from being dragged before a criminal tribunal, on so
horrible and degrading a charge. They applied, therefore,
to the regent to intervene his power; to treat the count as
having acted under an access of his mental malady; and to
shut him up in a madhouse. The regent was deaf to their
solicitations. He replied, coldly, that if the count was a
madman, one could not get rid too quickly of madmen who
were furious in their insanity. The crime was too public and
atrocious to be hushed up or slurred over; justice must take
its course.

Seeing there was no avoiding the humiliating scene of a
public trial, the noble relatives of the count endeavored to
predispose the minds of the magistrates before whom he was
to be arraigned. They accordingly made urgent and eloquent representations of the high descent and noble and
powerful connections of the count; set forth the circumstances of his early history; his mental malady; the nervous
irritability to which he was subject, and his extreme sensitiveness to insult or contradiction. By these means they
sought to prepare the judges to interpret everything in favor
of the count, and, even if it should prove that he had inflicted
the mortal blow on the usurer, to attribute it to access of
insanity provoked by insult.

To give full effect to these representations, the noble conclave determined to bring upon the judges the dazzling rays
of the whole assembled aristocracy. Accordingly, on the
day that the trial took place, the relations of the count, to
the number of fifty-seven persons, of both sexes, and of the
highest rank, repaired in a body to the Palace of Justice,
and took their stations in a long corridor which led to the
court-room. Here, as the judges entered, they had to pass in
review this array of lofty and noble personages, who saluted
them mournfully and significantly as they passed. Any one
conversant with the stately pride and jealous dignity of the
French noblesse of that day may imagine the extreme state
of sensitiveness that produced this self-abasement. It was
confidently presumed, however, by the noble suppliants that,
having once brought themselves to this measure, their influence over the tribunal would be irresistible. There was one
lady present, however, Madame de Beauffremont, who was
affected with the Scottish gift of second sight, and related
such dismal and sinister apparitions as passing before her

eyes that many of her female companions were filled with doleful presentiments.

Unfortunately for the count, there was another interest at work, more powerful even than the high aristocracy. The all-potent Abbe Dubois, the grand favorite and bosom counselor of the regent, was deeply interested in the scheme of Law, and the prosperity of his bank, and of course in the security of the stock-brokers. Indeed, the regent himself is said to have dipped deep in the Mississippi scheme. Dubois and Law, therefore, exerted their influence to the utmost to have the tragic affair pushed to the extremity of the law, and the murder of the broker punished in the most signal and appalling manner. Certain it is, the trial was neither long nor intricate. The count and his fellow-prisoner were equally inculpated in the crime, and both were condemned to a death the most horrible and ignominious—to be broken alive on the wheel!

As soon as the sentence of the court was made public, all the nobility, in any degree related to the house of Van Horn, went into mourning. Another grand aristocratical assemblage was held, and a petition to the regent, on behalf of the count, was drawn out and left with the Marquis de Crequi for signature. This petition set forth the previous insanity of the count, and showed that it was a hereditary malady of his family. It stated various circumstances in mitigation of his offense, and implored that his sentence might be commuted to perpetual imprisonment.

Upward of fifty names of the highest nobility, beginning with the Prince de Ligne, and including cardinals, archbishops, dukes, marquises, etc., together with ladies of equal rank, were signed to this petition. By one of the caprices of human pride and vanity, it became an object of ambition to get enrolled among the illustrious suppliants; a kind of testimonial of noble blood, to prove relationship to a murderer! The Marquis de Crequi was absolutely besieged by applicants to sign, and had to refer their claims to this singular honor to the Prince de Ligne, the grandfather of the count. Many who were excluded were highly incensed, and numerous feuds took place. Nay, the affronts thus given to the morbid pride of some aristocratical families passed from generation to generation; for, fifty years afterward, the Duchess of Mazarin complained of a slight which her father had received from the Marquis de Crequi; which proved to be something connected with the signature of this petition.

This important document being completed, the illustrious body of petitioners, male and female, on Saturday evening, the eve of Palm Sunday, repaired to the Palais Royal, the residence of the regent, and were ushered, with great cere- mony, but profound silence, into his hall of council. They had appointed four of their number as deputies to present the petition; viz., the Cardinal de Rohan, the Duke de Havre, the Prince de Ligne, and the Marquis de Crequi. After a little while the deputies were summoned to the cabinet of the regent. They entered, leaving the assembled petitioners in a state of the greatest anxiety. As time slowly wore away, and the evening advanced, the gloom of the company in- creased. Several of the ladies prayed devoutly; the good Princess of Armagnac told her beads.

The petition was received by the regent with a most un- propitious aspect. "In asking the pardon of the criminal," said he, "you display more zeal for the house of Van Horn than for the service of the king." The noble deputies en- forced the petition by every argument in their power. They supplicated the regent to consider that the infamous punish- ment in question would reach not merely the person of the condemned, not merely the house of Van Horn, but also the genealogies of princely and illustrious families, in whose armorial bearings might be found quarterings of this dis- honored name.

"Gentlemen," replied the regent, "it appears to me the disgrace consists in the crime rather than in the punishment."

The Prince de Ligne spoke with warmth: "I have in my genealogical standard," said he, "four escutcheons of Van Horn, and of course have four ancestors of that house. I must have them erased and effaced, and there would be so many blank spaces, like holes, in my heraldic ensigns. There is not a sovereign family which would not suffer through the rigor of your Royal Highness; nay, all the world knows that in the thirty-two quarterings of madame, your mother, there is an escutcheon of Van Horn."

"Very well," replied the regent, "I will share the dis- grace with you, gentlemen."

Seeing that a pardon could not be obtained, the Cardinal de Rohan and the Marquis de Crequi left the cabinet; but the Prince de Ligne and the Duke de Havre remained be- hind. The honor of their houses, more than the life of the unhappy count, was the great object of their solicitude. They now endeavored to obtain a minor grace. They represented that in the Netherlands, and in Germany, there was an important difference in the public mind as to the mode of inflicting the punishment of death upon persons of quality. That decapitation had no influence on the fortunes of the family of the executed, but that the punishment of the wheel was such an infamy that the uncles, aunts, brothers, and sisters of the criminal, and his whole family, for three succeeding generations, were excluded from all noble chapters, princely abbeys, sovereign bishoprics, and even Teutonic commanderies of the Order of Malta. They showed how this would operate immediately upon the fortunes of a sister of the count, who was on the point of being received as a canoness into one of the noble chapters.

While this scene was going on in the cabinet of the regent, the illustrious assemblage of petitioners remained in the hall of council, in the most gloomy state of suspense. The re-entrance from the cabinet of the Cardinal de Rohan and the Marquis de Crequi, with pale, downcast countenances, had struck a chill into every heart. Still they lingered until near midnight to learn the result of the after application. At length the cabinet conference was at an end. The regent came forth, and saluted the high personages of the assemblage in a courtly manner. One old lady of quality, Madame de Guyon, whom he had known in his infancy, he kissed on the cheek, calling her his "good aunt." He made a most ceremonious salutation to the stately Marchioness de Crequi, telling her he was charmed to see her at the Palais Royal; "a compliment very ill-timed," said the marchioness, "considering the circumstance which brought me there." He then conducted the ladies to the door of the second saloon, and there dismissed them, with the most ceremonious politeness.

The application of the Prince de Ligne and the Duke de Havre, for a change of the mode of punishment, had, after much difficulty, been successful. The regent had promised solemnly to send a letter of commutation to the attorney-general on Holy Monday, the 25th of March, at five o'clock in the morning. According to the same promise, a scaffold would be arranged in the cloister of the Conciergerie or prison, where the count would be beheaded on the same morning, immediately after having received absolution. This mitigation of the form of punishment gave but little consolation to the great body of petitioners, who had been anxious for the pardon of the youth: it was looked upon as all-important, however, by the Prince de Ligne, who, as has been before observed, was exquisitely alive to the dignity of his family.

The Bishop of Bayeux and the Marquis de Crequi visited the unfortunate youth in prison. He had just received the communion in the chapel of the Conciergerie, and was kneeling before the altar, listening to a mass for the dead, which was performed at his request. He protested his innocence of any intention to murder the Jew, but did not deign to allude to the accusation of robbery. He made the bishop and the marquis promise to see his brother the prince, and inform him of this his dying asseveration.

Two other of his relations, the Prince Rebecq-Montmorency and the Marshal Van Isenghien, visited him secretly, and offered him poison, as a means of evading the disgrace of a public execution. On his refusing to take it, they left him with high indignation. "Miserable man!" said they. "You are fit only to perish by the hand of the executioner!"

The Marquis de Crequi sought the executioner of Paris, to bespeak an easy and decent death for the unfortunate youth. "Do not make him suffer," said he; "uncover no part of him but the neck; and have his body placed in a coffin before you deliver it to his family." The executioner promised all that was requested, but declined a rouleau of a hundred louis-d'ors which the marquis would have put into his hand. "I am paid by the king for fulfilling my office," said he; and added that he had already refused a like sum, offered by another relation of the marquis.

The Marquis de Crequi returned home in a state of deep affliction. There he found a letter from the Duke de St. Simon, the familiar friend of the regent, repeating the promise of that prince that the punishment of the wheel should be commuted to decapitation.

"Imagine," says the Marchioness de Crequi, who in her memoirs gives a detailed account of this affair, "imagine what we experienced, and what was our astonishment, our grief, and indignation, when, on Tuesday, the 26th of March, an hour after midday, word was brought us that the Count Van Horn had been exposed on the wheel, in the Place de Greve, since half-past six in the morning, on the same scaffold with the Piedmontese de Mille, and that he had been tortured previous to execution!"

One more scene of aristocratic pride closed this tragic story. The Marquis de Crequi, on receiving this astounding news, immediately arrayed himself in the uniform of a general officer, with his cordon of nobility on the coat. He ordered six valets to attend him in grand livery, and two of his carriages, each with six horses, to be brought forth. In this sumptuous state, he set off for the Place de Greve, where he had been preceded by the Princes de Ligne, de Rohan, de Croüy, and the Duke de Havre.

The Count Van Horn was already dead, and it was believed that the executioner had had the charity to give him the coup de grace, or "death-blow," at eight o'clock in the morning. At five o'clock in the evening, when the Judge Commissary left his post at the Hotel de Ville, these noblemen, with their own hands, aided to detach the mutilated remains of their relation; the Marquis de Crequi placed them in one of his carriages, and bore them off to his hotel, to receive the last sad obsequies.

The conduct of the regent in this affair excited general indignation. His needless severity was attributed by some to vindictive jealousy; by others to the persevering machinations of Law. The house of Van Horn, and the high nobility of Flanders and Germany, considered themselves flagrantly outraged: many schemes of vengeance were talked of, and a hatred engendered against the regent that followed him through life, and was wreaked with bitterness upon his memory after his death.

The following letter is said to have been written to the regent by the Prince Van Horn, to whom the former had adjudged the confiscated effects of the count:

"I do not complain, sir, of the death of my brother, but I complain that your Royal Highness has violated in his person the rights of the kingdom, the nobility, and the nation. I thank you for the confiscation of his effects; but I should think myself as much disgraced as he should I accept any favor at your hands. *I hope that God and the king may render to you as strict justice as you have rendered to my unfortunate brother.*"

END OF VOLUME FOUR